Probability and Statistics for Actuaries

First Edition

Natalia A Humphreys and Yuly Koshevnik

University of Texas - Dallas

SAN DIEGO

Bassim Hamadeh, CEO and Publisher
John Remington, Acquisitions Editor
Gem Rabanera, Senior Project Editor
Christian Berk, Production Editor
Emely Villavicencio, Senior Graphic Designer
Trey Soto, Licensing Coordinator
Natalie Piccotti, Director of Marketing
Kassie Graves, Vice President of Editorial
Jamie Giganti, Director of Academic Publishing

cognella® | ACADEMIC PUBLISHING

3970 Sorrento Valley Blvd., Ste. 500, San Diego, CA 92121

Contents

Preface

This book originated as a helpful tool for the audience interested in probabilistic and statistical aspects of actuarial science. These two disciplines lie at the root of a number of professional exams given by the Society of Actuaries (SOA) and Casualty Actuarial Society (CAS).

While teaching courses at the University of Texas at Dallas in the Actuarial Science program, the authors identified particular areas of interest and difficulty voiced by their students. Based on the authors' experiences, accumulated through dozens of lectures, seminars and discussions, they were motivated to provide structured and detailed explanation to help students formalize and deepen their knowledge in these areas.

While writing this book, the authors pursued the following goals:

- To ensure that students sharpen their knowledge accrued from the previously taken probability and statistics courses. This was accomplished by providing an extensive review of probabilistic and statistical models and techniques presented in the first chapters of each part of the book.

- To enhance the students' knowledge obtained in the courses that contained elements of credibility theory. This was achieved by highlighting an important role of the Bayesian approach. In particular, the authors sought to emphasize elements of statistical decision theory along with conditioning techniques.

- To provide detailed explanation of the Bayesian approach as it is related to prior distribution and alleviate analytical challenges in various applications. This was accomplished by employing alternative methods in credibility studies, such as a Bühlmann framework and empirical Bayes approach.

- To deepen the students' knowledge of statistical inference. This was completed in the last chapter of the book by detailed presentation of several parametric approaches to model data behavior.

As they present their joint work, the authors remain hopeful that readers will expand and deepen their understanding of the probabilistic and statistical processes, gain confidence in preparation for actuarial exams, and succeed in their career growth.

Natalia A. Humphreys and Yuly Koshevnik
Richardson, TX
December, 2020

Part I

Probability Review and Elements of Credibility Theory

Chapter 1

Probability Review

Probability theory course is a prerequisite for all statistics-related studies. This chapter allows readers to refresh their knowledge accrued from the past.

Commonly used discrete and continuous distributions are presented in the first three sections. Readers are prepared to work with probabilistic statements related to large samples, including the **law of large numbers** and **normal approximation**, also known as the **central limit theorem (CLT)**.

Readers will familiarize themselves with commonly used probability models and their applications.

After completing this chapter, readers will be prepared to handle more specific topics that are covered in the rest of the text.

Exercises will further deepen and develop readers' knowledge of material presented in this chapter.

1.1 Discrete and Continuous Random Variables

In probability and statistics, a random variable can informally be described as a variable whose values depend on outcomes of a random phenomenon. In probability theory a random variable is formally understood as a measurable function defined on a probability space that maps from the sample space to the real numbers.

1.1.1 Probability

Probability is the measure of the likelihood that an event will occur.

Probability quantifies as a number between 0 and 1, where 0 indicates impossibility and 1 indicates certainty.

The higher the probability of an event, the more likely it is that the event will occur.

Example. An example of probability is the tossing of a fair (balanced) coin. Since the coin is fair, the two outcomes, "heads" and "tails," are equally probable. The probability of "heads" equals the probability of "tails." Since no other outcomes are possible, the probability of either "heads" or "tails" is 1/2, which could also be written as 0.5 or 50%.

Probability is typically denoted by $\mathbf{P}$. For example, $\mathbf{P}(X \leq 0.4) = 0.3$ means the probability that the random variable X is not greater than 0.4 is equal to 0.3.

1.1.2 Types of Random Variables

Let X be a random variable.

A random variable X is **discrete** or has a **discrete distribution** if its list of all possible values can be presented by a finite or countable set of distinct values x, with $\mathbf{P}(X = x) > 0$ for each of these values.

A random variable X is **continuous** or has a **continuous distribution** if $\mathbf{P}(X = x) = 0$ for each x.

A random variable X is **mixed** or has a **mixed distribution** if it is continuous except at a finite or countable set of points.

1.1.3 Cumulative Distribution and Related Functions

The **cumulative distribution function,** or the (**CDF**), denoted $F_X(x)$ or $F(x)$, is the probability
$$F_X(x) = \mathbf{P}(X \le x).$$

$F_X(x)$ is right-continuous:
$$\lim_{h \to 0} F_X(x + h) = F_X(x), \ h > 0$$

The **survival function**, denoted $S_X(x)$ or $S(x)$, is the complement of $F(x)$ and is the probability
$$S(x) = 1 - F(x) = \mathbf{P}(X > x).$$

The **cumulative hazard function**, denoted $H_X(x)$ or $H(x)$, is defined as
$$H(x) = -\ln S(x).$$

1.1.4 Probability Density and Hazard Rate Functions

For a continuous random variable, the **probability density function,** or the **pdf**, denoted $f_X(x)$ or $f(x)$, is the derivative of $F(x)$:
$$f(x) = \frac{d}{dx} F(x) = \lim_{\Delta x \to 0} \frac{\mathbf{P}(X \le x + \Delta x) - \mathbf{P}(X \le x)}{\Delta x}$$

For a discrete random variable, the **pdf** is replaced by the **probability mass function, ** or the **pmf**, and is defined as
$$f(x) = \mathbf{P}(X = x),$$

where x belongs to a countable set $\mathcal{X}$.

The **hazard rate function**, denoted $h_X(x)$ or $h(x)$, is defined as
$$h(x) = \frac{f(x)}{S(x)} = \lim_{\Delta x \to 0} \frac{\mathbf{P}(X \le x + \Delta x | X > x)}{\Delta x},$$

where conditional probability is defined as
$$\mathbf{P}(A|B) = \frac{\mathbf{P}(A \cap B)}{\mathbf{P}(B)}.$$

Note that for a continuous random variable, hazard rate function can be expressed as

$$h(x) = -\frac{d \ln S(x)}{dx} = \frac{f(x)}{1 - F(x)}.$$

Thus, for real-valued continuous random variables on $x \in (-\infty, \infty)$, the **CDF**, the survival, and the cumulative hazard rate functions could be defined as

$$H(x) = \int_{-\infty}^{x} h(t)\, dt$$

$$S(x) = \int_{x}^{\infty} f(t)\, dt = \exp(-H(x))$$

$$F(x) = \int_{-\infty}^{x} f(t)\, dt = 1 - \exp(-H(x))$$

and for the discrete random variables as

$$H(x) = -\ln\left[\sum_{t>x} \mathbf{P}[X = t] \right]$$

$$S(x) = \sum_{t>x} \mathbf{P}[X = t] = \sum_{t>x} f(t)$$

$$F(x) = \sum_{t\le x} \mathbf{P}[X = t] = \sum_{t\le x} f(t).$$

The **probability distribution** of a random variable can be described in terms of the cumulative distribution function. Another way to describe it is through the probability density function for continuous random variables or the probability mass function for discrete random variables.

Following are characteristics of random variables based on their distribution.

1.1.5 Expectation and Variance

For continuous random variables the **expected value** of X, $\mathbf{E}[X]$, is defined as

$$\mathbf{E}[X] = \int_{-\infty}^{\infty} x f(x)\, dx.$$

If $T = g(X)$ is a transformed variable, then the **expected value** of T, $\mathbf{E}[T]$, is defined as

$$\mathbf{E}[T] = \mathbf{E}[g(X)] = \int_{-\infty}^{\infty} g(x) f(x)\, dx,$$

provided the integrals are absolutely convergent.

For discrete variables, defining $p_n = \mathbf{P}\{N = n\}$, the expected values are defined as

$$\mathbf{E}[N] = \sum_{n=0}^{\infty} n p_n, \quad \mathbf{E}[g(N)] = \sum_{n=0}^{\infty} g(n) p_n,$$

provided the series are absolutely convergent.

For any two random variables X and Y and any two constants a and b

$$\mathbf{E}(aX + bY) = a\mathbf{E}(X) + b\mathbf{E}(Y).$$

Thus, $\mathbf{E}[\cdot]$ is a linear operator.

Another commonly used characteristic of random variables is **variance** X, $\mathbf{Var}(X)$, defined as

$$\mathbf{Var}(X) = \mathbf{E}[(X - \mathbf{E}[X])^2] = \sigma^2.$$

Note that σ^2 is always nonnegative.

The **standard deviation** is the square root of variance:

$$\sigma = \sqrt{\mathbf{Var}(X)}$$

Since $\mathbf{E}[\cdot]$ is a linear operator, the variance of a random variable can also be expressed as the following difference:

$$\mathbf{Var}(X) = \mathbf{E}[X^2] - (\mathbf{E}[X])^2$$

1.1.6   Moments

The nth **raw** moment of a random variable X, μ'_n, is defined as

$$\mu'_n = \mathbf{E}[X^n], \ n = 1, 2, \ldots$$

Note that the first raw moment of X is the expected value or the mean of X:

$$\mu_1 = \mu = \mathbf{E}[X]$$

Likewise, the nth **central** moment of a random variable X, μ_n, is defined as

$$\mu_n = \mathbf{E}[(X - \mu)^n], \ n = 1, 2, \ldots$$

Note that the second central moment of X is the variance of X:

$$\mathbf{Var}(X) = \mathbf{E}[(X - \mu)^2] = \mu_2$$

Again, since the expectation $\mathbf{E}[\cdot]$ is a linear operator, there is a connection between the raw moments and the central moments through the Pascal triangle:

$$
\begin{array}{ccccccccc}
 & & & & 1 & & & & \\
 & & & 1 & & 1 & & & \\
 & & 1 & & 2 & & 1 & & \\
 & 1 & & 3 & & 3 & & 1 & \\
1 & & 4 & & 6 & & 4 & & 1 \\
\end{array}
$$

$$\cdots$$

For example, the first four central moments can be expressed through the corresponding raw moments as follows:

$$
\begin{aligned}
\mu_2 &= \mathbf{E}[(X - \mu)^2] = \mu'_2 - 2\mu'_1\mu + \mu^2 = \mu'_2 - \mu^2 \\
\mu_3 &= \mathbf{E}[(X - \mu)^3] = \mu'_3 - 3\mu'_2\mu + 3\mu'_1\mu^2 - \mu^3 = \mu'_3 - 3\mu'_2\mu + 2\mu^3 \\
\mu_4 &= \mathbf{E}[(X - \mu)^4] = \mu'_4 - 4\mu'_3\mu + 6\mu'_2\mu^2 - 4\mu'_1\mu^3 + \mu^4 = \mu'_4 - 4\mu'_3\mu + 6\mu'_2\mu^2 - 3\mu^4
\end{aligned}
$$

In general, using the **binomial theorem**, an nth central moment can be evaluated as

$$\mu_n = \sum_{k=0}^{n} (-1)^{n-k} \binom{n}{k} \mu_k' \mu^{n-k}$$

The following three special moments are often used in probability and statistics:

1) The **skewness**, defined as

$$\gamma_1 = \frac{\mu_3}{\sigma^3},$$

is a measure of symmetry of a distribution. Skewness is approximately zero if the distribution is nearly symmetric.

2) The **kurtosis**, defined as

$$\gamma_2 = \frac{\mu_4}{\sigma^4} - 3,$$

is a measure of normality of a distribution. Kurtosis is approximately zero if the distribution is nearly normal.

3) The **coefficient of variation**, defined as

$$CV = \frac{\sigma}{\mu},$$

is a statistical measure of variability (dispersion) in a population around the mean.

1.1.7   Probability- and Moment-Generating Functions

The probability-generating function of a discrete random variable N is a power series representation of the probability mass function of the random variable. It is defined as

$$P_N(z) = \mathbf{E}[z^N] = \sum_{n=0}^{\infty} z^n \cdot \mathbf{P}[N = n].$$

By definition, a moment-generating function of a random variable N is

$$M_N(z) = \mathbf{E}\left[e^{zN}\right], \ |z| < 1.$$

Thus,

$$P_N(z) = \mathbf{E}[e^{N \ln z}] = M_N(\ln z).$$

1.1.8   Covariance

For two random variables X and Y, their **covariance** is

$$\mathbf{Cov}(X, Y) = \mathbf{E}[(X - \mu_X)(Y - \mu_Y)] = \mathbf{E}[XY] - \mathbf{E}[X]\mathbf{E}[Y].$$

For independent random variables $\mathbf{Cov}(X, Y) = 0$. Hence, if X and Y are independent and their first moments exist

$$\mathbf{E}[XY] = \mathbf{E}[X]\mathbf{E}[Y].$$

The **correlation coefficient** is defined as

$$\rho_{X,Y} = \frac{\mathbf{Cov}(X,Y)}{\sigma_X \sigma_Y}.$$

For any two random variables X and Y and any two constants a and b

$$\mathbf{Var}(aX + bY) = a^2\mathbf{Var}(X) + 2ab\mathbf{Cov}(X,Y) + b^2\mathbf{Var}(Y) = a^2\sigma_X^2 + 2ab\rho_{X,Y}\sigma_X\sigma_Y + b^2\sigma_Y^2.$$

In particular,

$$\mathbf{Var}(X + Y) = \mathbf{Var}(X) + 2\mathbf{Cov}(X,Y) + \mathbf{Var}(Y)$$
$$\mathbf{Var}(X - Y) = \mathbf{Var}(X) - 2\mathbf{Cov}(X,Y) + \mathbf{Var}(Y).$$

Therefore, the covariance of the two random variables can be expressed as

$$\mathbf{Cov}(X,Y) = \frac{\mathbf{Var}(X + Y) - \mathbf{Var}(X - Y)}{4}.$$

Since the covariance of any two independent random variables is zero, for n independent random variables $X_1, X_2, \ldots, X_n$,

$$\mathbf{Var}\left(\sum_{i=1}^{n} X_i\right) = \sum_{i=1}^{n} \mathbf{Var}(X_i).$$

A **covariance matrix** for n random variables $X_1, X_2, \ldots, X_n$ is an $n \times n$ matrix $\mathbf{A}$, with entries $a_{ij} = \mathbf{Cov}(X_i, X_j)$ for $i \neq j$ and $a_{ii} = \mathbf{Var}(X_i)$ for $i = j$:

$$\mathbf{A} = \begin{bmatrix} a_{11} & a_{12} & \cdots & a_{1n} \\ a_{21} & a_{22} & \cdots & a_{2n} \\ a_{31} & a_{32} & \cdots & a_{3n} \\ & & \cdots & \\ a_{n1} & a_{n2} & \cdots & a_{nn} \end{bmatrix}$$

1.1.9 Percentiles

The **lower** $100p^{th}$ **percentile** is a number π_p such that

$$F(\pi_p) \geq p \text{ and } F(\pi_p^-) \leq p,$$

where

$$F(\pi_p^-) = \lim_{h \to 0} F(\pi_p - h).$$

The **upper** $100p^{th}$ **percentile** is a number π_{1-p} such that

$$F(\pi_{1-p}) \geq 1 - p \text{ and } F(\pi_{1-p}^-) \leq 1 - p.$$

If F_X is strictly increasing, it is the unique point at which

$$F_X(\pi_p) = \mathbf{P}(X \leq \pi_p) = p.$$

Note that the 50th percentile of a random variable is called the **median**.

In the following section we will present a few commonly used discrete distributions.

1.2   Commonly Used Discrete Distributions

Recall that a random variable X is **discrete** or has a **discrete distribution** if its list of all possible values can be presented by a finite or countable set of distinct values.

For a discrete random variable, the key notion that describes its distribution is the **pmf**,

$$f(x) = \mathbf{P}[X = x], \tag{1.1}$$

where x belongs to a set $\mathcal{X}$ of distinct integer values. Usually, it is either a set of natural numbers or so-called **whole** numbers, starting with $x = 0$.

Generally, the notion of **CDF** could be introduced in the discrete case, as follows:

$$F(t) = \sum_{x \le t} \mathbf{P}[X = x] = \sum_{x \le t} f(x).$$

Two discrete random variables, X and Y, are **independent** if

$$\mathbf{P}(X = x, Y = y) = \mathbf{P}(X = x) \cdot \mathbf{P}(Y = y) \quad \text{for all } x \text{ and } y.$$

Following is the description of the most commonly used discrete distributions.

1.2.1   Discrete Uniform Distribution

The distribution is supported by a finite set of integer values, $\mathcal{X} = \{1, 2, \ldots, n\}$, and has the probabilities assigned as follows:

$$\mathbf{P}[X = k] = \frac{1}{n} \quad \text{for} \quad k = 1, 2, \ldots, n. \tag{1.2}$$

We may denote this distribution as $\mathbf{DU}[n]$.

The expected value of X is

$$\mu_X = \mathbf{E}[X] = \frac{1}{n} \sum_{k=1}^{n} k = \frac{1}{n} \times \frac{n(n+1)}{2} = \frac{n+1}{2}. \tag{1.3}$$

The **second moment** of X is

$$\mathbf{E}[X^2] = \frac{1}{n} \sum_{k=1}^{n} k^2 = \frac{1}{n} \times \frac{n(n+1)(2n+1)}{6} = \frac{(n+1)(2n+1)}{6}.$$

Calculating the variance of X, we have

$$\sigma_X^2 = \mathbf{Var}[X] = \mathbf{E}\left[(X - \mu)^2\right] = \mathbf{E}[X^2] - \mu^2 = \frac{(n+1)(2n+1)}{6} - \left[\frac{n+1}{2}\right]^2 =$$

$$= \frac{n+1}{12}(2(2n+1) - 3(n+1)) = \frac{(n+1)(n-1)}{12} = \frac{(n^2-1)}{12}.$$

Thus, the variance of $X \in \mathbf{DU}[n]$ is

$$\sigma_X^2 = \mathbf{Var}[X] = \frac{n^2 - 1}{12}. \tag{1.4}$$

1.2.2   Empirical Distribution

Consider a **random sample** of a random variable X that is formed by n independent observations, $X_1, X_2, \ldots, X_n$, each with the same distribution as X.

An **empirical distribution** is associated with the empirical measure of a sample such that

$$\mathbf{P}(X = X_i) = \frac{1}{n}, \quad i = 1, 2, \ldots, n.$$

The empirical cumulative distribution function is defined as

$$\hat{F}_n(t) = \frac{\text{number of elements in the sample} \leq t}{n} = \frac{1}{n} \sum_{i=1}^{n} \mathbf{1}\{x_i \leq t\},$$

where $\mathbf{1}\{A\}$ is the indicator function of event A.

The analogue of **pdf** of the empirical distribution is sometimes called the **histogram** and is defined as

$$\hat{f}_n(t) = \frac{\text{number of elements in the sample} = t}{n} = \frac{1}{n} \sum_{i=1}^{n} \mathbf{1}\{x_i = t\},$$

where again $\mathbf{1}\{A\}$ is the indicator function of event A.

The mean of the empirical distribution associated with a random sample $X_1, X_2, \ldots, X_n$ is the **sample mean**, defined as

$$\hat{\mu}_1 = \bar{X} = \frac{1}{n} \sum_{i=1}^{n} X_i.$$

Similarly, an empirical or the sample k^{th} raw moment is

$$\hat{\mu}'_k = \frac{1}{n} \sum_{i=1}^{n} X_i^k; \tag{1.5}$$

and an empirical or the sample k^{th} central moment is

$$\hat{\mu}_k = \frac{1}{n} \sum_{i=1}^{n} (X_i - \bar{X})^k.$$

1.2.3   Bernoulli Distribution

The Bernoulli distribution is a special distribution with the support $X = \{0, 1\}$, where the value of $X = 1$ is usually considered as a **success** and the value of $X = 0$ is interpreted as a **failure**.

Accordingly, the probability of success, $p = \mathbf{P}[X = 1]$, is usually referred to as a **success rate**, and the probability of failure, $1 - p = \mathbf{P}[X = 0]$, is then named a **failure rate**.

Thus, X can be represented as

$$X = \begin{cases} 1, & \text{with probability } p \\ 0, & \text{with probability } 1 - p. \end{cases}$$

For a Bernoulli random variable, **pmf** can be represented as

$$\mathbf{P}\,[X = x] = p^x\,(1-p)^{1-x}, \quad \text{where } x = 0, 1 \text{ and } 0 \le p \le 1.$$

The expected value of X and any moment of X are easy to derive:

$$\mu = \mu_X = \mathbf{E}\,[X] = \mathbf{E}\,[X^r] = p, \text{ for any natural } r \tag{1.6}$$

Hence, the variance of X is

$$\sigma^2 = \sigma_X^2 = \mathbf{Var}\,[X] = \mathbf{E}\,[X^2] - \mathbf{E}\,[X]^2 = p - p^2 = p(1-p). \tag{1.7}$$

A **generalized** Bernoulli random variable Y is defined as

$$Y = \begin{cases} a, & \text{with probability } p \\ b, & \text{with probability } 1 - p. \end{cases}$$

If X is a **standard** Bernoulli random variable and Y is a **generalized** Bernoulli random variable, then $Y = (a - b)X + b$, and

$$\mathbf{E}[Y] = (a - b)p + b \text{ and } \mathbf{Var}(Y) = (a - b)^2 p(1 - p).$$

This technique is often referred to as the **Bernoulli shortcut**.

1.2.4 Binomial Distribution

A common extension of the Bernoulli distribution is known as **binomial** distribution, which is usually denoted as $\mathbf{Bin}(n, p)$.

If $\{X_j : 1 \le j \le n\}$ represents n independent and identically distributed random variables, each following the Bernoulli distribution, then the sum,

$$Y = \sum_{j=1}^{n} X_j,$$

follows the binomial distribution, with parameters n and p, $\mathbf{Bin}(n, p)$.

For a binomial random variable, **pmf** can be represented as

$$\mathbf{P}\,[Y = k] = \frac{n!}{k!\,(n-k)!}\,p^k\,(1-p)^{n-k} \quad \text{for} \quad k = 0, 1, \ldots, n. \tag{1.8}$$

If $n = 1$, this distribution is the Bernoulli one, with the success rate equal to p. Thus, Bernoulli can be denoted as $\mathbf{Bin}(1, p)$.

Probability theory shows that

$$\mu_Y = \mathbf{E}\,[Y] = np \text{ and } \sigma_Y^2 = \mathbf{Var}\,[Y] = np(1 - p). \tag{1.9}$$

A single Bernoulli variable is usually identified with the result of one game, while Y, that is, the sum of n independent binary (Bernoulli) variables, measures the number of victories after a set of n games.

Note that a sum of n independent binomial random variables $X_1, X_2, \ldots, X_m$, having the same p and sizes $n_1, n_2, \ldots, n_m$, has a binomial distribution with parameter p and size

$$n = \sum_{k=1}^{m} n_k.$$

Binomial distribution is used to model the number of successes in a sample of size n, drawn with replacement from a large population.

1.2.5 Geometric Distribution

A random variable X has a **geometric** distribution with parameter p, also referred to as a **success rate**, if it takes an integer value from $\mathcal{X} = \{0, 1, \ldots\}$, with probabilities

$$p_k = \mathbf{P}\left[X = k\right] = p\left(1 - p\right)^k \quad \text{for} \quad k = 0, 1, \ldots \tag{1.10}$$

Under this definition, X is interpreted as a number of losses (or failures) prior to the first success.

If you consider a **shifted** variable, $W = X + 1$, then W indicates the **time** when the first success occurs. Equivalently, $W = m$ if and only if the first $(m - 1)$ trials result in failures, and the trial m results in a success.

Expected value and variance of W can be found as follows:

$$\mathbf{E}\left[W\right] = \frac{1}{p} \quad \text{and} \quad \mathbf{Var}\left[W\right] = \frac{1 - p}{p^2}. \tag{1.11}$$

Using the relationship $X = W - 1$, we obtain

$$\mathbf{E}\left[X\right] = \frac{1}{p} - 1 = \frac{1 - p}{p} \quad \text{and} \quad \mathbf{Var}\left[X\right] = \frac{1 - p}{p^2}. \tag{1.12}$$

Note that $\mathbf{Var}\left[X\right] = \mathbf{Var}\left[W\right]$.

Sometimes, a different parametrization is used for the geometric distribution. In this case the probabilities are defined as

$$p_k = \mathbf{P}\left[X = k\right] = \left(\frac{1}{1 + \beta}\right)\left(\frac{\beta}{1 + \beta}\right)^k, \quad \text{where} \quad \beta > 0 \ \text{ and } \ k = 0, 1, \ldots$$

Since

$$p_0 = \frac{1}{1 + \beta},$$

this expression can be written as

$$p_k = \left(\frac{\beta}{1 + \beta}\right)^k \cdot p_0,$$

or, recursively,

$$p_k = \frac{\beta}{1 + \beta} \cdot p_{k-1}.$$

The mean and variance of X will be then expressed as

$$\mathbf{E}[X] = \beta \quad \text{and} \quad \mathbf{Var}(X) = \mathbf{E}[X](1 + \beta) = \beta(1 + \beta).$$

Note that for the geometric distribution $\mathbf{Var}(X) > \mathbf{E}[X]$.

Also note that the geometric distribution is the discrete counterpart of the exponential distribution and has a similar memoryless property:

$$\mathbf{P}(X \geq n + k | X \geq n) = \mathbf{P}(X \geq k).$$

This can be proven using a property of a geometric series:

$$\mathbf{P}(X \geq n) = \sum_{i=n}^{\infty} \frac{1}{1 + \beta} \left(\frac{\beta}{1 + \beta} \right)^i = \left(\frac{\beta}{1 + \beta} \right)^n.$$

1.2.6   Negative Binomial Distribution

The **negative binomial** distribution relates to the geometric distribution in a way similar to what the binomial was for the Bernoulli variable.

If $\{W_j : j = 1, 2, \ldots, r\}$ are independent random variables, each having the **same** geometric distribution, **Geom**$[p]$; then their sum, $Y = \sum_{j=1}^{r} W_j$, is said to have the **negative binomial** distribution, with parameters r and p, denoted as **NB**$[r, p]$.

The event, $[Y = k]$, states that the rth success occurs at the trial number k in a sequence of independent identically distributed (iid) Bernoulli trials.

For example, if 1 is a success and non-1 are failures, throwing a dice repeatedly until the third time 1 appears ($r = 3$ successes) produces the probability distribution of the number of non-1 that is negative binomial.

For a negative binomial random variable, **pmf** can be represented as

$$\mathbf{P}[Y = k] = \frac{(k - 1)!}{(r - 1)!(k - r)!} \, p^r \, (1 - p)^{k-r} \quad \text{for} \ \ k = r, r + 1, \ldots. \tag{1.13}$$

The variable $T = Y - r$, measuring the total number of failures before the rth success occurs, has a **shifted** distribution,

$$\mathbf{P}[T = k] = \frac{(k + r - 1)!}{(r - 1)!(k!)} \, p^r \, (1 - p)^k, \quad \text{for} \ \ k = 0, 1, \ldots. \tag{1.14}$$

The expected value and variance for either version of the negative binomial distribution are calculated in a probability theory course.

Using the same convention, that is, Y is the time of the rth success and T is the count of failures that preceded this success, we have

$$\mathbf{E}[Y] = \frac{r}{p} \quad \text{and} \ \ \mathbf{E}[T] = \frac{r(1 - p)}{p}, \tag{1.15}$$

while

$$\mathbf{Var}[Y] = \mathbf{Var}[T] = \frac{r(1 - p)}{p^2}. \tag{1.16}$$

Using $p = 1/(1 + \beta)$ parametrization for $\beta > 0$, we can rewrite the probabilities as

$$p_k = \binom{k + r - 1}{k} \left(\frac{1}{1 + \beta}\right)^r \left(\frac{\beta}{1 + \beta}\right)^k.$$

Since

$$p_0 = \left(\frac{1}{1 + \beta}\right)^r,$$

this expression can be written as

$$p_k = \binom{k + r - 1}{k} \left(\frac{\beta}{1 + \beta}\right)^k \cdot p_0,$$

or, recursively,

$$p_k = \frac{\beta}{1 + \beta} \cdot \frac{r + k - 1}{k} \cdot p_{k-1}.$$

The mean and variance of X will be then expressed as

$$\mathbf{E}[X] = r\beta \text{ and } \mathbf{Var}(X) = \mathbf{E}[X](1 + \beta) = r\beta(1 + \beta).$$

Again, $\mathbf{Var}(X) > \mathbf{E}[X]$.

Note that a sum of n independent negative binomial random variables, $X_1, X_2, \ldots, X_n$, sharing the same β and parameters $r_1, r_2, \ldots, r_n$, has a negative binomial distribution, with parameters β and

$$r = \sum_{k=1}^{n} r_k.$$

1.2.7 Poisson Distribution

Poisson distribution is another type of discrete distribution, also with a countable set of distinct values. A random variable Y follows a Poisson distribution with the intensity parameter $\lambda > 0$ if

$$p_k = \mathbf{P}[Y = k] = \frac{\lambda^k}{k!} e^{-\lambda} \text{ for } k = 0, 1, 2, \ldots. \tag{1.17}$$

Since

$$p_0 = e^{-\lambda},$$

this expression can be written as

$$p_k = \frac{\lambda^k}{k!} \cdot p_0,$$

or, recursively,

$$p_k = \frac{\lambda}{k} \cdot p_{k-1}.$$

Note that a sum of n independent Poisson random variables, $X_1, X_2, \ldots, X_n$, with parameters $\lambda_1, \lambda_2, \ldots, \lambda_n$, has a Poisson distribution with parameter

$$\lambda = \sum_{k=1}^{n} \lambda_k.$$

In probability theory, the **law of rare events** or **Poisson limit theorem**, states that the Poisson distribution may be used as an approximation to the binomial distribution, under certain conditions. Specifically, the Poisson distribution is a limiting case of the binomial distribution when the number of trials n increases indefinitely while the limit of the product $\lim_{n \to \infty} np_n$, the expected value of the number of successes from the trials, remains constant.

Lemma 1.2.1 *Let p_n be a sequence of real numbers in $[0, 1]$ such that the sequence np_n converges to a finite limit λ. Let*

$$b(k; n, p) = \frac{n!}{k! \, (n - k)!} \, p^k \, (1 - p)^{n-k}$$

be the binomial probability mass function.

Then,

$$\lim_{n \to \infty} b(k; n, p) = \frac{\lambda^k}{k!} \, e^{-\lambda} \quad for \quad k = 0, 1, 2, \ldots.$$

Proof. Since $np = \lambda$, it follows that $p = \lambda/n$. Then the binomial **pmf** can be represented as

$$\frac{n!}{k! \, (n - k)!} \, p^k \, (1 - p)^{n-k} = \frac{\lambda^k}{k!} \cdot \frac{n!}{(n - k)! \, n^k} \left(1 - \frac{\lambda}{n} \right)^n \left(1 - \frac{\lambda}{n} \right)^{-k}.$$

Note that

$$\lim_{n \to \infty} \frac{n!}{(n - k)! \, n^k} = \lim_{n \to \infty} \frac{n(n - 1) \ldots (n - k + 1)}{n^k} = 1$$

$$\lim_{n \to \infty} \left(1 - \frac{\lambda}{n} \right)^n = e^{-\lambda}, \text{ and } \lim_{n \to \infty} \left(1 - \frac{\lambda}{n} \right)^{-k} = 1.$$

Therefore,

$$\lim_{n \to \infty} \frac{n!}{k! \, (n - k)!} \, p^k \, (1 - p)^{n-k} = \frac{\lambda^k}{k!} \cdot 1 \cdot e^{-\lambda} \cdot 1 = \frac{\lambda^k}{k!} \, e^{-\lambda}.$$

The expectation and variance of the Poisson distribution are derived in probability theory

$$\mathbf{E}[Y] = \lambda \quad \text{and} \quad \mathbf{Var}[Y] = \lambda. \tag{1.18}$$

Note that both negative binomial and Poisson distributions have a **countable** supporting set, while the binomial distribution has a **finite** one.

1.3   Common Continuous Distributions

For continuous random variables, especially real-valued ones, let $f(x)$ denote the **pdf**. The **CDF**, denoted $F(x)$, is defined as

$$F(x) = \int_{-\infty}^{x} f(t) \, dt \quad \text{for all} \quad x \in (-\infty, \infty). \tag{1.19}$$

Following is the description of the most commonly used continuous distributions.

1.3.1 Uniform Distribution

A real-valued random variable U follows the uniform distribution over the unit interval $(0, 1)$ if its density is

$$f(x) = 1 \quad \text{for} \quad 0 < x < 1 \quad \text{and} \quad f(x) = 0 \quad \text{elsewhere.} \tag{1.20}$$

Often we need to extend the uniform distribution by considering the distribution over an interval (a, b), where $a < b$. The general uniform distribution has the density function

$$f(x) = f(x \mid a, b) = \frac{1}{b-a} \quad \text{for} \quad a < x < b \quad \text{and} \quad f(x) = 0 \quad \text{elsewhere.} \tag{1.21}$$

Note that X has the uniform distribution over the interval (a, b) if and only if

$$U = \frac{X - a}{b - a}$$

is uniformly-distributed over the unit interval $(0, 1)$.

Solving this equation for X, we obtain

$$X = a + (b - a) U. \tag{1.22}$$

Recall that the moments of a continuous random variable X are defined as integrals.

If $T = T(X)$ is a transformed random variable, such as a power of X or a polynomial of X, then

$$\mathbf{E}[T] = \int_{-\infty}^{\infty} T(x) f(x) \, dx, \tag{1.23}$$

provided this (generally improper) integral converges to a finite value.

For a uniformly-distributed random variable, the expected value and variance are

$$\mathbf{E}[X] = \frac{a+b}{2} \quad \text{and} \quad \mathbf{Var}[X] = \frac{(b-a)^2}{12}. \tag{1.24}$$

In particular, if U is uniformly-distributed over the unit interval $(0, 1)$, we obtain

$$\mathbf{E}[U] = \frac{1}{2} \quad \text{and} \quad \mathbf{Var}[U] = \frac{1}{12}.$$

In addition,

$$\mathbf{E}[U^r] = \frac{1}{r+1} \quad \text{for any} \quad r > -1.$$

If $r \leq -1$, this integral diverges.

1.3.2 Gamma and Beta Functions

To discuss other continuous distributions, it is useful to remind the readers of the definitions of the gamma and beta functions introduced by Leonard Euler.

The **gamma** function is defined for all complex numbers, except for the negative integers and zero. For complex numbers with a positive real part, it is defined via a convergent improper integral for the argument $a > 0$:

$$\Gamma(a) = \int_0^\infty x^{a-1} e^{-x} \, dx. \tag{1.25}$$

It can be shown for any a in the domain $\{a > 0\}$ that

$$\Gamma(a+1) = a \cdot \Gamma(a),$$

and $\Gamma(1) = 1$. Using induction, for any natural n, we obtain

$$\Gamma(n) = (n-1)!$$

Thus, $\Gamma(2) = 1$, and $\Gamma(3) = 2! = 2$, and so on.

Consider the integral

$$I(\beta, \delta) = \int_0^\infty x^\beta e^{-\delta x} \, dx.$$

Making a substitution, $u = \delta \cdot x$, we have

$$du = \delta dx; \quad x = \frac{u}{\delta}.$$

Hence,

$$I(\beta, \delta) = \frac{1}{\delta^{\beta+1}} \int_0^\infty u^\beta e^{-u} \, du = \frac{\Gamma(\beta+1)}{\delta^{\beta+1}}.$$

In particular, if $\beta = n$, an integer, then

$$I(n, \delta) = \int_0^\infty x^n e^{-\delta x} \, dx = \frac{\Gamma(n+1)}{\delta^{n+1}} = \frac{n!}{\delta^{n+1}}. \tag{1.26}$$

The **beta** function is defined as

$$\mathbf{B}(a, b) = \int_0^1 x^{a-1} (1-x)^{b-1} \, dx, \quad \text{where } a > 0, \ b > 0. \tag{1.27}$$

Euler established the identity connecting the beta and the gamma functions:

$$\mathbf{B}(a, b) = \frac{\Gamma(a)\Gamma(b)}{\Gamma(a+b)}. \tag{1.28}$$

1.3.3 Beta Distribution

A random variable X has the **beta** distribution, with parameters (a, b) if its density function is defined for $0 < x < 1$ as

$$f(x) = f(x \,|\, a, b) = \frac{\Gamma(a+b)}{\Gamma(a)\Gamma(b)} x^{a-1} (1-x)^{b-1} \quad \text{and} \quad f(x) = 0 \ \text{otherwise.} \tag{1.29}$$

Two parameters are assumed to be strictly positive real numbers: $a > 0$ and $b > 0$.

Based on the definition (1.27) of the beta function and formula (1.28), it follows that

$$\int_0^1 f(x)\ dx = 1.$$

Due to the definition of the beta function and properties of the gamma function, the first two moments of beta distribution can be derived as follows:

$$\mathbf{E}[X] = \frac{\Gamma(a+b)}{\Gamma(a)\,\Gamma(b)} \int_0^1 x^a\,(1-x)^{b-1}\ dx = \frac{\Gamma(a+b)}{\Gamma(a)\,\Gamma(b)} \cdot \frac{\Gamma(a+1)\,\Gamma(b)}{\Gamma(a+b+1)} =$$

$$= \frac{\Gamma(a+b)\cdot\Gamma(a+1)}{\Gamma(a)\,\Gamma(a+b+1)} = \frac{a}{a+b}$$

Thus,

$$\mathbf{E}[X] = \frac{a}{a+b}. \tag{1.30}$$

Similarly, the second moment is

$$\mathbf{E}[X^2] = \frac{\Gamma(a+b)}{\Gamma(a)\,\Gamma(b)} \int_0^1 x^{a+1}\,(1-x)^{b-1}\ dx = \frac{\Gamma(a+b)}{\Gamma(a)\Gamma(b)} \cdot \frac{\Gamma(a+2)\,\Gamma(b)}{\Gamma(a+b+2)} =$$

$$= \frac{\Gamma(a+b)\cdot\Gamma(a+2)}{\Gamma(a)\,\Gamma(a+b+2)} = \frac{a(a+1)}{(a+b)(a+b+1)}.$$

Thus,

$$\mathbf{E}[X^2] = \frac{a(a+1)}{(a+b)(a+b+1)}. \tag{1.31}$$

Calculating $\mathbf{Var}(X)$, we obtain

$$\mathbf{Var}(X) = \mathbf{E}[X^2] - \mathbf{E}[X]^2 = \frac{a(a+1)}{(a+b)(a+b+1)} - \left(\frac{a}{a+b}\right)^2 =$$

$$= \frac{a}{a+b}\left(\frac{a+1}{a+b+1} - \frac{a}{a+b}\right) = \frac{ab}{(a+b)^2\cdot(a+b+1)}.$$

Thus,

$$\mathbf{Var}(X) = \frac{ab}{(a+b)^2\cdot(a+b+1)}. \tag{1.32}$$

In general, any k^{th} raw moment of X is

$$\mathbf{E}[X^k] = \frac{\Gamma(a+b)\,\Gamma(a+k)}{\Gamma(a)\,\Gamma(a+b+k)},\ k > -a.$$

Note that the standard uniform distribution is a particular case of a beta distribution, with parameters $a = 1$ and $b = 1$.

1.3.4   Exponential Distribution

A random variable X has an exponential distribution with a scale parameter $b > 0$ if its **pdf** is of the form

$$f(x) = f(x \mid b) = \frac{1}{b} e^{-x/b}. \tag{1.33}$$

Then, the expected value and variance are

$$\mathbf{E}[X] = b \quad \text{and} \quad \mathbf{Var}[X] = b^2.$$

Sometimes, a different parametrization is used, with the scale parameter b replaced by its reciprocal, $\lambda = 1/b$. In this case, the equation (1.33) is replaced by

$$f(x) = \lambda \cdot e^{-\lambda x}, \quad \text{where } x > 0. \tag{1.34}$$

Then the expected value and variance are

$$\mathbf{E}[X] = \frac{1}{\lambda} \quad \text{and} \quad \mathbf{Var}[X] = \frac{1}{\lambda^2}.$$

1.3.5   Gamma Distribution

A random variable X has a **standardized** gamma distribution with parameter $\alpha > 0$ if its **pdf** is of the form

$$f(x) = f(x \mid \alpha, 1) = \frac{1}{\Gamma(\alpha)} x^{\alpha-1} e^{-x} \quad \text{for } 0 < x < \infty. \tag{1.35}$$

It is zero otherwise. By the definition (1.25) of a gamma function, the density (1.35) satisfies a standard condition of any continuous density:

$$\int_{-\infty}^{\infty} f(x) \, dx = 1,$$

with integration actually performed over the interval $(0, \infty)$.

The kth raw moments of the standardized gamma distribution are defined as

$$\mathbf{E}[X^k] = \frac{\Gamma(\alpha+k)}{\Gamma(\alpha)}, \quad k > -\alpha.$$

In particular, the first two moments are

$$\mathbf{E}[X] = \frac{\Gamma(\alpha+1)}{\Gamma(a)} = \alpha \quad \text{and} \quad \mathbf{E}[X^2] = \frac{\Gamma(\alpha+2)}{\Gamma(a)} = \alpha(\alpha+1). \tag{1.36}$$

Thus, the variance of standardized gamma-distributed random variable is

$$\mathbf{Var}[X] = \mathbf{E}[X^2] - (\mathbf{E}[X])^2 = \alpha(\alpha+1) - \alpha^2 = \alpha. \tag{1.37}$$

A general gamma distribution has **two** parameters, α and θ, α being viewed as the **shape** and θ indicating the **scale**.

The density function of a general gamma distribution is defined as

$$f(x) = f(x \mid \alpha, \theta) = \frac{1}{\theta^\alpha \, \Gamma(\alpha)} \, x^{\alpha-1} \, e^{-x/\theta} \quad \text{for} \ \ 0 < x < \infty. \tag{1.38}$$

Note that if Y has the density (1.38), then $X = Y/\theta$ follows the distribution (1.35).

The first two central moments of a general gamma-distributed random variable Y are

$$\mathbf{E}[Y] = \alpha\theta \quad \text{and} \quad \mathbf{Var}[Y] = \alpha\theta^2. \tag{1.39}$$

The kth raw moments of the general gamma distribution are defined as

$$\mathbf{E}[X^k] = \frac{\theta^k \Gamma(\alpha+k)}{\Gamma(\alpha)}, \ \ k > -\alpha.$$

For an **integer** α the gamma distribution is also called an **Erlang** distribution.

Note that the exponential distribution is a particular case of a gamma distribution, with $\alpha = 1$ and θ. Thus, the sum of n independent exponential random variables with common mean θ follows a gamma, or Erlang, distribution, with parameters $\alpha = n$ and θ.

In addition, the cumulative distribution function of $X = X_1 + X_2 + \cdots + X_n$ is

$$F_X(x) = 1 - \sum_{j=0}^{n-1} e^{-x/\theta} \frac{(x/\theta)^j}{j!}.$$

1.3.6 Inverse Gamma Distribution

Consider a continuous random variable X that is positive, with probability 1, and the density function $f_X(x) = f(x)$ defined for $x > 0$.

Consider a transformed variable,

$$Y = X^{-1} = \frac{1}{X}.$$

Deriving its **CDF**, we have

$$F_Y(y) = \mathbf{P}[Y \le y] = \mathbf{P}[X \ge y^{-1}] = 1 - F_X(y^{-1}),$$

where $F_X(x)$ is the CDF for X.

Differentiating $F_Y(y)$, we obtain

$$f_Y(y) = \frac{1}{y^2} \cdot f\left(\frac{1}{y}\right), \ y > 0. \tag{1.40}$$

Let X follow a gamma distribution, with parameters (α, β), with $\alpha > 0$ and $\beta > 0$, and with density

$$f_X(x) = \frac{1}{\Gamma(\alpha) \cdot \beta^\alpha} \, x^{\alpha-1} \cdot e^{-x/\beta}, \ x > 0. \tag{1.41}$$

Then the random variable $Y = X^{-1} = 1/X$ follows the inverse gamma distribution, with parameters $(\alpha, \theta = \beta^{-1})$.

Indeed. By (1.40), the density of Y is

$$f_Y(y) = \frac{1}{y^2} \cdot \frac{1}{\Gamma(\alpha) \cdot \beta^\alpha} \, y^{-(\alpha-1)} \cdot e^{-1/(y\beta)} = \frac{1}{y^2} \cdot \frac{\theta^\alpha}{\Gamma(\alpha)} \cdot \frac{1}{y^{\alpha-1}} \cdot e^{-\theta/y} =$$
$$= \frac{\theta^\alpha}{\Gamma(\alpha) \, y^{\alpha+1}} \cdot e^{-\theta/y}. \tag{1.42}$$

Sometimes this definition is written in the equivalent form as

$$f_Y(y) = \frac{(\theta/y)^\alpha \cdot e^{-\theta/y}}{y \cdot \Gamma(\alpha)}.$$

Let us calculate the n-th moment of Y.

Lemma 1.3.1 *If Y has inverse gamma distribution, with parameters $\alpha > n$ and $\theta > 0$, then*

$$E[Y^n] = \frac{\theta^n}{(\alpha-1)(\alpha-2)\dots(\alpha-n)}. \tag{1.43}$$

Proof. Since Y has inverse gamma distribution, with parameters α and θ, $X = 1/Y$ has a gamma distribution, with parameters α and $1/\theta$. Its **pdf** is

$$f_X(x) = \frac{\theta^\alpha}{\Gamma(\alpha)} \, x^{\alpha-1} \cdot e^{-\theta x}. \tag{1.44}$$

By the definition of an expected value, for any function $g(x)$,

$$\mathbf{E}[(g(X)] = \int_{-\infty}^{\infty} g(x) f_X(x) \, dx.$$

In particular, for the function $g(x) = 1/x^n = y^n$, we have

$$\mathbf{E}[Y^n] = \mathbf{E}[X^{-n}] = \frac{\theta^\alpha}{\Gamma(\alpha)} \int_0^{\infty} x^{-n} \cdot x^{\alpha-1} \cdot e^{-\theta x} \, dx = \frac{\theta^\alpha}{\Gamma(\alpha)} \int_0^{\infty} x^{\alpha-n-1} \cdot e^{-\theta x} \, dx.$$

Using (1.26), we obtain

$$\mathbf{E}[Y^n] = \frac{\theta^\alpha}{\Gamma(\alpha)} \int_0^{\infty} x^{\alpha-n-1} \cdot e^{-\theta x} \, dx = \frac{\theta^\alpha \cdot \Gamma(\alpha-n)}{\Gamma(\alpha) \cdot \theta^{\alpha-n}} = \frac{\theta^n \cdot \Gamma(\alpha-n)}{\Gamma(\alpha)}.$$

Since

$$\frac{\Gamma(z+n+1)}{\Gamma(z)} = z(z+1)\cdots(z+n),$$

we obtain

$$\mathbf{E}[Y^n] = \frac{\theta^n \cdot \Gamma(\alpha-n)}{\Gamma(\alpha)} = \frac{\theta^n}{(\alpha-1)(\alpha-2)\dots(\alpha-n)}.$$

Actuarial applications of the inverse gamma operate with moments of this distribution, especially those of the first and second order.

Corollary 1. If Y has inverse gamma distribution, with parameters $\alpha > 1$ and $\theta > 0$, then

$$\mathbf{E}\left[Y\right] = \frac{\theta}{\alpha - 1}. \tag{1.45}$$

Corollary 2. If Y has inverse gamma distribution, with parameters $\alpha > 2$ and $\theta > 0$, then

$$\mathbf{E}\left[Y^2\right] = \frac{\theta^2}{(\alpha - 1)(\alpha - 2)}. \tag{1.46}$$

This identity leads to the formula for variance of Y:

$$\mathbf{Var}\left[Y\right] = \frac{\theta^2}{(\alpha - 1)^2(\alpha - 2)} \tag{1.47}$$

Indeed.

$$\mathbf{Var}\left[Y\right] = \mathbf{E}\left[Y^2\right] - \left(\mathbf{E}\left[Y\right]\right)^2 = \frac{\theta^2}{(\alpha - 1)(\alpha - 2)} - \left(\frac{\theta}{\alpha - 1}\right)^2 =$$

$$= \frac{\theta^2}{(\alpha - 1)}\left(\frac{1}{\alpha - 2} - \frac{1}{\alpha - 1}\right) = \frac{\theta^2}{(\alpha - 1)^2(\alpha - 2)}(\alpha - 1 - \alpha + 2) = \frac{\theta^2}{(\alpha - 1)^2(\alpha - 2)}.$$

1.3.7 Normal Distribution

A real-valued random variable Z follows the **standard** normal distribution if its **pdf** is

$$f\left(x\right) = \frac{1}{\sqrt{2\pi}} e^{-x^2/2} \quad \text{for} \quad -\infty < x < \infty. \tag{1.48}$$

It can be shown that

$$\mathbf{E}\left[Z\right] = 0 \quad \text{and} \quad \mathbf{E}\left[Z^2\right] = 1.$$

Thus, the variance of the standard normal random variable is

$$\mathbf{Var}\left[Z\right] = \mathbf{E}\left[Z^2\right] - \left(\mathbf{E}\left[Z\right]\right)^2 = 1.$$

A random variable X has a **general** normal distribution, with parameters μ and σ^2 if its **pdf** is

$$f\left(x \,|\, \mu,\, \sigma\right) = \frac{1}{\sqrt{2\pi}\sigma} \exp\left\{-\frac{(x - \mu)^2}{2\sigma^2}\right\}, \tag{1.49}$$

where $-\infty < \mu < \infty$ and $\sigma > 0$. This distribution is usually denoted as $\mathbf{N}\left[\mu,\, \sigma^2\right]$.

The standard normal distribution $\mathbf{N}\left[0,\, 1\right]$ is a particular case of the general normal distribution, with parameters $\mu = 0$ and $\sigma^2 = 1$.

Moments of the general normal distribution are

$$\mathbf{E}\left[X\right] = \mu \quad \text{and} \quad \mathbf{Var}\left[X\right] = \sigma^2. \tag{1.50}$$

Moreover, the transformed variable,

$$Z = \frac{1}{\sigma}\left(X - \mu\right),$$

follows the standard normal distribution with the density (1.48). Alternatively, if Z is a standard normal random variable, then $X = \mu + \sigma Z$ will have the normal distribution with parameters (μ, σ^2), described by (1.49).

If X and Y are independent random variables with $X \sim \mathbf{N}(\mu_X, \sigma_X^2)$ and $Y \sim \mathbf{N}(\mu_Y, \sigma_Y^2)$, then $W = aX + bY \sim \mathbf{N}(\mu_W, \sigma_W^2)$.

In particular, if n random variables X_i are independent and normally-distributed, with parameters μ and σ^2, their sum is normally-distributed, with parameters $n\mu$ and $n\sigma^2$.

1.3.8 Lognormal Distribution

Let X be a normally-distributed random variable, $X \sim \mathbf{N}\left[\mu, \sigma^2\right]$, then a transformed variable, $Y = \exp[X]$, will follow the **lognormal** distribution, with parameters μ and σ.

One can derive the density of the lognormal distribution; however, all moments for Y can be found by using the moment-generating function (MGF) for the normal distribution.

Recall that the MGF for X is defined as

$$\mathbf{M}(t) = \mathbf{E}\left[e^{tX}\right] = \exp\left[\mu t + \frac{1}{2}\sigma^2 t^2\right]. \tag{1.51}$$

This function exists (the integral converges) for any real t.

Using the identity (1.51), moments of the lognormal distribution are:

$$\mathbf{E}\left[Y\right] = \mathbf{M}(1) = \exp\left[\mu + \frac{1}{2}\sigma^2\right] \quad \text{and}$$

$$\mathbf{E}\left[Y^2\right] = \mathbf{M}(2) = \exp\left[2\mu + \frac{1}{2}\cdot 2^2\sigma^2\right] = \exp\left[2\mu + 2\sigma^2\right]. \tag{1.52}$$

This implies the formula for the variance of a lognormal random variable:

$$\mathbf{Var}\left[Y\right] = \exp\left[2\mu + 2\sigma^2\right] - \exp\left[2\mu + \sigma^2\right] = \exp\left[2\mu + \sigma^2\right]\left(e^{\sigma^2} - 1\right)$$

In general, using (1.51) again,

$$\mathbf{E}[Y^k] = \exp\left[k\mu + 0.5k^2\sigma^2\right], \quad k = 1, 2, \ldots.$$

1.3.9 Pareto Distribution

A random variable X has a two-parameter Pareto or Lomax distribution, with parameters α and θ, if its **pdf** and **CDF** functions are given by

$$f_X(x) = \frac{\alpha\theta^\alpha}{(x+\theta)^{\alpha+1}} \quad \text{and} \quad F_X(x) = 1 - \left(\frac{\theta}{x+\theta}\right)^\alpha. \tag{1.53}$$

For any integer $-1 < n < \alpha$,

$$\mathbf{E}[X^n] = \frac{\theta^n \Gamma(n+1)\Gamma(\alpha-n)}{\Gamma(\alpha)} = \frac{\theta^n \cdot n!}{(\alpha-1)(\alpha-2)\ldots(\alpha-n)}.$$

In particular,

$$\mathbf{E}[X] = \frac{\theta}{\alpha - 1} \text{ and } \mathbf{E}[X^2] = \frac{2\theta^2}{(\alpha-1)(\alpha-2)}. \tag{1.54}$$

Thus,

$$\mathbf{Var}(X) = \frac{\theta^2 \cdot \alpha}{(\alpha-1)^2(\alpha-2)}.$$

Indeed.

$$\mathbf{Var}(X) = \mathbf{E}[X^2] - \mathbf{E}[X]^2 = \frac{2\theta^2}{(\alpha-1)(\alpha-2)} - \left(\frac{\theta}{\alpha-1}\right)^2 =$$

$$= \frac{\theta^2}{\alpha-1}\left(\frac{2}{\alpha-2} - \frac{1}{\alpha-1}\right) = \frac{\theta^2}{(\alpha-1)^2(\alpha-2)}(2\alpha - 2 - \alpha + 2) = \frac{\theta^2 \cdot \alpha}{(\alpha-1)^2(\alpha-2)}.$$

1.3.10 Beta and Pareto Distributions Connected

Recall that a continuous random variable Q has beta distribution, with parameters (a,b), where $a > 0$ and $b > 0$, if its density is

$$f(q) = f_Q(q) = \frac{\Gamma(a+b)}{\Gamma(a) \cdot \Gamma(b)} \cdot q^{a-1} \cdot (1-q)^{b-1}, \ 0 < q < 1, \tag{1.55}$$

where $\Gamma(a)$ is defined by (1.25).

Various actuarial applications operate with either

$$W = \frac{1-Q}{Q} \text{ or } Y = \frac{1}{Q}, \ W = Y - 1.$$

Distribution of W and Y are similar and can be derived using (1.40). They are variations of what is known as Pareto distribution. In view of applications needed for credibility theory, our attention will be focused on particular cases of Pareto distributions and their first and second moments.

Since $0 < Q < 1$, the range of $Y = Q^{-1}$ is $1 < Y < \infty$. Bounds of W, respectively, are $0 < W < \infty$. For $y > 1$ the density for $Y = Q^{-1}$, according to (1.40), is

$$g(y) = f_Y(y) = y^{-2} \cdot \frac{\Gamma(a+b)}{\Gamma(a) \cdot \Gamma(b)} \cdot \frac{1}{y^{a-1}} \cdot \left(1 - \frac{1}{y}\right)^{b-1} = \frac{\Gamma(a+b)}{\Gamma(a) \cdot \Gamma(b)} \cdot \frac{(y-1)^{b-1}}{y^{a+b}}. \tag{1.56}$$

Since $W = Y - 1$, its density is

$$f_W(w) = g(w+1) = \frac{\Gamma(a+b)}{\Gamma(a) \cdot \Gamma(b)} \cdot \frac{w^{b-1}}{(w+1)^{a+b}}, \tag{1.57}$$

which corresponds to a three-parameter Pareto distribution with $\theta = 1$.

Let us evaluate first and second moments for W and Y.

Lemma 1.3.2 *If W has density (1.57) and $a > 1$, then*

$$\boldsymbol{E}[W] = \frac{b}{a-1}. \tag{1.58}$$

Proof. Since $W = (1 - Q)/Q$, its expected value is

$$\mathbf{E}[W] = \frac{\Gamma(a+b)}{\Gamma(a) \cdot \Gamma(b)} \int_0^1 \frac{1-q}{q} \cdot q^{a-1} \cdot (1-q)^{b-1} \, dq = \frac{\Gamma(a+b)}{\Gamma(a) \cdot \Gamma(b)} \int_0^1 q^{a-2} \cdot (1-q)^b \, dq.$$

Using (1.28), we have

$$\mathbf{E}[W] = \frac{\Gamma(a+b)}{\Gamma(a) \cdot \Gamma(b)} \cdot \frac{\Gamma(a-1) \cdot \Gamma(b+1)}{\Gamma(a+b)} = \frac{\Gamma(a-1) \cdot \Gamma(b+1)}{\Gamma(a) \cdot \Gamma(b)} = \frac{b}{a-1}.$$

Notice that for $Y = W + 1$ the expectation is

$$\mathbf{E}[Y] = \frac{b}{a-1} + 1 = \frac{a+b-1}{a-1}. \tag{1.59}$$

Lemma 1.3.3 *If $W = Q^{-1} - 1$ has density (1.57) with $a > 2$, then*

$$\boldsymbol{E}[W^2] = \frac{b \cdot (b+1)}{(a-1) \cdot (a-2)}. \tag{1.60}$$

Proof.

$$\mathbf{E}[W^2] = \frac{\Gamma(a+b)}{\Gamma(a) \cdot \Gamma(b)} \cdot \int_0^1 \left(\frac{1-q}{q} \right)^2 \cdot q^{a-1} \cdot (1-q)^{b-1} \, dq =$$

$$= \frac{\Gamma(a+b)}{\Gamma(a) \cdot \Gamma(b)} \cdot \frac{\Gamma(a-2) \cdot \Gamma(b+2)}{\Gamma(a) \cdot \Gamma(b)} = \frac{b \cdot (b+1)}{(a-1) \cdot (a-2)}.$$

Lemma 1.3.4 *If $Y = Q^{-1}$ has density (1.56) with $a > 2$, then*

$$\boldsymbol{E}[Y^2] = \frac{(a+b-1)(a+b-2)}{(a-1)(a-2)}.$$

Proof.

$$\mathbf{E}[Y^2] = \frac{\Gamma(a+b)}{\Gamma(a)\Gamma(b)} \int_0^1 q^{-2} \cdot q^{a-1} (1-q)^{b-1} \, dq = \frac{\Gamma(a+b)}{\Gamma(a)\Gamma(b)} \int_0^1 q^{a-3} (1-q)^{b-1} \, dq =$$

$$= \frac{\Gamma(a+b)}{\Gamma(a)\Gamma(b)} \cdot \frac{\Gamma(a-2)\Gamma(b)}{\Gamma(a+b-2)} = \frac{(a+b-1)(a+b-2)}{(a-1)(a-2)}$$

Since $Y = W + 1$, their variances coincide:

$$\mathbf{Var}[W] = \mathbf{Var}[Y] = \frac{b(a+b-1)}{(a-1)^2(a-2)} \tag{1.61}$$

1.4   Law of Large Numbers

The law of large numbers (LLN) is a theorem that describes the result of performing the same experiment a large number of times. According to the law, the average of the results obtained from a large number of trials should be close to the expected value and will tend to become closer as more trials are performed.

There are two versions of the law of large numbers: **strong law** and **weak law**.

Both versions of the law state that if $X_1, X_2, \ldots$ is an infinite sequence of the independent, identically distributed (iid) random variables with the expected value $\mathbf{E}[X_i] = \mu$, then the sample mean

$$\bar{X}_n = \frac{1}{n}\left(X_1 + X_2 + \cdots + X_n\right)$$

converges to the expected value,

$$\bar{X}_n \to \mu \ \text{ as } n \to \infty,$$

with virtual certainty.

The difference between the strong and the weak version is concerned with the mode of convergence being asserted.

1.4.1 The Weak Law of Large Numbers

The weak law of large numbers states that the sample average **converges in probability** toward the expected value:

$$\bar{X}_n \xrightarrow{P} \mu \ \text{ as } n \to \infty$$

That is, for any $\epsilon > 0$,

$$\lim_{n\to\infty} \mathbf{P}\left(|\bar{X}_n - \mu| > \epsilon\right) = 0.$$

Interpreting this result, the weak law states that for any nonzero margin specified, no matter how small, with a sufficiently large sample there will be a very high probability that the average of the observations will be close to the expected value, that is within the margin.

1.4.2 The Strong Law of Large Numbers

The strong law of large numbers states that the sample average **converges almost surely** toward the expected value:

$$\bar{X}_n \xrightarrow{a.s.} \mu \ \text{ as } n \to \infty$$

That is,

$$\mathbf{P}\left(\lim_{n\to\infty} \bar{X}_n = \mu\right) = 1.$$

What this means is that as the number of trials n increases, the probability that the average of the observations is approaching the expected value will be equal to one.

1.5   Central Limit Theorem

The classical **central limit theorem (CLT)** establishes that, in some situations, when independent random variables are added, their properly normalized sum tends toward a normal distribution (informally a "bell curve"), even if the original variables themselves are not normally-distributed. It states that if $\{X_1, X_2, \cdots, X_n\}$ is a random sample of size n, that is, a sequence of iid random variables drawn from a distribution with expected value $\mathbf{E}[X_i] = \mu$ and finite variance $\mathbf{Var}[X_i] = \sigma^2$, then the random variable $\sqrt{n}\left(\bar{X}_n - \mu\right)$ approximates the normal distribution with mean 0 and variance σ^2:

$$\lim_{n \to \infty} \mathbf{P}\left(\sqrt{n}\left(\bar{X}_n - \mu\right) \leq z\right) = \Phi\left(\frac{z}{\sigma}\right),$$

where $\Phi(x)$ is the standard normal **CDF** evaluated at x.

1.5.1   Normal Approximation to the Binomial

Let Y be a binomially-distributed random variable, with parameters n and p: $Y \sim \mathbf{Bin}[n, p]$. Its expectation and variance are

$$\mathbf{E}[Y] = np \quad \text{and} \quad \mathbf{Var}[Y] = np(1-p).$$

Since Y can be presented as a sum of n Bernoulli random variables,

$$Y = \sum_{i=1}^{n} X_i,$$

by the CLT, as n increases, the distribution of a sample proportion,

$$\hat{p} = \bar{X} = \frac{Y}{n},$$

becomes approximately normal, with parameters

$$\mu = \frac{1}{n} \cdot \mathbf{E}[Y] = \frac{1}{n} \cdot np = p \text{ and}$$

$$\sigma^2 = \frac{1}{n^2} \cdot \mathbf{Var}(Y) = \frac{1}{n^2} \cdot n\mathbf{Var}(X) = \frac{p(1-p)}{n}.$$

Since for a large sample size n the distribution of Y is approximately normal, with parameters $(np;\ np(1-p))$, a statistic

$$Z_n = \frac{Y - np}{\sqrt{np(1-p)}} = \frac{\hat{p} - p}{\sqrt{p(1-p)/n}}, \tag{1.62}$$

is approximately normal, $\mathbf{N}[0, 1]$, or, equivalently,

$$\lim_{n \longrightarrow \infty} \mathbf{P}[Z_n \leq z] = \Phi(z),$$

where $\Phi(z)$ denotes CDF of the standard normal distribution.

Note that since (1.62) holds, the same statistic Z_n appears in the normal approximation to the sample proportion.

Conclusion

In this chapter we reviewed commonly used notions and definitions used in probability theory. Detailed explanations may be found in Sheldon M. Ross[8] although any textbook covering random variables, probability distributions, expected values, and higher moments would also be appropriate.

As readers refreshed their knowledge of probability, it is helpful to practice and assure that important notions and techniques can be efficiently utilized. Exercises at the end of this chapter highlight commonly used probability models, distributions, and relations carried out by expectations and moments. In addition, they provide the opportunity to distinguish between discrete and continuous models.

Exercises

1.1. Probability: Binomial Distribution

Let X be the random variable for number of claims, X is binomially-distributed, with parameters $m = 10$ and $q = 0.1$.

Calculate the probability of having two or more claims.

1.2. Moments: Binomial Distribution

Let X be again binomially-distributed, with parameters $m = 10$ and $q = 0.1$.

Calculate the first and second moments of X.

1.3. Probability: Geometric Distribution

Suppose the claim rate is $q = 0.1$ per year. Assume that the variable X represents the number of years preceding the first claim for the insured. Such variable has a geometric distribution with parameter q.

Calculate the following:

(a) The probability that there will be **precisely** 5 years before the first claim occurs

(b) The probability that there will be **at least** 5 years before the first claim occurs

(c) The probability that the first claim occurs **before** the fifth year

(d) The probability that there will be **at least** 8 years with no claim, given that there were 4 years with no claim

1.4. Moments: Negative Binomial Distribution

Let X be a negatively binomial-distributed random variable, with parameters $r = 10$ and $q = 0.1$.

Calculate the expected value and the variance of X.

1.5. Probabilities and Percentiles: Normal Distribution

Suppose that X has a normal distribution, with parameters $\mu = 3$ and $\sigma^2 = 4$.

Calculate the following:

(a) The probability that $X < 4$

(b) The probability that $X \geq 2$

(c) The probability that $-1 \leq X < 4$

(d) The upper-fifth percentile for X

(e) The lower-fifth percentile for X

(f) The proportion of X values between the lower- and upper-fifth percentiles.

1.6. Moments: Lognormal Distribution

Suppose the random variable Y has a lognormal distribution, with parameters $\mu = 3$ and $\sigma = 2$.

Calculate the following:

(a) The mean and variance of Y

(b) The median of Y

(c) The upper- and lower-fifth percentiles for Y, given that the top fifth percentile for Z is $Z_{0.05} = 1.645$

(d) The probability that Y will exceed its expected value

1.7. Independence of Two Discrete Random Variables

Suppose variables (X, Y) are purely discrete.

In this case, $p(x, y) = \mathbf{P}\left[(X = x) \bigcap (Y = y)\right]$ is the **joint pmf**.

Suppose the joint distribution of two discrete random variables X and Y is

$$\mathbf{P}(X = 0, Y = 0) = 0.35; \quad \mathbf{P}(X = 0, Y = 1) = 0.15;$$
$$\mathbf{P}(X = 1, Y = 0) = 0.15; \quad \mathbf{P}(X = 1, Y = 1) = 0.35.$$

Determine if these random variables are independent.

1.8. Correlation of Two Discrete Random Variables

You are given the following joint distribution of two random variables X and Y:

(x, y)	$\mathbf{P}((X, Y) = (x, y))$	(x, y)	$\mathbf{P}((X, Y) = (x, y))$	(x, y)	$\mathbf{P}((X, Y) = (x, y))$
(0, 0)	0.35	(1, 0)	0.15	(2, 0)	0.05
(0, 1)	0.10	(1, 1)	0.10	(2, 1)	0.05
(0, 2)	0.05	(1, 2)	0.05	(2, 2)	0.10

Calculate the correlation of X and Y.

1.9. Empirical Moments

A doughnut shop has purchased a liability policy for its doughnut-making machines from the same insurance company for the past 5 years. The number of service calls by the company as the result of machine malfunctions is shown in the following table:

Year	Service Calls
2010	5
2009	2
2008	4
2007	3
2006	9

Calculate the **variance** of the empirical distribution of the number of service calls per year.

1.10. Functions of Moments

For a random variable X you are given the following:

(i) $\mathbf{E}[X] = 4$

(ii) $\mathbf{Var}(X) = 90$

(iii) $\mathbf{E}[X^3] = 20$

Let μ_n be the nth **central** moment of X and let σ be its standard deviation.

Define the **skewness** of X as

$$\gamma_1 = \frac{\mu_3}{\sigma^3}.$$

Calculate γ_1.

1.11. Definition of an Expectation

By definition, a continuous random variable X has two-parameter Pareto distribution if its probability density function $f(x)$ is defined as follows:

$$f(x) = \frac{\alpha\theta^\alpha}{(x+\theta)^{\alpha+1}}, \; x > 0, \; \theta > 0, \; \alpha > 1$$

Using definition of expectation, show that

$$\mathbf{E}[X] = \frac{\theta}{\alpha - 1}.$$

1.12. Mode of a Random Variable

The random variable X has the density function

$$f(x) = \frac{5x^2}{(2+x^3)^4}, \; 0 < x < \infty.$$

Determine the **mode** of X.

1.13. Poisson Random Variable

Suppose a count of exposures (N) has Poisson distribution, with intensity $\lambda = 2$ events per year.

Calculate the following:

(a) The probability that N takes an **odd** value

(b) The conditional distribution of N, given that N takes an **odd** value

(c) The conditional expectation of N, given that N is **odd**, and evaluate it for $\lambda = 4$.

1.14. Probability of Choosing an Item

Two baskets contain 10 similarly shaped balls. The first basket contains 2 blue and 8 red balls. The second one has 5 blue and 5 red balls. It is known that the first basket is **three times** as likely to be selected than the second one. Suppose that the ball chosen is red.

Calculate the probability that it was drawn from the first basket.

1.15. Correlation of Two Random Variables

Let X and Y be Poisson random variables. You are given the following information about the expected values for X and Y and the variance of their difference:

(i) $\mathbf{E}[X] = 16$ and $\mathbf{E}[Y] = 9$

(ii) $\mathbf{Var}[X - Y] = 13$

Calculate the following:

(a) The **covariance** between X and Y

(b) Their **correlation** coefficient

Solutions

1.1. Recall that if

$$\{X_j\}, \quad j = 1, 2, \ldots, m$$

are m independent observations of a zero-one variable, associated with the claim occurrence, so that $X_j = 1$ if the jth insured has a claim and $X_j = 0$ otherwise, then the random variable, $X = \sum_{j=1}^{m} X_j$, represents the total number of claims within the observation period. Suppose $\mathbf{P}[X_j = 1] = q$, where $0 < q < 1$ is a claim rate. Then $X = \sum_{j=1}^{m} X_j$ is binomially-distributed, with parameters m and q.

To find $\mathbf{P}[X \geq 2]$, we may want to add 9 individual probabilities for events,

$$(X = 2), \ldots, (X = 10).$$

However, there is a faster way to get the result, by using the **complementary event**:

$$\mathbf{P}[X \geq 2] = 1 - \mathbf{P}\left[(X = 0) \bigcup (X = 1)\right]$$

Using (1.8), we have

$$\mathbf{P}[X = k] = \frac{m!}{k!\,(m-k)!}\, q^k\, (1-q)^{m-k} \quad \text{for} \quad k = 0, 1, \ldots, m.$$

Therefore,

$$\mathbf{P}[X \geq 2] = 1 - (1 - 0.1)^{10} - 10 \cdot (0.1)(1 - 0.1)^9 = 1 - (0.9)^{10} - (0.9)^9$$
$$= 1 - [0.3487 + 0.3874] = 1 - 0.7361 = 0.2639 \approx \mathbf{0.26}.$$

1.2. Using (1.9) for an expectation and variance of a binomially-distributed random variable, we have

$$\mathbf{E}[X] = mq = 10 \cdot 0.1 = 1 \quad \text{and} \quad \mathbf{Var}[X] = mq(1-q) = 10 \cdot (0.1) \cdot (1 - 0.1) = 0.9.$$

Calculating the second moment of X, we obtain

$$\mathbf{E}[X^2] = \mathbf{Var}[X] + (\mathbf{E}[X])^2 = 0.9 + (1)^2 = \mathbf{1.9}.$$

1.3. (a) Recall that, by (1.10), if X is a geometrically-distributed random variable, with parameter q,

$$p_k = \mathbf{P}[X = k] = q\,(1-q)^k \quad \text{for} \quad k = 0, 1, \ldots$$

Then, for $k = 5$ and $q = 0.1$, we have

$$\mathbf{P}[X = 5] = (1 - q)^5 \cdot q = (0.9)^5 \cdot 0.1 = 0.05905 \approx \mathbf{0.059}.$$

(b) The probability that there will be **at least** 5 years before the first claim occurs can be represented as the sum

$$\mathbf{P}\left[X \geq 5\right] = \sum_{k=5}^{\infty} \mathbf{P}\left[X = k\right] = \sum_{j=0}^{\infty} \mathbf{P}\left[X = 5 + j\right] = \sum_{j=0}^{\infty} q \cdot (1-q)^{j+5} =$$

$$= (1-q)^5 \cdot q \cdot \sum_{j=0}^{\infty} (1-q)^j = (1-q)^5 \cdot q \frac{1}{1-(1-q)} = (1-q)^5.$$

Thus, for any n,

$$\mathbf{P}\left[X \geq n\right] = (1-q)^n.$$

Using $q = 0.1$, we obtain

$$\mathbf{P}\left[X \geq 5\right] = (0.9)^5 = 0.59049 \approx \mathbf{0.59}.$$

(c) To find the probability that the first claim occurs **before** the fifth year, we use the complementary event rule:

$$\mathbf{P}\left[X < 5\right] = 1 - \mathbf{P}\left[X \geq 5\right] = 1 - (0.9)^5 = 1 - 0.59049 = 0.40951 \approx \mathbf{0.41}.$$

(d) The probability that there will be **at least** 8 years with no claim, given that there were 4 years with no claim, can be found by using the definition of a conditional probability:

$$\mathbf{P}\left[X \geq 8 \,|\, X \geq 4\right] = \frac{\mathbf{P}\left[(X \geq 8) \cap (X \geq 4)\right]}{\mathbf{P}\left[X \geq 4\right]} = \frac{\mathbf{P}\left[X \geq 8\right]}{\mathbf{P}\left[X \geq 4\right]} = \frac{(1-q)^8}{(1-q)^4} = (1-q)^4$$

Thus, for any $n \geq m$,

$$\mathbf{P}\left[X \geq n \,|\, X \geq m\right] = (1-q)^{n-m}.$$

Using $q = 0.1$, we obtain

$$\mathbf{P}\left[X \geq 8 \,|\, X \geq 4\right] = (1-q)^4 = 0.6561 \approx \mathbf{0.66}.$$

1.4. Recall that if instead of one insured with X_j, viewed as the number of years prior to the first claim, we consider the sum of $r = 10$ independent observations, each of them being geometrically-distributed, with the claim rate $q = 0.1$, then $X = \sum_{j=1}^{r} X_j$ will have the negative binomial distribution, with parameters r and q.

X can be interpreted as the event such that $[X = k]$ occurs if and only if there are k years with no claim among r observed policies.

Using the formula (1.14) for the expectation and variance of X, we have

$$\mathbf{E}\left[X\right] = r \cdot \frac{1-q}{q} = 10 \cdot \frac{0.9}{0.1} = 9, \quad \text{and}$$

$$\mathbf{Var}\left[X\right] = r \cdot \frac{(1-q)}{q^2} = 10 \cdot \frac{0.9}{0.01} = 900.$$

1.5. Assume that X has a normal distribution, $\mathbf{N}\left[\mu, \sigma^2\right]$. Then $Z = (X - \mu)/\sigma$ is standard normal with parameters $\mu = 0$ and $\sigma^2 = 1$.

Using the table for cumulative distribution function associated with the standard normal random variable, Z, one can determine various probabilities, such as

$$\mathbf{P}\left[Z \leq a\right] = \mathbf{P}\left[Z < a\right] = \Phi\left(a\right), \quad \text{or}$$

$$\mathbf{P}\left[Z > b\right] = \mathbf{P}\left[Z \geq b\right] = 1 - \Phi(b).$$

The probability that Z falls into an interval, open-ended or closed, is calculated as

$$\mathbf{P}\left[a \leq Z \leq b\right] = \Phi\left(b\right) - \Phi\left(a\right), \ a < b.$$

Since $\mu = 3$ and $\sigma^2 = 4$, the variable $Z = (X - 3)/2$ has the standard normal distribution. Therefore,

(a)

$$\mathbf{P}\left[X < 4\right] = \mathbf{P}\left[Z < \frac{4 - 3}{2}\right] = \mathbf{P}\left[Z < 0.5\right] = \Phi(0.5) = \mathbf{0.6915}.$$

(b)

$$\mathbf{P}\left[X \geq 2\right] = 1 - \mathbf{P}\left[X < 2\right] = 1 - \mathbf{P}\left[Z < \frac{2 - 3}{2} = -0.5\right] =$$

$$= 1 - \mathbf{P}\left[Z < -0.5\right] = 1 - \Phi(-0.5) = 1 - 0.3085 = \mathbf{0.6915}.$$

(c)

$$\mathbf{P}\left[-1 \leq X < 4\right] = \mathbf{P}\left[\frac{-1 - 3}{2} < Z < \frac{4 - 3}{2}\right] = \mathbf{P}\left[-2 < Z < 0.5\right] =$$

$$= \Phi(0.5) - \Phi(-2) = 0.6915 - 0.0228 = \mathbf{0.6687}.$$

The upper $100q$ **percentile** for any continuous random variable W is defined for any number $0 < q < 1$, as the solution of the equation $\mathbf{P}\left[W \geq W_q\right] = q$, or, equivalently,

$$W_q = F^{-1}\left(1 - q\right).$$

The lower $100q$ percentile is $F^{-1}\left(q\right)$ and can be identified with w_{1-q}.

(d) The upper-fifth percentile, $X_{0.05}$, is defined as

$$X_{0.05} = \mu + \sigma \cdot Z_{0.05} = 3 + 2 \cdot 1.645 = \mathbf{6.29}.$$

(e) The lower-fifth percentile for X is the 95th-upper percentile, so

$$X_{0.95} = \mu + \sigma \cdot Z_{0.95} = 3 + 2 \cdot (-1.645) = \textbf{-0.29}.$$

(f) The proportion of X values between the lower- and upper-fifth percentiles is

$$\mathbf{P}\left[-0.29 \leq X \leq 6.29\right] = 0.95 - 0.05 = \mathbf{0.90}.$$

This is not surprising, since 5% of the population of X values is below (-0.29) and also 5% of the population will exceed 6.29. Therefore, the remaining part, which is

$$100\% - 5\% - 5\% = 90\%,$$

will be between the percentiles.

1.6. Recall that if X has a normal distribution, $\mathbf{N}\left[\mu, \sigma^2\right]$, then $Y = \exp\left[X\right]$ has log-normal distribution with the same parameters.

Note that

$$Z = \frac{\ln\left(Y\right) - \mu}{\sigma}$$

has the standard normal distribution.

(a) Using (1.52), the expected value and the variance of a lognormally-distributed random variable, with parameters μ and σ, is calculated as follows:

$$\mathbf{E}\left[Y\right] = \exp\left[\mu + \frac{1}{2}\sigma^2\right]$$

and

$$\mathbf{Var}\left[Y\right] = \exp\left[2\mu + \sigma^2\right]\left(\exp\left[\sigma^2\right] - 1\right)$$

Therefore,

$$\mathbf{E}\left[Y\right] = e^{(3+0.5\cdot4)} = e^5 = \mathbf{148.41} \text{ and}$$

$$\mathbf{Var}\left[Y\right] = e^{(2\cdot3+4)} \cdot \left(e^4 - 1\right) = e^{10} \cdot \left(e^4 - 1\right) = \mathbf{22{,}080.06}.$$

(b) The median of Y is determined by the median of X as

$$Y_{0.5} = \exp\left[X_{0.5}\right] = e^3 = \mathbf{20.09}.$$

(c) Given that the top-fifth percentile for Z is $Z_{0.05} = 1.645$, the upper- and lower-fifth percentiles for Y can be derived using the inverse transformation. Thus, since

$$Z = \frac{\ln\left(Y\right) - \mu}{\sigma},$$

the inverse transformation is

$$Y = \exp\left[\mu + \sigma \cdot Z\right] = e^{3+2\cdot Z}.$$

Hence, the upper- and lower-fifth percentile for Y are

$$Y_{0.05} = e^{(3+2\cdot1.645)} = \mathbf{539.15}$$

$$Y_{0.95} = e^{(3-2\cdot1.645)} = \mathbf{0.75}.$$

(d) The probability that Y will exceed its expected value can be determined as

$$\mathbf{P}\left[Y > \mathbf{E}\left[Y\right]\right] = \mathbf{P}\left[Y > \exp\left(\mu + \frac{1}{2}\sigma^2\right)\right] = \mathbf{P}\left[\ln Y > \mu + 0.5\sigma^2\right] =$$

$$= 1 - \Phi\left(\frac{0.5\sigma^2}{\sigma}\right) = 1 - \Phi\left(0.5\sigma\right) = 1 - \Phi(1) = 1 - 0.8413 = \mathbf{0.1587}.$$

1.7. The joint distribution of (X, Y) can be described as follows:

	$x = 0$	$x = 1$
$y = 0$	0.35	0.15
$y = 1$	0.15	0.35

To find $f_X(x)$, we use the formula $f_X(x) = \sum_y f(x, y)$. Then,

$$f_X(0) = \sum_y f(0, y) = 0.35 + 0.15 = 0.5$$

$$f_X(1) = \sum_y f(1, y) = 0.15 + 0.35 = 0.5.$$

Similarly, to find $f_Y(y)$, we use the formula $f_Y(y) = \sum_x f(x, y)$. Then,

$$f_Y(0) = \sum_x f(x, 0) = 0.35 + 0.15 = 0.5$$

$$f_Y(1) = \sum_x f(x, 1) = 0.15 + 0.35 = 0.5.$$

Note that

$$\sum_x f_X(x) = \sum_y f_Y(y) = 1.$$

Then,

$$\mu_X = 0 \cdot 0.5 + 1 \cdot 0.5 = 0.5$$
$$\mu_Y = 0 \cdot 0.5 + 1 \cdot 0.5 = 0.5.$$

Let $Z = X \cdot Y$. Then,

$$Z = \begin{cases} 0, & p = 0.35 + 0.15 + 0.15 = 0.65 \\ 1, & p = 0.35. \end{cases}$$

Thus, $\mathbf{E}[Z] = \mathbf{E}[XY] = 0 \cdot 0.65 + 1 \cdot 0.35 = 0.35$.

Note that $\mathbf{E}[X]\mathbf{E}[Y] = 0.5^2 = 0.25$.

Since $\mathbf{E}[X]\mathbf{E}[Y] \neq \mathbf{E}[X]\mathbf{E}[Y]$, these random variables are not independent.

In fact, since

$$\mathbf{Cov}(X, Y) = \mathbf{E}[XY] - \mathbf{E}[X]\mathbf{E}[Y] = 0.35 - 0.25 = 0.10,$$

these random variables are positively correlated.

1.8. The given probability table can be recast as follows:

	x = 0	x = 1	x = 2
y = 0	0.35	0.15	0.05
y = 1	0.10	0.10	0.05
y = 2	0.05	0.05	0.10

To find $f_X(x)$, we use the formula $f_X(x) = \sum_y f(x, y)$ Then,

$$f_X(0) = \sum_{y} f(0, y) = 0.35 + 0.1 + 0.05 = 0.5$$

$$f_X(1) = \sum_{y} f(1, y) = 0.15 + 0.1 + 0.05 = 0.3$$

$$f_X(2) = \sum_{y} f(2, y) = 0.05 + 0.05 + 0.1 = 0.2.$$

Similarly, to find $f_Y(y)$, we use the formula $f_Y(y) = \sum_x f(x, y)$ Then,

$$f_Y(0) = \sum_{x} f(x, 0) = 0.35 + 0.15 + 0.05 = 0.55$$

$$f_Y(1) = \sum_{x} f(x, 1) = 0.1 + 0.1 + 0.05 = 0.25$$

$$f_Y(2) = \sum_{x} f(x, 2) = 0.05 + 0.05 + 0.1 = 0.2.$$

Note that

$$\sum_{x} f_X(x) = \sum_{y} f_Y(y) = 1.$$

Then,

$$\mu_X = 0 \cdot 0.5 + 1 \cdot 0.3 + 2 \cdot 0.2 = 0.7$$
$$\mu_Y = 0 \cdot 0.55 + 1 \cdot 0.25 + 2 \cdot 0.2 = 0.65$$
$$\mathbf{E}[X^2] = 0 \cdot 0.5 + 1 \cdot 0.3 + 4 \cdot 0.2 = 1.1$$
$$\mathbf{E}[Y^2] = 0 \cdot 0.55 + 1 \cdot 0.25 + 4 \cdot 0.2 = 1.05$$
$$\mathbf{Var}(X) = 1.1 - 0.7^2 = 0.61$$
$$\mathbf{Var}(Y) = 1.05 - 0.65^2 = 0.6275.$$

Let $Z = X \cdot Y$. Then,

$$Z = \begin{cases} 0, & p = 0.7 \\ 1, & p = 0.1 \\ 2, & p = 0.1 \\ 4, & p = 0.1. \end{cases}$$

Hence, $\mathbf{E}[Z] = 0.1 + 2 \cdot 0.1 + 4 \cdot 0.1 = 0.7$ and

$$\mathbf{Cov}(X, Y) = \mathbf{E}[XY] - \mathbf{E}[X]\mathbf{E}[Y] = 0.7 - 0.7 \cdot 0.65 = 0.245,$$

and the correlation coefficient is

$$\rho_{XY} = \frac{\mathbf{Cov}(X, Y)}{\sigma_X \sigma_Y} = \frac{0.245}{(0.61 \cdot 0.6275)^{0.5}} = \mathbf{0.40}.$$

1.9. By definition of a variance of the empirical distribution,

$$\mathbf{Var}(X) = \frac{1}{5} \sum_{i=1}^{5} (X_i - \bar{X})^2.$$

The sample mean is

$$\bar{X} = \frac{1}{5} \sum_{i=1}^{5} X_i = \frac{1}{5}(5 + 2 + 4 + 3 + 9) = 4.6$$

and

$$X_i - \bar{X} \text{ are } 0.4, \ -2.6, \ -0.6, \ -1.6, \ 4.4.$$

Therefore,

$$\mathbf{Var}(X) = \frac{1}{5}\left(0.16 + 6.76 + 0.36 + 2.56 + 19.36\right) = \frac{1}{5} \cdot 29.2 = \mathbf{5.84}.$$

1.10. We have

$$\gamma_1 = \frac{\mu_3}{\sigma^3}; \ \sigma^3 = (\sigma^2)^{3/2} = (90)^{3/2} = 853.815$$

$$\mu_3 = \mu_3' - 3\mu_2'\mu + 2\mu^3$$

$$\mu_2 = \mu_2' - \mu^2 \Rightarrow \mu_2' = \mu_2 + \mu^2 = 90 + 16 = 106$$

$$\mu_3 = 20 - 3 \cdot 106 \cdot 4 + 2 \cdot 64 = 20 - 1272 + 128 = -1124$$

$$\gamma_1 = -\frac{1124}{853.815} = \mathbf{-1.3164}.$$

1.11. By definition of expectation

$$\mathbf{E}[X] = \int_{-\infty}^{\infty} x f(x) dx = \int_{0}^{\infty} x \cdot \frac{\alpha \theta^\alpha}{(x + \theta)^{\alpha+1}} dx = \alpha \theta^\alpha \int_{0}^{\infty} \frac{x}{(x + \theta)^{\alpha+1}} dx.$$

Let us make a substitution: $u = x + \theta$. Then $x = u - \theta$ and $dx = du$ and the expected value is

$$\mathbf{E}[X] = \alpha \theta^\alpha \int_{\theta}^{\infty} \frac{u - \theta}{u^{\alpha+1}} du = \alpha \theta^\alpha \left(\int_{\theta}^{\infty} u^{-\alpha} du - \theta \int_{\theta}^{\infty} u^{-\alpha-1} du \right) =$$

$$= \alpha \theta^\alpha \left(\frac{u^{-\alpha+1}}{1 - \alpha} \Big|_{\theta}^{\infty} + \frac{\theta u^{-\alpha}}{\alpha} \Big|_{\theta}^{\infty} \right) = \alpha \theta^\alpha \left(-\frac{\theta^{1-\alpha}}{1 - \alpha} - \frac{\theta^{1-\alpha}}{\alpha} \right) = \frac{\theta}{\alpha - 1}.$$

1.12. By definition, a **mode** of the distribution is x such that $f(x)$ is maximized.

Differentiating $f(x)$, we obtain

$$f'(x) = 5 \cdot \frac{2x(2+x^3)^4 - x^2 \cdot 4(2+x^3)^3 \cdot 3x^2}{(2+x^3)^8} = 10 \cdot \frac{x(2+x^3) - 6x^4}{(2+x^3)^5} =$$

$$= 10 \cdot \frac{x(2 - 5x^3)}{(2+x^3)^5}.$$

Solving $f'(x) = 0$, we obtain

$$x(2 - 5x^3) = 0 \Leftrightarrow \left[\begin{array}{l} x = 0 = x_{min} \\ x = \sqrt[3]{2/5} = \sqrt[3]{0.4} =\approx 0.7368 = x_{max}. \end{array} \right.$$

Therefore, the mode is 0.7368.

1.13. Recall that a Taylor series for exponential function for any real u can be written as

$$e^u = \sum_{n=0}^{\infty} \frac{u^n}{n!} \quad \text{and} \quad e^{-u} = \sum_{n=0}^{\infty} \frac{(-u)^n}{n!}.$$

Splitting the sum for e^u into even- and odd-numbered terms, we have

$$e^u = A(u) + B(u) = \sum_{n=0}^{\infty} \frac{u^{2n}}{(2n)!} + \sum_{n=0}^{\infty} \frac{u^{2n+1}}{(2n+1)!},$$

where

$$A = A(u) = \sum_{n=0}^{\infty} \frac{u^{2n}}{(2n)!} \quad \text{and} \quad B = B(u) = \sum_{n=0}^{\infty} \frac{u^{2n+1}}{(2n+1)!}.$$

Note that

$$A + B = e^u \quad \text{and} \quad A - B = e^{-u}.$$

Solving this system of two equations for A and for B, we obtain

$$A = A(u) = \frac{1}{2}\left(e^u + e^{-u}\right) \quad \text{and} \quad B = B(u) = \frac{1}{2}\left(e^u - e^{-u}\right).$$

(a) Recall from (1.17) that if a random variable (Y) follows a Poisson distribution with the intensity parameter λ, then its probability density function is defined as

$$p_k = \mathbf{P}\,[Y = k] = \frac{\lambda^k}{k!}\,e^{-\lambda} \quad \text{for} \quad k = 0, 1, 2, \ldots.$$

Then the probability that N takes an odd value is

$$\mathbf{P}\,[N \text{ is odd}] = \sum_{n=0}^{\infty} \mathbf{P}\,[N = 2n + 1] = \sum_{n=0}^{\infty} \frac{\lambda^{2n+1}}{(2n+1)!}\,e^{-\lambda} =$$

$$= e^{-\lambda} \cdot B\,(\lambda) = e^{-\lambda} \cdot \frac{1}{2}\left(e^{\lambda} - e^{-\lambda}\right) = \frac{1}{2}\left(1 - e^{-2\lambda}\right).$$

Since $\lambda = 2$, we obtain

$$\mathbf{P}\left[N \text{ is odd }\right] = \frac{1}{2}\left[1 - e^{-2\cdot 2}\right] \approx \mathbf{0.4908}.$$

Similarly,

$$\mathbf{P}\left[N \text{ is even }\right] = \sum_{n=0}^{\infty} \mathbf{P}\left[N = 2n\right] = \sum_{n=0}^{\infty} \frac{\lambda^{2n}}{(2n)!}\, e^{-\lambda} = e^{-\lambda} \cdot A\left(\lambda\right) =$$

$$= e^{-\lambda} \cdot \frac{1}{2}\left(e^{u} + e^{-u}\right) = \frac{1}{2}\left(1 + e^{-2\lambda}\right).$$

Since $\lambda = 2$, we obtain

$$\mathbf{P}\left[N \text{ is even }\right] = \frac{1}{2}\left[1 + e^{-4}\right] \approx \mathbf{0.5092}.$$

(b) To find the conditional distribution of N, given that N takes an odd value, let us introduce the event F that is favored by all odd numbers and use the following formula:

$$P\left[N = 2n + 1 \,|\, N \in F\right] = \frac{\mathbf{P}\left[N = 2n + 1\right]}{\mathbf{P}\left[N \in F\right]} = \frac{\lambda^{2n+1}}{(2n+1)!}\, e^{-\lambda} \div e^{-\lambda} \cdot B\left(\lambda\right) =$$

$$= \frac{\lambda^{2n+1}}{(2n+1)!} \div B\left(\lambda\right) = \frac{\lambda^{2n+1}}{(2n+1)!} \cdot \frac{2}{e^{\lambda} - e^{-\lambda}}$$

Also,

$$\mathbf{P}\left[N = 2n \,|\, N \text{ is odd}\right] = 0$$

for any natural n.

(c) The conditional expectation of N, given that N is odd, can be found using the following formula:

$$\mathbf{E}\left[N \,|\, N \in F\right] = \sum_{n=0}^{\infty} (2n + 1) \cdot P\left[N = 2n + 1 \,|\, N \in F\right] =$$

$$= \sum_{n=0}^{\infty} (2n + 1) \cdot \mathbf{P}\left[N = 2n + 1\right] \div \mathbf{P}\left[N \in F\right] =$$

$$= \sum_{n=0}^{\infty} (2n + 1) \cdot \frac{\lambda^{2n+1}}{(2n+1)!}\, e^{-\lambda} \div \mathbf{P}\left[N \in F\right] =$$

$$= \sum_{n=0}^{\infty} (2n + 1) \cdot \frac{\lambda^{2n+1}}{(2n+1)!}\, e^{-\lambda} \div e^{-\lambda} \cdot B\left(\lambda\right) =$$

$$= \sum_{n=0}^{\infty} (2n + 1) \cdot \frac{\lambda^{2n+1}}{(2n+1)!} \div B\left(\lambda\right) =$$

$$= \frac{\lambda}{B\left(\lambda\right)} \sum_{n=0}^{\infty} \frac{\lambda^{2n}}{(2n)!} = \lambda \cdot \frac{A\left(\lambda\right)}{B\left(\lambda\right)} = \lambda \cdot \frac{1 + e^{-2\lambda}}{1 - e^{-2\lambda}}$$

For $\lambda = 4$, this expectation equals

$$\mathbf{E}\left[N \,|\, N \in F\right] = 4 \cdot \frac{1 + e^{-8}}{1 - e^{-8}} \approx \mathbf{4}.$$

1.14. Let us introduce event E, that the first basket was selected. Then $\mathbf{P}[E] = 3/4$ and $\mathbf{P}[E'] = 1/4$. Given E, the event R (red ball is drawn) is $8/10$, while given E' the conditional probability of R is $5/10$. Hence,

$$\mathbf{P}[R] = \mathbf{P}[E] \cdot \mathbf{P}[R|E] + \mathbf{P}[E'] \cdot \mathbf{P}[R|E'] =$$
$$= \left(\frac{3}{4}\right) \cdot \left(\frac{8}{10}\right) + \left(\frac{1}{4}\right) \cdot \left(\frac{5}{10}\right) = \frac{29}{40} = 0.725.$$

The conditional probability, then, is

$$\mathbf{P}[E\,|R] = \frac{\mathbf{P}[E \cap R]}{\mathbf{P}[R]} = \frac{\mathbf{P}[E]\,\mathbf{P}[R|E]}{\mathbf{P}[R]} = \left(\frac{3}{4} \cdot \frac{8}{10}\right) \div \frac{29}{40} = \frac{24}{29} = \mathbf{0.8276}.$$

1.15. (a) Using the formula for a variance of $Z = X - Y$, we have

$$\mathbf{Var}[X - Y] = \mathbf{Var}[X] - 2 \times \mathbf{COV}[X, Y] + \mathbf{Var}[Y].$$

Since X and Y both are Poisson-distributed, $\mathbf{Var}[X] = \mathbf{E}[X] = 16$ and $\mathbf{Var}[Y] = \mathbf{E}[Y] = 9$.

Therefore, $13 = 16 + 9 - 2 \cdot \mathbf{COV}[X, Y]$, which implies that

$$\mathbf{COV}[X, Y] = \frac{1}{2}(25 - 13) = \mathbf{6}.$$

(b) The correlation coefficient, or just correlation, is defined as the ratio

$$\rho_{X,Y} = \mathbf{Corr}[X, Y] = \frac{\mathbf{COV}[X, Y]}{\sqrt{\mathbf{Var}[X]} \cdot \sqrt{\mathbf{Var}[Y]}} = \frac{6}{\sqrt{16} \cdot \sqrt{9}} = \frac{6}{4 \cdot 3} = \mathbf{0.5}.$$

Chapter 2

Conditional Probability, Variance, and Expectation

In this chapter we present conditional probability and expectation that form the foundation of Bayesian inferences. The framework known as **conditioning** is focused on developing the skills required for conclusions, such as prediction, based on observations.

When a sample is drawn from a distribution that is partially known, the value of the parameter itself is treated as a random variable. Its distribution is called **prior**, and joint behavior of observed values is then derived using Bayes' theorem.

Parameter and sample can follow either discrete or continuous distribution. Thus, the topics presented are structured as follows:

1. Purely discrete case: Both parameter and data; that is, the sample of conditionally independent observations, are discrete.

2. Purely continuous case: Both parameter and data are continuously distributed.

3. Mixed case: Either parameter is continuous and data follows a discrete distribution or the other way around.

After studying this chapter, readers will recognize **prior** and data distributions and will be able to evaluate conditional and marginal moments.

Exercises will further deepen and develop readers' knowledge of the material presented in this chapter.

2.1 Conditional Distribution

To provide a clarified vision of conditioning, we first focus on two real-valued variables, (X, Y). In general, both X and Y can also be vectors.

Consider the following three cases:

1. Variables (X, Y) are purely discrete.

   In this case, $p(x, y) = \mathbf{P}\left[(X = x) \bigcap (Y = y)\right]$ is the **joint pmf**.

   The following two assumptions ensure that the **pmf** is a properly defined probability distribution:

1) $p(x, y) \geq 0, \quad \forall (x, y)$
2) $\sum_x \sum_y p(x, y) = 1$

2. (X, Y) is purely continuous.

   In this case, the function $p(x, y)$ represents the **joint pdf**.

   The following two assumptions ensure that the **pdf** is a properly defined probability distribution:

   1) $p(x, y) \geq 0, \quad \forall (x, y)$
   2) $\int_{-\infty}^{\infty} \int_{-\infty}^{\infty} p(x, y) \, dx \, dy = 1$

3. One component, (X), is discrete and the other, (Y), is continuous.

   It is reasonable to describe the **joint** distribution in terms of a **probability** function that behaves like a **pdf** in y and like a **pmf** in x.

   The following two assumptions ensure that the $p(x, y)$ is a properly defined probability distribution:

   1) $p(x, y) \geq 0, \quad \forall (x, y)$
   2) $\sum_x \left[\int_{-\infty}^{\infty} p(x, y) \, dy \right] = 1$

In general, for any event, A, and a random variable, $W = W(X, Y)$, the conditional probability, $\mathbf{P}[A|W]$, is a **function** of a random variable W. Its value for $W = w$ is interpreted as $\mathbf{P}[A|W = w]$.

Similarly, for a random variable, $T = T(X, Y)$, its **conditional** expectation, $\mathbf{E}[T|W]$, is a function of W. Its value, given $W = w$, is $\mathbf{E}[T|W = w]$.

The following two theorems relate marginal probabilities to conditional probabilities.

2.2 Bayes' Theorem

Bayes' theorem describes the probability of an event based on prior knowledge of conditions that might be related to the event. It states that

$$\mathbf{P}[A|B] = \frac{\mathbf{P}[B|A]\mathbf{P}[A]}{\mathbf{P}[B]}, \text{ where}$$

- $\mathbf{P}[A|B]$ is a conditional probability: likelihood of event A occurring given that B is true

- $\mathbf{P}[B|A]$ is also a conditional probability: likelihood of event B occurring given that A is true

- $\mathbf{P}[A]$ and $\mathbf{P}[B]$ are the probabilities of observing A and B independently of each other. They are also known as the **marginal probabilities**.

For continuous distributions, Bayes' theorem is stated in terms of the probability density functions:

$$f_{X|Y}(x|y) = \frac{f_{Y|X}(y|x) f_X(x)}{f_Y(y)}$$

2.3   Law of Total Probability

The law of total probability is a fundamental rule relating marginal probabilities to conditional probabilities. It expresses the total probability of an outcome, which can be realized via several distinct events.

Let B_i, $i = 1, 2, 3, \ldots$ be a finite or countable partition of a sample space; that is, a set of pairwise disjoint events $\mathbf{P}[B_i \cap B_j] = 0$ for $i \neq j$ whose union is the entire sample space $\mathbf{P}[\cup_i B_i] = 1$. Then for any event A of the same probability space,

$$\mathbf{P}[A] = \sum_i \mathbf{P}[A \cap B_i] = \sum_i \mathbf{P}[B_i]\mathbf{P}[A|B_i]. \tag{2.1}$$

For continuous distributions,

$$\mathbf{P}[A] = \int_{-\infty}^{\infty} \mathbf{P}[A|x] f(x) dx. \tag{2.2}$$

Based on the definition of the expectation as either

$$\mathbf{E}[g(X)] = \sum_k g(k) \cdot p_k \quad \text{or} \quad \mathbf{E}[g(X)] = \int_{-\infty}^{\infty} g(x) \cdot f_X(x)\, dx,$$

the probability of A can then be expressed as either

$$\mathbf{P}[A] = \sum_i \mathbf{P}[B_i]\mathbf{P}[A|B_i] \quad \text{or} \quad \mathbf{P}[A] = \int \mathbf{P}[A|x] f(x) dx,$$

depending on whether B is discrete or continuous.

Let us review the discrete, continuous, and mixed case of (X, Y).

2.4   Discrete Case

Suppose X and Y are both discrete. For each component, X and Y, we introduce **marginal** probability mass functions as

$$f_X(x) = \sum_y p(x, y) \quad \text{and} \quad f_Y(y) = \sum_x p(x, y).$$

Then, similar to the multiplication rule for probabilities, the conditional mass functions can be introduced:

$$f_{X|Y}(x|y) = \frac{p(x, y)}{f_Y(y)} \quad \text{and} \quad f_{Y|X}(y|x) = \frac{p(x, y)}{f_X(x)} \tag{2.3}$$

According to the stated convention, $f_{X|Y}(x|Y)$ is viewed as the conditional **pmf** for (X), given $Y = y$, and its value at $X = x$ is $f_{X|Y}(x|y)$.

A similar interpretation is applicable to $f_{Y|X}(y|X)$, which is viewed as a function of the random variable X taking the value $f_{Y|X}(y|x)$ at $Y = y$.

Note that the conditional probability mass function and conditional densities are later presented as functions of **two** variables. The second variable (Y) specifying the condition will play the role of a parameter for the distribution of the first component (X), given $Y = y$.

Thus, $(X \,|\, Y = y)$, has the **pmf** with the parameter equal to y. Similarly, $(Y \,|\, X = x)$ has the **pmf** with parameter equal to x.

The conditional expectation, $\mathbf{E}\,[T \,|\, X = x]$, of a transformed variable is defined as the **expected value** of $T = T(X, Y)$, evaluated with respect to the conditional distribution, or

$$\mathbf{E}\,[T(X,Y) \,|\, Y = y] = \sum_x T(x, y) \cdot f_{X|Y}(x \,|\, y). \tag{2.4}$$

Several examples illustrate these definitions.

2.4.1 Poisson-Binomial Model

Let us consider an example of marginal probability derived from joint probability distribution of a Poisson and binomial.

Suppose that N follows the Poisson distribution with parameter $\lambda > 0$:

$$\mathbf{P}\,[N = n] = \frac{\lambda^n}{n!}\, e^{-\lambda}, \quad \text{for } n = 0, 1, \ldots,$$

and $(X \,|\, N = n)$ has the binomial distribution $\mathbf{Bin}\,[n, p]$, where $0 < p < 1$:

$$\mathbf{P}\,[X = k \,|\, N = n] = \binom{n}{k} p^k (1-p)^{n-k}, \quad k = 0, 1, \cdots, n$$

1. The joint probability mass function is the product

$$p(k, n) = \mathbf{P}\left[(X = k)\bigcap(N = n)\right] = \mathbf{P}\,[X = k \,|\, N = n] \cdot \mathbf{P}\,[N = n] =$$
$$= \binom{n}{k} p^k (1-p)^{n-k} \cdot \frac{\lambda^n}{n!}\, e^{-\lambda}.$$

2. By the law of total probability, the **marginal** distribution of X can be obtained as the sum

$$\mathbf{P}\,[X = k] = \sum_n \mathbf{P}\,[N = n] \cdot \mathbf{P}\,[X = k \,|\, N = n] = \sum_{n=k}^{\infty} \binom{n}{k} p^k (1-p)^{n-k} \cdot \frac{\lambda^n}{n!}\, e^{-\lambda} =$$

$$= \sum_{n=k}^{\infty} \frac{n!}{k!(n-k)!} \cdot p^k (1-p)^{n-k} \cdot \frac{\lambda^n}{n!}\, e^{-\lambda} = \sum_{n=k}^{\infty} \frac{1}{k!(n-k)!} \cdot p^k (1-p)^{n-k} \cdot \lambda^n\, e^{-\lambda} =$$

$$= \frac{(\lambda p)^k e^{-\lambda}}{k!} \sum_{n=k}^{\infty} \frac{1}{(n-k)!} \cdot (1-p)^{n-k} \cdot \lambda^{n-k} = \frac{(\lambda p)^k e^{-\lambda}}{k!} \sum_{m=0}^{\infty} \frac{1}{m!} \cdot (1-p)^m \cdot \lambda^m =$$

$$= \frac{(\lambda p)^k e^{-\lambda}}{k!} \cdot e^{\lambda(1-p)} = \frac{(\lambda p)^k e^{-\lambda p}}{k!}.$$

Thus, X is Poisson-distributed, with the parameter $\tilde{\lambda} = \lambda p$.

3. The conditional distribution of $(N\,|X=k)$ for $N\geq k$ can be obtained using Bayes' theorem:

$$\mathbf{P}\left[N\,|X=k\right]=\frac{\mathbf{P}\left[X=k\,|N=n\right]\cdot\mathbf{P}\left[N=n\right]}{\mathbf{P}\left[X=k\right]}=$$

$$\left(\binom{n}{k}p^{k}(1-p)^{n-k}\cdot\frac{\lambda^{n}}{n!}\,e^{-\lambda}\right)/\left(\frac{(\lambda p)^{k}e^{-\lambda p}}{k!}\right)=$$

$$=\frac{n!}{(n-k)!k!}\,p^{k}(1-p)^{n-k}\frac{\lambda^{n}}{n!}\,e^{-\lambda}\cdot\frac{k!}{(\lambda p)^{k}e^{-\lambda p}}=$$

$$=\frac{1}{(n-k)!}\,\lambda^{n-k}e^{-\lambda(1-p)}(1-p)^{n-k}=\frac{1}{(n-k)!}(\lambda(1-p))^{n-k}e^{-\lambda(1-p)}$$

Thus, for $N\geq k$, $(N-k|X=k)$ is also Poisson-distributed, with the parameter $\lambda\,(1-p)$.

Consider a random variable, $M=N-X$. Note that, conditionally, given $(X=k)$, the distribution of M **does not depend** on the current value of $X=k$. Thus, the marginal joint distribution of the pair $(X,M=N-X)$ satisfies the assumption of independence.

Notice the common paradox. Although conditionally, given N, the variables X and $M=N-X$ are dependent, they become **marginally** independent.

2.4.2 Sum-of-Poisson Model

Suppose that (X,Y) are two **independent** Poisson-distributed random variables, with intensities λ and μ, respectively, and $W=X+Y$ is observable.

1. The probability mass function for W can be found by conditioning:

$$\mathbf{P}\left[W=n\right]=\mathbf{E}\left[\mathbf{P}\left[X=k\,|Y\right]\right]=\sum_{r=0}^{n}\mathbf{P}\left[X=n-r\right]\cdot\mathbf{P}\left[Y=r\right]=$$

$$=\sum_{r=0}^{n}e^{-\lambda}\frac{\lambda^{n-r}}{(n-r)!}\,e^{-\mu}\frac{\mu^{r}}{r!}=\frac{e^{-(\lambda+\mu)}}{n!}\sum_{r=0}^{n}\frac{n!}{(n-r)!r!}\,\lambda^{n-r}\mu^{r}=\frac{e^{-(\lambda+\mu)}}{n!}\,(\lambda+\mu)^{n}$$

Thus, W has the Poisson distribution with the rate $\lambda+\mu$.

2. Calculating the conditional distribution of $(X\,|W=n)$, by Bayes' theorem we have

$$\mathbf{P}\left[X\,|W=n\right]=\frac{\mathbf{P}\left[X=k\cap W=n\right]}{\mathbf{P}\left[W=n\right]}=\frac{\mathbf{P}\left[X=k\cap Y=n-k\right]}{\mathbf{P}\left[W=n\right]}=$$

$$=\frac{\mathbf{P}\left[X=k\right]\mathbf{P}\left[Y=n-k\right]}{\mathbf{P}\left[W=n\right]}=e^{-\lambda}\frac{\lambda^{k}}{k!}\cdot e^{-\mu}\frac{\mu^{n-k}}{(n-k)!}/e^{-(\lambda+\mu)}\frac{(\lambda+\mu)^{n}}{n!}=$$

$$=\frac{n!}{k!(n-k)}\cdot\frac{\lambda^{k}\mu^{n-k}}{(\lambda+\mu)^{n}}=\binom{n}{k}\left(\frac{\lambda}{\lambda+\mu}\right)^{k}\left(\frac{\mu}{\lambda+\mu}\right)^{n-k}=\binom{n}{k}q^{k}(1-q)^{n-k},$$

where $q=\dfrac{\lambda}{\lambda+\mu}$.

Thus, the conditional distribution of $(X\,|W=n)$ is binomial, **Bin** $[n,q]$, where $q=\lambda/(\lambda+\mu)$.

2.4.3 Moments of the Geometric via Conditioning

Consider the geometric distribution, which can be viewed as the distribution of the **time** when the first success occurs in a run of Bernoulli trials with the success rate equal to q.

Let $\{U_1, U_2, \ldots\}$, be a potentially unlimited run of Bernoulli or "zero-one" random variables, with

$$\mathbf{P}\left[U_j = 1\right] = q \ \text{ and } \ \mathbf{P}\left[U_j = 0\right] = 1 - q \ \text{ for each } \ j.$$

For a geometric random variable N with parameter q,

$$N = n \Leftrightarrow U_j = 0 \text{ for } j = 1, 2, \ldots, n - 1 \text{ and } U_n = 1.$$

The joint distribution of a Bernoulli random variable U and a geometric random variable N can be obtained as follows:

$$\mathbf{P}\left[(U = 1) \bigcap (N = 1)\right] = q,$$
$$\mathbf{P}\left[(U = 0) \bigcap (N = k + 1)\right] = (1 - q)^k \cdot q, \ k \geq 1$$

Hence,

$$\mathbf{P}\left[N = k + 1 \,|\, U = 0\right] = \frac{\mathbf{P}\left[N = k + 1 \cap U = 0\right]}{\mathbf{P}\left[U = 0\right]} = \frac{(1 - q)^k \cdot q}{1 - q} =$$
$$= (1 - q)^{k-1} \cdot q = \mathbf{P}\left[N = k\right].$$

Thus, $(N \,|\, U = 0)$ has the same distribution as $(N + 1)$.

Let $\mathbf{E}\left[N\right] = \mu$. Let us calculate the first and second moments of N.

1. By the **double expectation** theorem,

   $$\mu = \mathbf{E}\left[N\right] = \mathbf{E}\left[\mathbf{E}\left[N \,|\, U\right]\right] = \mathbf{E}\left[N \,|\, U = 1\right] \cdot \mathbf{P}\left[U = 1\right] + \mathbf{E}\left[N \,|\, U = 0\right] \cdot \mathbf{P}\left[U = 0\right].$$

   By definition, $\mathbf{E}\left[N \,|\, U = 1\right] = 1$, and $\mathbf{P}\left[U = 1\right] = q$.

   Since $(N \,|\, U = 0)$ has the same distribution as $(N + 1)$, it follows that

   $$\mathbf{E}\left[N \,|\, U = 0\right] = \mathbf{E}\left[N + 1\right] = \mu + 1.$$

   Therefore,

   $$\mu = 1 \cdot q + (\mu + 1)(1 - q) = q + \mu(1 - q) + 1 - q = 1 + \mu(1 - q) \Leftrightarrow$$
   $$\mu \cdot q = 1 \Leftrightarrow \mu = \frac{1}{q}.$$

2. Applying similar reasoning to the second moment of N, we have

   $$\mathbf{E}\left[N^2\right] = \mathbf{E}\left[\mathbf{E}\left[N^2 \,|\, U\right]\right] = \mathbf{E}\left[N^2 \,|\, U = 1\right] \cdot \mathbf{P}\left[U = 1\right] + \mathbf{E}\left[N^2 \,|\, U = 0\right] \cdot \mathbf{P}[U = 0].$$

Note that $\mathbf{E}\left[N^2 \mid U = 1\right] = 1$. In addition, $(N^2 \mid U = 0)$ has the **same** distribution as $(N+1)^2 = N^2 + 2N + 1$.

Let $\mu_2' = \mathbf{E}\left[N^2\right]$. Then, using the additive property of expectations,

$$\mathbf{E}\left[N^2 \mid U = 0\right] = \mathbf{E}\left[N^2 + 2N + 1\right] = \mathbf{E}\left[N^2\right] + 2\mathbf{E}\left[N\right] + 1 = \mu_2' + 2\mu + 1.$$

Thus,

$$\mu_2' = 1 \cdot q + (\mu_2' + 2\mu + 1) \cdot (1 - q) \Leftrightarrow \mu_2' \cdot q = q + \left(\frac{2}{q} + 1\right)(1 - q) = \frac{2}{q} - 1 \Leftrightarrow$$

$$\mathbf{E}\left[N^2\right] = \frac{2 - q}{q^2}.$$

Calculating the variance of N, we obtain

$$\mathbf{Var}\left[N\right] = \mu_2' - \mu^2 = \frac{2 - q}{q^2} - \left(\frac{1}{q}\right)^2 = \frac{1 - q}{q^2}.$$

Consider a random variable, $M = N - 1$, that indicates a number of failures **before** the first success occurs. Then M has a modified geometric distribution, defined as

$$\mathbf{P}\left[M = k\right] = q(1 - q)^k, \ k = 0, 1, \ldots.$$

Then, using the properties of expectation and variance, we obtain

$$\mathbf{E}\left[M\right] = \frac{1}{q} - 1 = \frac{1 - q}{q} \quad \text{and} \quad \mathbf{Var}\left[M\right] = \mathbf{Var}\left[N\right] = \frac{1 - q}{q^2}.$$

2.5   Continuous Case

In a purely continuous situation, the bivariate distribution of a pair (X, Y) is determined by their joint density.

As in the previous section, the following **joint density** defines **marginal** density of one component and **conditional** density of the other, so that

$$p\left(x, y\right) = f_X\left(x\right) \cdot f_{Y \mid X}\left(y \mid x\right) = f_Y\left(y\right) \cdot f_{X \mid Y}\left(x \mid y\right),$$

where the marginal densities for X and for Y are

$$f_X\left(x\right) = \int_{-\infty}^{\infty} p\left(x, y\right) \, dy \quad \text{and} \quad f_Y\left(y\right) = \int_{-\infty}^{\infty} p\left(x, y\right) \, dx. \tag{2.5}$$

Conditional densities for $(Y \mid X = x)$ and for $(Y \mid X = x)$ are

$$f_{Y \mid X}\left(y \mid x\right) = \frac{p\left(x, y\right)}{f_X\left(x\right)} \quad \text{and} \quad f_{X \mid Y}\left(x \mid y\right) = \frac{p\left(x, y\right)}{f_Y\left(y\right)}. \tag{2.6}$$

Recall that the **marginal** density function for Y is

$$f_Y\left(y\right) = \int_{-\infty}^{\infty} f_{Y \mid X}\left(y \mid x\right) \cdot f_X\left(x\right) \, dx,$$

and the cumulative distribution function for Y is

$$\mathbf{P}\left[Y \le t\right] = F_Y\left(t\right) = \int_{-\infty}^{t} f_Y\left(y\right)\,dy.$$

The **marginal** raw k^{th} moments for Y can be evaluated by taking the integrals:

$$\mathbf{E}\left[Y^k\right] = \int_{-\infty}^{\infty} y^r f_Y\left(y\right)\,dy. \tag{2.7}$$

The **conditional** expectation of $T = T\left(X, Y\right)$, given $X = x$, is

$$\mathbf{E}\left[T\,|X = x\right] = \int_{-\infty}^{\infty} T\left(x, y\right) \cdot f_{Y|X}\left(y\,|x\right)\,dx. \tag{2.8}$$

Consider the sum $W = X + Y$. Note that, conditionally, given $X = x$, the cumulative distribution function of $(W|X = x)$ is

$$F_{W|X}(w|x) = F_Y(w - x).$$

Differentiating in w, the conditional density of $(W|X = x)$ is

$$f_{W|X}(w|x) = f_Y(w - x), \tag{2.9}$$

which coincides with density for Y shifted x units to the right.

This identity can be utilized for the joint density for (X, W) as

$$f_{X,W}(x, w) = f_X(x) \cdot f_{W|X}(w|x) = f_X(x) \cdot f_Y(w - x). \tag{2.10}$$

The conditional density for $(X|W)$ can be evaluated as follows:

$$f_{X|W}(x|w) = \frac{f_X(x) \cdot f_Y(w - x)}{f_W(w)} \tag{2.11}$$

This expression can be used for analysis of various models related to gamma distribution as either model or prior.

2.5.1 Gamma-Uniform Model

Suppose that X has a **gamma** $[\alpha = 2, \theta = 1]$ distribution with the density

$$f\left(x\right) = xe^{-x},\ x > 0.$$

Given $X = x$, a random variable Y is uniformly-distributed over the interval $(0, x)$. Thus, its conditional density is

$$f_{Y|X}\left(y\,|x\right) = \frac{1}{x},\ 0 < y < x.$$

The joint density of the pair (X, Y) is

$$p\left(x, y\right) = f_X\left(x\right) \cdot f_{Y|X}\left(y\,|x\right) = e^{-x},\ 0 < y < x.$$

1. Calculating the marginal density of Y, by integrating the joint density in x from y to ∞, we obtain

$$f_Y(y) = \int_y^\infty e^{-x}\,dx = e^{-y}, \ y > 0.$$

2. Calculating the conditional density of X, given $Y = y$, by dividing the joint density, $p(x, y)$, by the marginal density for Y, we have

$$f_{X|Y}(x\,|y) = \frac{p(x, y)}{f_Y(y)} = e^{-x}/e^{-y} = e^{-(x-y)}, \ 0 < y < x.$$

Thus, given $Y = y$, the variable $X - y$ has the exponential distribution with parameter 1.

3. Calculating the first two conditional moments of $(X\,|Y = y)$ we have

$$\mathbf{E}[X\,|Y = y] = y + \mathbf{E}[X - y\,|Y = y] = y + 1, \text{ and}$$
$$\mathbf{Var}[X\,|Y = y] = \mathbf{Var}[X - y\,|Y = y] = 1.$$

The second conditional moment of $(X\,|Y = y)$ is

$$\mathbf{E}\left[(X\,|Y = y)^2\right] = \mathbf{Var}[X\,|Y = y] + \mathbf{E}[X\,|Y = y]^2 = 1 + (y + 1)^2.$$

Similar to what was noted in the discrete situation, the variables Y and $W = X - Y$ are marginally independent, while, conditionally, $(Y|X = x)$ and $(W = X - Y|X = x)$ are dependent because $[Y + W|X = x]$ is a constant x.

2.5.2   Gamma and Conditioning

Conversely, given two independent exponentially-distributed random variables (X, Y), we can derive the distribution of their sum $Z = X+Y$, as well as conditional distribution of $(X\,|Z = z)$.

The joint density function is the product of two exponential densities sharing the same parameter λ:

$$p(x, y) = \lambda^2 \cdot e^{-\lambda(x+y)}, \ x > 0, \ y > 0$$

Suppose that the observed variable is $Z = X + Y$.

Since both X and Y are positive with probability 1, it follows that $0 < X < Z$ and $0 < Y < Z$.

1. Calculating the distribution of Z, we obtain the convolution of the two random variables X and Y:

$$F_Z(t) = \mathbf{P}[Z \le t] = \mathbf{P}[X + Y \le t] = \int_0^t \left[\int_0^{t-y} f_X(x) f_Y(y) dx\right] dy =$$

$$= \int_0^t F_X(t - y) f_Y(y)\,dy$$

Similarly,

$$F_Z(t) = \mathbf{P}[Z \le t] = \mathbf{P}[X + Y \le t] = \int_0^t \left[\int_0^{t-x} f_X(x) f_Y(y) dy\right] dx =$$

$$= \int_0^t F_Y(t - x) f_X(x)\,dx.$$

For an exponential random variable,

$$F_X(x) = 1 - e^{-\lambda x}, \quad f_X(x) - \lambda e^{-\lambda x}.$$

Therefore,

$$\mathbf{P}\left[Z \leq t\right] = \lambda \int_0^t \left(1 - e^{-\lambda(t-y)}\right) e^{-\lambda y} \, dy = \lambda \int_0^t \left(e^{-\lambda y} - e^{-\lambda t}\right) \, dy.$$

Differentiating with respect to t, using the Leibniz's rule, we obtain

$$h_Z(t) = \lambda \int_0^t \frac{\partial}{\partial t} \left(e^{-\lambda y} - e^{-\lambda t}\right) \, dy = \lambda^2 \int_0^t e^{-\lambda t} \, dy = \lambda^2 t e^{-\lambda t}.$$

Recall, that the **pdf** for the gamma distribution, with parameters α and λ, is

$$f(t) = \frac{(\lambda t)^\alpha e^{-\lambda t}}{t \Gamma(\alpha)}.$$

Therefore, Z has a gamma distribution, with parameters $\alpha = 2$ and λ.

2. Joint density for (X, Z) is

$$p(x, z) = \lambda e^{-\lambda x} \cdot \lambda e^{-\lambda(z-x)} = \lambda^2 e^{-\lambda z}, \ 0 < x < z < \infty.$$

3. Conditional density of $(X \,|\, Z = z)$ is uniform over the interval $(0, z)$. Indeed,

$$f_{X|Z} = \frac{p(x, z)}{f_Z(z)} = \left(\lambda^2 e^{-\lambda z}\right) / \left(\lambda^2 z e^{-\lambda z}\right) = \frac{1}{z}, \ 0 < x < z < \infty.$$

4. Calculating conditional moments of $(X \,|\, Z = z)$ we obtain

$$\mathbf{E}\left[X | Z = z\right] = \frac{1}{z} \int_0^z x^r \, dx = \frac{z^r}{r+1}.$$

2.6 Mixed Case: Discrete Prior and Continuous Model

Note that in this situation we face neither density nor mass function. It is rather a **hybrid** of both. Assume that Y is a discrete random variable with the **pmf**,

$$f_Y(y) = g(y) = \mathbf{P}[Y = y]$$

for $y \sim \mathcal{Y}$, where $\mathcal{Y}$ is a finite or countable set.

This distribution will be referred as **prior** for the **parameter** Y. Like any **pmf**, this function should satisfy these conditions:

$$g(y) \geq 0 \quad \text{and} \quad \sum_{y \sim \mathcal{Y}} g(y) = 1$$

Recall that the joint distribution of a pair (X, Y) is determined by the joint density–mass function, $p(x, y) \geq 0$.

Then

$$f_X(x) = h(x) = \sum_y p(x, y)$$

is a **marginal** density of X and

$$\int_{-\infty}^{\infty} p(x, y) \; dx = g(y) = \mathbf{P}\,[Y = y]$$

is the probability mass function for Y.

Conditional probability mass functions are defined as follows:

The **model** describing the distribution of X, given $Y = y$, is

$$f_{X|Y}(x\,|Y = y) = \mathbf{P}\,[X = x\,|Y = y] = \frac{p(x, y)}{g(y)}. \qquad (2.12)$$

The **model** describing the distribution of Y, given $X = x$, is

$$f_{Y|X}(y\,|X = x) = \mathbf{P}\,[Y = y\,|X = x] = \frac{p(x, y)}{h(x)}. \qquad (2.13)$$

2.6.1   Discrete Mixture of Exponentials Model

Suppose that Y has the purely discrete distribution determined by a **pmf** $g(y)$ and the **model** is the exponential with

$$f(x\,|Y = y) = \frac{1}{y}\,e^{-x/y} \text{ for } x > 0.$$

Let us calculate the first two moments of X in terms of the moments of Y.

The **marginal pdf** for X is

$$f_X(x) = \sum_y p(x, y) = \sum_y f_Y(y)\, f_{X|Y}(x\,|y),$$

that is, a mixture of exponential distributions.

To determine the **marginal** moments of X, note that $\mathbf{E}\,[X\,|Y = y] = y$. Indeed,

$$\mathbf{E}\,[X\,|Y = y] = \int_0^{\infty} x f_{X|Y}(x\,|y) \; dx = \int_0^{\infty} x \cdot \frac{1}{y} e^{-x/y} \; dx =$$

$$= \left[u = \frac{x}{y} \Rightarrow x = uy \Rightarrow dx = y du \right] = \int_0^{\infty} u e^{-u} y \; du = y \int_0^{\infty} u e^{-u} \; du =$$

$$= \left[\Gamma(z) = \int_0^{\infty} x^{z-1} e^{-x} \; dx, \; \Gamma(n) = (n-1)! \right] = y\Gamma(2) = y \cdot 1! = y.$$

Since $\mathbf{E}\,[X\,|Y = y] = y$, using the **double expectation** property of conditional expectations we obtain

$$\mathbf{E}\,[X] = \mathbf{E}\,[\mathbf{E}\,[X\,|Y]] = \mathbf{E}\,[Y] = \sum_y y \cdot g(y).$$

Similarly, calculating $\mathbf{E}\left[X^2\,|Y=y\right]$, we obtain

$$\mathbf{E}\left[X^2\,|Y=y\right] = \int_0^\infty x^2 f_{X|Y}\left(x\,|y\right)\,dx = \int_0^\infty x^2 \frac{1}{y} e^{-x/y}\,dx = \left[u = \frac{x}{y}\right] =$$

$$= \int_0^\infty u^2 e^{-u} y^2\,du = y^2 \int_0^\infty u^2 e^{-u}\,du = y^2 \Gamma(3) = y \cdot 2! = 2y^2.$$

Thus, for the second moment, $\mathbf{E}\left[X^2\right]$, we have

$$\mathbf{E}\left[X^2\right] = \mathbf{E}\left[\mathbf{E}\left[X^2\,|Y\right]\right] = 2\cdot\mathbf{E}\left[Y^2\right] = 2\sum_y y^2\cdot g\left(y\right).$$

Proceeding with the **marginal variance** of X, we obtain

$$\mathbf{Var}\left[X\right] = \mathbf{E}\left[X^2\right] - \left(\mathbf{E}\left[X\right]\right)^2 = 2\cdot\mathbf{E}\left[Y^2\right] - \left(\mathbf{E}\left[Y\right]\right)^2.$$

2.6.2   Numerical Illustration

Suppose Y can take values from $\mathcal{Y} = \{1,2,5\}$, with probabilities

$$g\left(1\right) = 0.55,\quad g\left(2\right) = 0.35,\quad\text{and}\quad g\left(5\right) = 0.1.$$

Then,

$$\mathbf{E}\left[Y\right] = 1\cdot0.55 + 2\cdot0.35 + 5\cdot0.1 = 1.75 \text{ and}$$
$$\mathbf{E}\left[Y^2\right] = 1^2\cdot0.55 + 2^2\cdot0.35 + 5^2\cdot0.1 = 4.45.$$

Using the formulae for marginal moments of X, we conclude that

$$\mathbf{E}\left[X\right] = 1.75 \quad\text{and}$$
$$\mathbf{Var}\left[X\right] = 2\cdot4.45 - \left(1.75\right)^2 = 1.3875.$$

2.7   General Mixed Case

So far we have considered (X, Y) as two observable **random** variables. Their joint distribution was shown to be the product of the marginal distribution of Y and a **model** distribution of X, given $Y = y$. In this section we will assume that Y is no longer observable. Thus, we will treat Y as a general parameter $Y = \Theta$ with $g\left(\theta\right)$ being either a **pmf** (if Θ is discrete) or a **pdf** (if Θ is continuous). The distribution of Θ is called the **prior** distribution.

The **model** distribution of observed records is then characterized by a function $f_{X|\Theta}\left(x\,|\theta\right)$, which also can be either a **pmf** (when X is discrete) or a **pdf** (when X is continuous).

Suppose we have observed $\mathbf{X} = x$, where $\mathbf{X} = \{X_1, X_2, \dots, X_n\}$ and $x = (x_1, x_2, \dots, x_n)$. Let $f\left(x_1, x_2, \dots, x_n\right)$ be the **unconditional** joint density function of the data $\mathbf{X}$.

Our goal is to estimate the conditional distribution of X_{n+1} given the distribution of $\mathbf{X}$. We will call $f(x_{n+1}|x_1, x_2, \dots, x_n)$ the **predictive** density. It will then be the **revised** unconditional $f(x)$ based on the observations $(x_1, x_2, \dots, x_n)$.

Let

$$f(\mathbf{x}|\theta) = f(x_1, x_2, \dots, x_n|\theta) = \prod_{i=1}^{n} f(x_i|\theta)$$

be the joint conditional **pmf** or **pdf** of the model and $g_\Theta(\theta)$ be the prior **pmf** or **pdf** for $\Theta = \theta$, or the **prior** density. Then,

$$f(x_1, x_2, \dots, x_n) = \int f(x_1, x_2, \dots, x_n|\theta)g(\theta) \, d\theta.$$

Suppose $g_{\Theta|X}(\theta|x_1, x_2, \dots, x_n)$ is the **posterior** density of parameter Θ. It is the revised density function for the parameter Θ based on data $x_1, x_2, \dots, x_n$.

Then the **predictive** density is

$$f(x_{n+1}|x_1, x_2, \dots, x_n) = \int f(x_{n+1}|\theta)g(\theta|x_1, x_2, \dots, x_n) \, d\theta.$$

Let us discuss posterior characteristics of Θ, such as moments of the first or second order and variance.

2.7.1   Uniform-Binomial Model

Suppose a continuous random variable Q is uniformly-distributed over the unit interval $[0, 1]$ and the conditional discrete variable $(Y|Q = q)$ has the binomial distribution $\mathbf{Bin}[n, q]$ so that its probability mass function is defined as

$$g(k|q) = \mathbf{P}[Y = k|Q = q] = \frac{n!}{k!(n-k)!} q^k (1-q)^{n-k}.$$

1. To find the **marginal** distribution of Y we need to integrate in q, that is

$$\mathbf{P}[Y = k] = \int_0^1 \mathbf{P}[Y = k|Q = q] \cdot g_Q(q) \, dq = \int_0^1 \frac{n!}{k!(n-k)!} q^k (1-q)^{n-k} \, dq =$$

$$= \frac{n!}{k!(n-k)!} \int_0^1 q^k (1-q)^{n-k} \, dq.$$

The integral is a well-known beta function,

$$B(a,b) = \int_0^1 u^{a-1} (1-u)^{b-1} \, du = \frac{\Gamma(a)\Gamma(b)}{\Gamma(a+b)},$$

where $\Gamma(r) = \int_0^\infty u^{r-1}e^{-u} \, du$.

Using the properties of the gamma function,

$$\Gamma(1) = 1, \; \Gamma(a+1) = a\Gamma(a)$$
$$\Gamma(k) = (k-1)! \text{ for any integer } k \geq 1,$$

we have

$$\int_0^1 q^k (1-q)^{n-k} \, dq = \frac{\Gamma(k+1)\,\Gamma(n-k+1)}{\Gamma(k+1+n-k+1)} = \frac{\Gamma(k+1)\,\Gamma(n-k+1)}{\Gamma(n+2)} =$$
$$= \frac{k!\,(n-k)!}{(n+1)!}.$$

Therefore,

$$\mathbf{P}\left[Y = k\right] = \frac{n!}{k!\,(n-k)!} \cdot \frac{k!\,(n-k)!}{(n+1)!} = \frac{1}{n+1}, \quad k = 0, 1, \ldots, n.$$

This is a **discrete uniform** distribution.

2. To find the **marginal** expectation of Y we need to evaluate the sum:

$$\mathbf{E}\left[Y\right] = \sum_{k=0}^{n} k \cdot \mathbf{P}\left[Y = k\right] = \sum_{k=0}^{n} k \cdot \frac{1}{n+1} = \frac{1}{n+1} \sum_{k=0}^{n} k = \frac{1}{n+1} \cdot \frac{n(n+1)}{2} = \frac{n}{2}.$$

3. To find the second moment, we need to evaluate the sum:

$$\mathbf{E}\left[Y^2\right] = \sum_{k=0}^{n} k^2 \cdot \mathbf{P}\left[Y = k\right] = \sum_{k=0}^{n} k^2 \cdot \frac{1}{n+1} = \frac{1}{n+1} \sum_{k=0}^{n} k^2 =$$
$$= \frac{1}{n+1} \cdot \frac{n(n+1)(2n+1)}{6} = \frac{n(2n+1)}{6}.$$

4. To find the **marginal** variance of Y we use the formula

$$\mathbf{Var}\left[Y\right] = \mathbf{E}\left[Y^2\right] - \left(\mathbf{E}\left[Y\right]\right)^2 = \frac{n(2n+1)}{6} - \left(\frac{n}{2}\right)^2 = \frac{2n^2+n}{6} - \frac{n^2}{4} =$$
$$= \frac{4n^2 + 2n - 3n^2}{12} = \frac{n^2 + 2n}{12} = \frac{n(n+2)}{12}.$$

5. To find the **conditional** density of $(Q|Y = k)$ at q we divide the joint mass-density function by the marginal mass function for Y at $Y = k$. This division results in

$$u(q\,|y = k) = \frac{g(k\,|q) \cdot g_Q(q)}{\mathbf{P}\left[Y = k\right]} = 1 \cdot \frac{(n)!}{k!\,(n-k)!} q^k (1-q)^{n-k} \div \frac{1}{n+1} =$$
$$= \frac{(n+1)!}{k!\,(n-k)!} q^k (1-q)^{n-k}.$$

Hence, conditionally, $(Q\,|Y = k)$ has beta distribution, with parameters $(a = k+1,\ b = n-k+1)$.

6. For a beta distribution, with parameters a and b, the kth raw moment is

$$\mathbf{E}\left[X^k\right] = \frac{\Gamma(a+b)\,\Gamma(a+k)}{\Gamma(a)\,\Gamma(a+b+k)}.$$

Since $\Gamma(a+1) = a\Gamma(a)$, we have

$$\mathbf{E}[X] = \frac{\Gamma(a+b)\,\Gamma(a+1)}{\Gamma(a)\,\Gamma(a+b+1)} = \frac{\Gamma(a+b)\,a\Gamma(a)}{\Gamma(a)\,(a+b)\Gamma(a+b)} = \frac{a}{a+b}$$

Therefore, the conditional expectation of $(Q|Y=k)$ is

$$\mathbf{E}[Q\,|Y=k] = \frac{a}{a+b} = \frac{k+1}{n+2}.$$

7. Similarly, the second raw moment of a beta distribution, with parameters a and b, is

$$\mathbf{E}\left[X^2\right] = \frac{\Gamma(a+b)\,\Gamma(a+2)}{\Gamma(a)\,\Gamma(a+b+2)} = \frac{\Gamma(a+b)\,a(a+1)\Gamma(a)}{\Gamma(a)\,(a+b+1)(a+b)\Gamma(a+b)} =$$

$$= \frac{a(a+1)}{(a+b+1)(a+b)}.$$

Thus, the variance of $X \sim \mathbf{Beta}[a,b]$ is

$$\mathbf{Var}(X) = \mathbf{E}\left[X^2\right] - \mathbf{E}[X]^2 = \frac{a(a+1)}{(a+b+1)(a+b)} - \left(\frac{a}{a+b}\right)^2 =$$

$$= \frac{a}{a+b}\left[\frac{a+1}{a+b+1} - \frac{a}{a+b}\right] = \frac{a}{a+b} \cdot \frac{a^2+ab+a+b-a^2-ab-a}{(a+b)(a+b+1)} =$$

$$= \frac{ab}{(a+b)^2(a+b+1)}.$$

Therefore, the conditional variance of $(Q|Y=k)$ is

$$\mathbf{Var}[Q\,|Y=k] = \frac{a \cdot b}{(a+b)^2\,(a+b+1)} = \frac{(k+1)\cdot(n-k+1)}{(n+2)^2\,(n+3)}.$$

2.7.2   Beta-Binomial Model

Suppose again a conditional discrete variable $(Y|Q=q)$ has the binomial distribution, $\mathbf{Bin}[n,q]$, with probability mass function

$$g(k\,|q) = \mathbf{P}[Y=k\,|Q=q] = \frac{n!}{k!\,(n-k)!}\,q^k\,(1-q)^{n-k}.$$

Generalizing the previous example, let us assume that the variable Q has a beta distribution, with parameters $(a>0, b>0)$. Then the **marginal** density of Q is

$$f(q) = \frac{\Gamma(a+b)}{\Gamma(a)\,\Gamma(b)}\,q^{a-1}\,(1-q)^{b-1}.$$

1. To find the marginal distribution of Y, let us integrate in q:

$$\mathbf{P}\left[Y = k\right] = \int_0^1 g\left(k\,|q\right) f\left(q\right)\, dq =$$

$$= \frac{n!}{k!\,(n-k)!} \cdot \frac{\Gamma\left(a+b\right)}{\Gamma\left(a\right)\Gamma\left(b\right)} \int_0^1 q^k\left(1-q\right)^{n-k} \cdot q^{a-1}\left(1-q\right)^{b-1}\, dq =$$

$$= \frac{n!}{k!\,(n-k)!} \cdot \frac{\Gamma\left(a+b\right)}{\Gamma\left(a\right)\Gamma\left(b\right)} \int_0^1 q^{k+a-1}\left(1-q\right)^{n-k+b-1}\, dq =$$

$$= \frac{n!}{k!\,(n-k)!} \cdot \frac{\Gamma\left(a+b\right)}{\Gamma\left(a\right)\Gamma\left(b\right)} \cdot \frac{\Gamma\left(k+a\right)\cdot\Gamma\left(n-k+b\right)}{\Gamma\left(a+b+n\right)} =$$

$$= \frac{\Gamma\left(k+a\right)}{\Gamma\left(k+1\right)} \cdot \frac{\Gamma\left(n-k+b\right)}{\Gamma\left(n-k+1\right)} \cdot \frac{\Gamma\left(n+1\right)}{\Gamma\left(n+a+b\right)} \cdot \frac{\Gamma\left(a+b\right)}{\Gamma\left(a\right)\Gamma\left(b\right)}$$

2. We now turn to the **conditional** density of $(Q|Y = k)$.

   Note that the joint mass–density function is

$$p\left(k,q\right) = g(k|q)f(q) = \frac{n!}{k!\,(n-k)!}\, q^k\left(1-q\right)^{n-k} \cdot \frac{\Gamma\left(a+b\right)}{\Gamma\left(a\right)\Gamma\left(b\right)}\, q^{a-1}\left(1-q\right)^{b-1} =$$

$$= \frac{n!}{k!\,(n-k)!} \cdot \frac{\Gamma\left(a+b\right)}{\Gamma\left(a\right)\Gamma\left(b\right)}\, q^{a+k-1}\left(1-q\right)^{n-k+b-1} = \mathbf{P}\left[Y = k\right] v(q|k).$$

   Using the result obtained for $\mathbf{P}\left[Y = k\right]$, we have

$$v\left(q\,|Y = k\right) = \frac{p\left(k,q\right)}{\mathbf{P}\left[Y = k\right]} = \frac{n!}{k!\,(n-k)!} \cdot \frac{\Gamma\left(a+b\right)}{\Gamma\left(a\right)\Gamma\left(b\right)}\, q^{a+k-1}\left(1-q\right)^{n-k+b-1} \cdot$$

$$\cdot \frac{\Gamma\left(k+1\right)}{\Gamma\left(k+a\right)} \cdot \frac{\Gamma\left(n-k+1\right)}{\Gamma\left(n-k+b\right)} \cdot \frac{\Gamma\left(n+a+b\right)}{\Gamma\left(n+1\right)} \cdot \frac{\Gamma\left(a\right)\Gamma\left(b\right)}{\Gamma\left(a+b\right)} =$$

$$= \frac{\Gamma\left(n+a+b\right)}{\Gamma\left(k+a\right)\Gamma\left(n-k+b\right)} \cdot q^{a+k-1}\left(1-q\right)^{n-k+b-1}.$$

   Thus, $(Q\,|N = k)$ has beta distribution, with parameters $(\tilde{a} = a+k,\ \tilde{b} = n+b-k)$.

3. The conditional expectation of $(Q\,|Y = k)$ is

$$\mathbf{E}\left[Q\,|Y = k\right] = \frac{\tilde{a}}{\tilde{a} + \tilde{b}} = \frac{a+k}{n+a+b}.$$

4. The conditional variance of $(Q\,|Y = k)$ is

$$\mathbf{Var}\left(Q\,|Y = k\right) = \frac{\tilde{a}\tilde{b}}{(\tilde{a} + \tilde{b})^2(\tilde{a} + \tilde{b} + 1)} = \frac{(a+k)(n-k+b)}{(a+b+n)^2(a+b+n+1)}.$$

2.7.3 Poisson-Exponential Model

Consider a discrete random variable, N, that, conditionally, given $\Lambda = \lambda$, has the Poisson distribution

$$\mathbf{P}\left[N = k\,|\Lambda = \lambda\right] = \frac{\lambda^k}{k!}\, e^{-\lambda},\ k = 0, 1, 2, \ldots.$$

Suppose the **random** parameter Λ is exponential with parameter θ:

$$g(\lambda) = \frac{1}{\theta} \cdot e^{-\lambda/\theta}, \ \lambda > 0$$

1. First note that the joint probability function is

$$p(k, \lambda) = \mathbf{P}[N = k \,|\, \Lambda = \lambda] \cdot g(\lambda) = \frac{\lambda^k}{k!} e^{-\lambda} \cdot \frac{1}{\theta} \cdot e^{-\lambda/\theta} = \frac{\lambda^k}{\theta k!} e^{-\lambda(1+1/\theta)}.$$

The **marginal** distribution of N is

$$\mathbf{P}[N = k] = f(k) = \int_0^\infty p(k, \lambda) \, d\lambda = \frac{1}{\theta k!} \int_0^\infty \lambda^k e^{-(1+1/\theta)\lambda} \, d\lambda.$$

Substituting $y = (1 + 1/\theta)\lambda$, we have

$$\lambda = \frac{y}{1 + 1/\theta} = \frac{y\theta}{1 + \theta}, \quad d\lambda = \frac{\theta}{1 + \theta} \, dy.$$

Therefore, for $k = 0, 1, \ldots$, we have

$$\mathbf{P}[N = k] = \frac{1}{\theta k!} \cdot \frac{\theta^k}{(1+\theta)^k} \cdot \frac{\theta}{1+\theta} \int_0^\infty y^k e^{-y} \, dy = \frac{\theta^k}{k!(1+\theta)^{k+1}} \int_0^\infty y^k e^{-y} \, dy =$$

$$= \frac{\theta^k}{k!(1+\theta)^{k+1}} \cdot \Gamma(k+1) = \frac{\theta^k}{k!(1+\theta)^{k+1}} \cdot k! = \frac{\theta^k}{(1+\theta)^{k+1}} = \frac{1}{1+\theta} \cdot \left(\frac{\theta}{1+\theta}\right)^k.$$

This is a geometric distribution, with the **success rate** equal to $q = \theta/\theta + 1$ starting at $k = 0$.

2. Calculating the **conditional** distribution of $(\Lambda \,|\, N = k)$, we have

$$g(\lambda \,|\, N = k) = p(\lambda, k) \div \mathbf{P}[N = k] = \frac{\lambda^k}{\theta k!} e^{-\lambda(1+1/\theta)} \cdot \frac{(1+\theta)^{k+1}}{\theta^k} =$$

$$= \frac{1}{\lambda k!} \left(\frac{\lambda(1+\theta)}{\theta}\right)^{k+1} \cdot e^{-\lambda((\theta+1)/\theta)},$$

which is a gamma distribution, with parameters $a = k + 1$ and $b = \theta/(1+\theta)$.

3. For a gamma distribution with parameters a and b, the kth raw moment is

$$\mathbf{E}[X^k] = b^k (a + k - 1)(a + k) \ldots a.$$

Thus, $\mathbf{E}[X] = ab$. Hence, the **conditional expectation** of Λ, given $N = k$, is

$$\mathbf{E}[\Lambda \,|\, N = k] = (k + 1) \cdot \frac{\theta}{1 + \theta}.$$

4. Similarly, the second raw moment of a gamma distribution, with parameters a and b, is

$$\mathbf{E}[X^2] = b^2 a(a + 1).$$

Thus, the variance of $X \sim \mathbf{Gamma}[a, b]$ is

$$\mathbf{Var}(X) = b^2 a(a + 1) - a^2 b^2 = ab^2.$$

Thus, the **conditional** variance of Λ, given $N = k$, is

$$\mathbf{Var}[\Lambda \,|\, N = k] = (k + 1) \left(\frac{\theta}{1 + \theta}\right)^2.$$

2.7.4 Poisson-Gamma Model

Consider a discrete random variable, N, that, conditionally, given $\Lambda = \lambda$, has the Poisson distribution

$$\mathbf{P}\left[N = k \,|\, \Lambda = \lambda\right] = \frac{\lambda^k}{k!}\, e^{-\lambda}, \ k = 0, 1, 2, \ldots.$$

Suppose the **random** parameter Λ is gamma-distributed, with parameters α and θ:

$$g\left(\lambda\right) = \frac{1}{\lambda\Gamma(\alpha)} \left(\frac{\lambda}{\theta}\right)^\alpha e^{-\lambda/\theta}, \ \lambda > 0$$

1. First note that the joint probability function is

$$p\left(k, \lambda\right) = \mathbf{P}\left[N = k \,|\, \Lambda = \lambda\right] \cdot g\left(\lambda\right) = \frac{\lambda^k}{k!}\, e^{-\lambda} \cdot \frac{1}{\Gamma(\alpha) \cdot \theta^\alpha} \lambda^{\alpha-1} e^{-\lambda/\theta} = \frac{\lambda^{\alpha+k-1}}{\theta^\alpha\Gamma(\alpha)k!}\, e^{-\lambda(1+1/\theta)}.$$

The **marginal** distribution of N is

$$\mathbf{P}\left[N = k\right] = f\left(k\right) = \int_0^\infty p\left(k, \lambda\right)\, d\lambda = \frac{1}{k! \cdot \Gamma(\alpha) \cdot \theta^\alpha} \int_0^\infty \lambda^{k+\alpha-1} \cdot e^{-\lambda(1+1/\theta)}\, d\lambda.$$

Using (1.26) with $\beta = n + \alpha - 1$ and $\delta = 1 + 1/\theta$, we obtain for $k = 0, 1, \ldots$

$$\mathbf{P}\left[N = k\right] = \frac{1}{k! \cdot \Gamma(\alpha) \cdot \theta^\alpha} \cdot \frac{\Gamma(k+\alpha)}{(1+1/\theta)^{k+\alpha}} = \frac{\Gamma(k+\alpha)}{k! \cdot \Gamma(\alpha)} \cdot \frac{\theta^{k+\alpha}}{\theta^\alpha (1+\theta)^{k+\alpha}} =$$

$$= \frac{\Gamma(k+\alpha)}{k! \cdot \Gamma(\alpha)} \cdot \left(\frac{1}{1+\theta}\right)^\alpha \cdot \left(\frac{\theta}{1+\theta}\right)^k.$$

This is a negative binomial distribution, with parameters $r = \alpha$, $\beta = \theta$, or an (r, q) parametrization with the success rate equal to $q = \theta/(\theta+1)$ starting at $k = 0$.

2. Calculating the **conditional** distribution of $(\Lambda \,|\, N = k)$, we have

$$g\left(\lambda \,|\, N = k\right) = p\left(\lambda, k\right) \div \mathbf{P}\left[N = k\right] = \frac{\lambda^{\alpha+k-1}}{\theta^\alpha\Gamma(\alpha)k!}\, e^{-\lambda(1+1/\theta)} \cdot \frac{k!\,\Gamma(\alpha)}{\Gamma(k+\alpha)} \frac{(1+\theta)^{\alpha+k}}{\theta^k} =$$

$$= \frac{\lambda^{\alpha+k-1}}{\Gamma(k+\alpha)} \left(\frac{1+\theta}{\theta}\right)^{\alpha+k} \cdot e^{-\lambda(1+\theta)/\theta},$$

which is a gamma distribution with parameters $a = \alpha + k$ and $b = \theta/(1+\theta)$.

3. Hence, the **conditional expectation** of Λ, given $N = k$, is

$$\mathbf{E}\left[\Lambda \,|\, N = k\right] = ab = (k + \alpha) \cdot \frac{\theta}{1+\theta}.$$

4. Similarly, the **conditional** variance of Λ, given $N = k$, is

$$\mathbf{Var}\left[\Lambda \,|\, N = k\right] = ab^2 = (k + \alpha) \left(\frac{\theta}{1+\theta}\right)^2.$$

Conclusion

This chapter was mainly focused on **conditioning techniques** that play an important role in actuarial models aimed at predicting credibility. Bayes' theorems provide tools suitable for evaluation of conditional distributions, expectations, and other moments. Readers are advised to practice with exercises, most of which are focused on these notions.

Combinations of discrete and continuous parts in prior and posterior distributions will help readers develop the self-confidence required for the next chapters.

Exercises

2.1. Discrete Mixture of Pareto Distributions

The severity distribution for losses on an auto collision coverage is

$$F(x) = 1 - 0.55 \left(\frac{1500}{1500 + x} \right)^3 - 0.45 \left(\frac{4500}{4500 + x} \right)^5, \quad x \geq 0.$$

Calculate the mean and the variance of the loss size.

2.2. Variance of a Portfolio of Insurance Risks

You are given the following information about a portfolio of insurance risks:

  (i) There are three classes of risks: A, B, and C.

 (ii) The number of risks in each class, and the mean and standard deviation of claim frequency for each class, are given in the following chart:

Class	Number of Risks	Claim Frequency Mean	Claim Frequency Standard Deviation
A	100	0.17	0.25
B	600	0.2	0.3
C	300	0.23	0.35

Calculate the variance of claim frequency for a risk randomly selected from a portfolio.

2.3. Variance of the Claim Size Distribution for a Portfolio

You are given the following information:

  (i) Risks in a portfolio are liability risks, with probability $1/3$, and property risks, with probability $2/3$.

 (ii) The risks have identical claim count distributions.

 (iii) Loss sizes for liability risks follow an inverse gamma distribution, with parameters $\theta = 200$ and $\alpha = 5$.

 (iv) Loss sizes for property risks follow an inverse gamma distribution, with parameters $\theta = 500$ and $\alpha = 4$.

Calculate the variance of the claim size distribution for this portfolio for a single claim.

2.4. Variance of a Random Claim

On auto collision coverage, there are two classes of policyholders, A and B; 70% of drivers are in class A and 30% in class B. The means and variances of losses for the drivers are as follows:

Class	Mean	Variance
A	300	30,000
B	800	50,000

A claim is submitted by a randomly selected driver.

Calculate the variance of the size of the claim.

2.5. Mixture of Binomial and Uniform

The number of losses on a homeowner's policy is binomially-distributed, with parameters $m = 5$ and q. The parameter q varies by policyholder uniformly between 0 and 0.4.

Calculate the probability of at least one loss for a policyholder.

2.6. Combination of Poisson and Gamma

The number of losses on a homeowner's policy is Poisson-distributed with parameter λ, which varies by policyholder exponentially with mean 10.

Calculate the probability of two or more losses for a policyholder.

2.7. Combination of Poisson and Gamma

Claims arrive at a Poisson rate of λ per hour. The parameter λ varies randomly from one day to the other. The distribution of λ over all days is a gamma, with mean 20 and variance 35.

Determine the probability of four claims arriving in 15 minutes on a randomly selected day.

2.8. Combination of Poisson and Gamma

Claims arrive at a Poisson rate of λ per minute. The parameter λ varies randomly from one minute to the other. The distribution of λ over all minutes is exponential with mean 4.

Determine the probability of three claims arriving in 2 minutes.

2.9. Combination of Poisson and Log-normal

The number of losses for the insurer follows a Poisson distribution with parameter λ, which varies randomly from one year to the other according to a gamma distribution, with parameters $\alpha = 5, \theta = 0.25$. Loss sizes are independent of the number of losses and are log-normally-distributed, with parameters $\mu = 9$, $\sigma = 2.3$.

A reinsurance agreement provides that the reinsurer reimburses the insurer for the excess of each loss over 900,000.

Calculate the probability that the reinsurer will pay exactly two losses in a year.

2.10. Combination of Poisson and Binomial

You are given the following:

(i) The count of exposures is presented as a random variable (N) that has a Poisson distribution with the intensity $\lambda = 10$.

(ii) Given $N = n$, the number of denied claims (X) has the binomial distribution $\mathbf{Bin}\,[n, q]$, where $q = 0.2$.

Derive and calculate the following:

(a) The **marginal** distribution of X; that is, $\mathbf{P}\,[X = k]$, for **any** natural k

(b) The **marginal** expected value of X; that is, $\mathbf{E}\,[X]$

(c) The **marginal** variance of X; that is, $\mathbf{Var}\,[X]$

2.11. Combination of Poisson and Binomial

You are given the following:

(i) The count of exposures is presented as a random variable (N) that has a Poisson distribution, with intensity $\lambda = 10$.

(ii) Given $N = n$, the number of denied claims (X) has the binomial distribution $\mathbf{Bin}\,[n, q]$, where $q = 0.2$.

Derive and find the following:

(a) The **conditional** distribution for a count of claims N, given that $X = k$ of them were denied

(b) The **conditional** distribution for the count of approved claims, $(N-X)$, given $X = k$

(c) The **marginal covariance** between X and $N - X$

2.12. Joint and Conditional Density

Suppose that X and Y are independent exponentially-distributed random variables, with the common density function

$$f(x) = f(x|\lambda) = \lambda e^{-\lambda x} \text{ for } x > 0 \text{ and } f(x) = 0 \text{ elsewhere.}$$

Let $T = X + Y$.

Determine the following:

(a) The **joint** density of (X, T)

(b) The **conditional** density of T, given $X = x$

(c) The **conditional** density of X, given $T = t$

2.13. Combination of Beta and Binomial

Suppose a continuous random variable Q follows beta distribution, with parameters $a = 3$ and $b = 4$.

Suppose further that, given $Q = q$, a discrete random variable $(X|Q = q)$ has a binomial distribution **Bin**$[5, q]$.

Determine the following:

(a) **Marginal** expectation of X

(b) **Marginal** variance of X

(c) **Conditional** expectation, $\mathbf{E}[Q\,|X = k]$, given $X = k$

2.14. Combination of Gamma and Poisson

Suppose a continuous random variable Λ follows a gamma distribution, with parameters $\alpha = 1$ and $\theta = 1/4$. Suppose, in addition, that, given $\Lambda = u$, a discrete random variable X has a conditional Poisson distribution with intensity u.

Determine the following:

(a) **Marginal** expectation of X

(b) **Marginal** variance of X

(c) **Conditional** (or **posterior**) density of Λ, given $X = k$

2.15. Moments of a Portfolio of Risks

A portfolio consists of three policies. The loss distribution for each policy is exponential with the following mean and weight:

Policy	I	II	III
Mean θ_i	10	5	4
Weight w_i	10%	40%	50%

A claim is submitted by a randomly selected policyholder.

Calculate the following:

(a) The expected size of the claim, $\mathbf{E}[X]$

(b) The variance of the size of the claim, $\mathbf{Var}[X]$

2.16. Conditional Probability of an Observation

The observation from a single experiment has distribution

$$\mathbf{P}[D = d \mid G = g] = g^{1-d} (1 - g)^d \quad \text{for } d = 0, 1.$$

The **prior** distribution of G is

$$\mathbf{P}\left[G = \frac{1}{3}\right] = \frac{2}{5} \quad \text{and} \quad \mathbf{P}\left[G = \frac{2}{5}\right] = \frac{3}{5}.$$

Calculate $\mathbf{P}\left[G = \frac{1}{3} \mid D = 1\right]$.

2.17. Marginal Expectation of a Poisson Random Variable

Suppose that the annual claim frequency N is Poisson-distributed, with the rate, $\lambda = 2$.

Suppose further that the variable X, conditionally, given $N = n$, has distribution **Beta**$[a = n, b = 1]$.

Evaluate $\mathbf{E}[X]$, the **marginal** expectation of X.

Solutions

2.1. This is a mixture of two Pareto distributions:

$$\alpha_1 = 3, \; \theta_1 = 1500, \; w_1 = 0.55 \;\; \text{and}$$
$$\alpha_2 = 5, \; \theta_2 = 4500, \; w_2 = 0.45$$

The first moment for each distribution and the mixture is

$$\mathbf{E}[X_1] = \frac{\theta}{\alpha - 1} = \frac{1500}{2} = 750, \; \mathbf{E}[X_2] = \frac{4500}{4} = 1125$$
$$\mathbf{E}[X] = 0.55 \cdot 750 + 0.45 \cdot 1125 = 918.75.$$

The second raw moment for each distribution and the mixture is

$$\mathbf{E}[X_1^2] = \frac{\theta^2 \cdot 2!}{(\alpha - 1)(\alpha - 2)} = \frac{1500^2 \cdot 2}{2 \cdot 1} = 1500^2 = 225 \cdot 10^4$$
$$\mathbf{E}[X_2^2] = \frac{4500^2 \cdot 2}{4 \cdot 3} = 337.5 \cdot 10^4$$
$$\mathbf{E}[X^2] = 0.55 \cdot 225 \cdot 10^4 + 0.45 \cdot 337.5 \cdot 10^4 = 2{,}756{,}250.$$

Therefore, the variance of the mixture is

$$\mathbf{Var}(X) = 2{,}756{,}250 - 918.75^2 = 1{,}912{,}148.44.$$

2.2. The total number of risks is

$$w = 100 + 600 + 300 = 1000.$$

Calculating the weights, we obtain

$$w_1 = \frac{100}{1000} = 0.1, \; w_2 = \frac{600}{1000} = 0.6, \; w_3 = \frac{300}{1000} = 0.3.$$

Thus, the expected values are

$$\mathbf{E}[X] = \sum_{i=1}^{3} w_i \mathbf{E}[X_i] = 0.1 \cdot 0.17 + 0.6 \cdot 0.2 + 0.3 \cdot 0.23 = 0.206$$
$$\mathbf{E}[X^2] = \sum_{i=1}^{3} w_i \mathbf{E}[X_i^2], \; \mathbf{E}[X_i^2] = \mathbf{Var}(X_i) + \mathbf{E}[X_i]^2$$
$$\mathbf{E}[X_1^2] = 0.25^2 + 0.17^2 = 0.0914, \; \mathbf{E}[X_2^2] = 0.3^2 + 0.2^2 = 0.13, \; \mathbf{E}[X_3^2] =$$
$$= 0.35^2 + 0.23^2 = 0.1754$$
$$\mathbf{E}[X^2] = 0.1 \cdot 0.0914 + 0.6 \cdot 0.13 + 0.3 \cdot 0.1754 = 0.13976$$
$$\mathbf{Var}(X) = 0.13976 - 0.206^2 = \mathbf{0.097324}.$$

2.3. Let X be the loss size, I be the risk. Then, for liability risks,

$$\mathbf{E}[X] = \frac{\theta}{\alpha - 1} = \frac{200}{4} = 50, \ \mathbf{E}[X^2] = \frac{\theta^2}{(\alpha - 1)(\alpha - 2)} = \frac{200^2}{4 \cdot 3} = \frac{1}{3} \cdot 10^4,$$

$$\mathbf{Var}(X) = \frac{1}{3} \cdot 10^4 - 25 \cdot 10^2 = 833.33.$$

For property risks,

$$\mathbf{E}[X] = \frac{\theta}{\alpha - 1} = \frac{500}{3} = 166.67, \ \mathbf{E}[X^2] = \frac{\theta^2}{(\alpha - 1)(\alpha - 2)} = \frac{500^2}{3 \cdot 2} = 41{,}666.67,$$

$$\mathbf{Var}(X) = 41{,}666.67 - 166.67^2 = 13{,}888.89.$$

Thus,

$$\mathbf{E}[X|I] = \left[\begin{array}{ll} 50, & p = 1/3 \\ 166.67, & p = 2/3 \end{array} \right. \quad \mathbf{Var}[X|I] = \left[\begin{array}{ll} 833.33, & p = 1/3 \\ 13{,}888.89, & p = 2/3. \end{array} \right.$$

Therefore,

$$\mathbf{Var}(X) = \mathbf{Var}\left(\mathbf{E}[X|I]\right) + \mathbf{E}\left[\mathbf{Var}(X|I)\right] = \left(833.33 \cdot \frac{1}{3} + 13{,}888.89 \cdot \frac{2}{3} \right) +$$

$$+ (166.67 - 50)^2 \cdot \frac{1}{3} \cdot \frac{2}{3} = 12{,}561.73.$$

2.4. This is a mixture situation: a single claim with probabilities of being one type or another. Let X be the claim size. Then,

$$\mathbf{E}[X] = 0.7 \cdot 300 + 0.3 \cdot 800 = 450$$
$$\mathbf{E}[X^2] = 0.7 \cdot \mathbf{E}[X_1^2] + 0.3 \cdot \mathbf{E}[X_2^2].$$

Calculating $\mathbf{E}[X_1^2]$ and $\mathbf{E}[X_2^2]$, we have

$$\mathbf{E}[X_1^2] = \mathbf{Var}(X_1) + (\mathbf{E}[X_1])^2 = 30{,}000 + 300^2 = 120{,}000$$
$$\mathbf{E}[X_2^2] = \mathbf{Var}(X_2) + (\mathbf{E}[X_2])^2 = 50{,}000 + 800^2 = 690{,}000.$$

Thus,

$$\mathbf{E}[X^2] = 0.7 \cdot 120{,}000 + 0.3 \cdot 690{,}000 = 291{,}000$$
$$\mathbf{Var}(X) = 291{,}000 - 450^2 = 291{,}000 - 202{,}500 = 88{,}500.$$

2.5. Let N be the number of losses on a homeowner's policy.

Recall that for a binomial distribution $\mathbf{Bin}[m, q]$,

$$p_0 = \mathbf{P}(N = 0) = (1 - q)^m.$$

Hence, for a single policyholder,

$$\mathbf{P}\left(N = 0|q\right) = (1 - q)^5.$$

To calculate the probability for a randomly selected policyholder, we integrate over q using the uniform density function. The probability of no loss is

$$\mathbf{P}\left(N=0\right)=\frac{1}{0.4}\int_0^{0.4}(1-q)^5\,dq=-\frac{1}{0.4}\cdot\frac{(1-q)^6}{6}\Big|_0^{0.4}=$$

$$=\frac{1}{2.4}(1-0.6^6)=\frac{5}{12}(1-0.6^6)=0.3972.$$

Hence, the the probability of at least one loss is

$$\mathbf{P}\left(N\geq 1\right)=1-\mathbf{P}\left(N=0\right)=1-0.3972=\mathbf{0.6028}.$$

2.6. There are two approaches to solving this problem.

1. The first approach uses the Poisson/Gamma principle, which states that if $(N|\lambda)\sim\mathbf{Poi}(\lambda)$, $\lambda\in\mathbf{Gamma}[\alpha,\theta[$, then $N\sim\mathbf{NB}[r,\beta]$, where $r=\alpha$, $\beta=\theta$.

   Since $(N|\lambda)\sim\mathbf{Poi}(\lambda)$, $\lambda\sim\mathbf{Exp}[\theta=10]\sim\mathbf{Gamma}[\alpha=1,\theta=10]$, it follows that $N\sim\mathbf{NB}[r,\beta]$, where $r=\alpha=1$, $\beta=\theta=10$; that is, N has a geometric distribution, with $\beta=10$.

$$\mathbf{P}\left(N\geq 2\right)=1-\left(\mathbf{P}\left(N=0\right)+\mathbf{P}\left(N=1\right)\right)=1-p_0-p_1$$

   For a geometric distribution,

$$p_0=\frac{1}{1+\beta}=\frac{1}{11},\quad p_1=\frac{\beta}{(1+\beta)^2}=\frac{10}{121}.$$

   Thus,

$$\mathbf{P}\left(N\geq 2\right)=1-\frac{1}{11}-\frac{10}{121}=1-\frac{21}{121}=\frac{100}{121}=\mathbf{0.8264}.$$

2. The second approach is based on the law of total probability. Let N be the number of losses on a homeowner's policy.

   Recall that for a Poisson distribution,

$$p_0=\mathbf{P}(N=0)=e^{-\lambda}$$

$$p_k=\mathbf{P}(N=k)=e^{-\lambda}\cdot\frac{\lambda^k}{k!}.$$

   Hence, for a single policyholder,

$$\mathbf{P}\left(N=0|\lambda\right)=e^{-\lambda}$$
$$\mathbf{P}\left(N=1|\lambda\right)=\lambda\cdot e^{-\lambda}.$$

To calculate the probability for a randomly selected policyholder, we integrate over λ using the exponential density function:

$$f_\Lambda(\lambda)=\frac{1}{\theta}e^{-\lambda/\theta}=\frac{1}{10}e^{-\lambda/10},\ 0<\lambda<\infty$$

The probability of no losses is

$$\mathbf{P}\left(N=0\right) = \frac{1}{\theta}\int_0^\infty e^{-\lambda} \cdot e^{-\lambda/\theta} \, d\lambda = \frac{1}{\theta}\int_0^\infty e^{-\lambda(1+1/\theta)} \, d\lambda =$$

$$= -\frac{1/\theta}{1+1/\theta} \cdot e^{-\lambda(1+1/\theta)}\Big|_0^\infty = \frac{1}{1+\theta} = \frac{1}{11} = 0.\overline{09} \approx 0.091.$$

The probability of one loss is

$$\mathbf{P}\left(N=1\right) = \frac{1}{\theta}\int_0^\infty \lambda \cdot e^{-\lambda} \cdot e^{-\lambda/\theta} \, d\lambda = \frac{1}{\theta}\int_0^\infty \lambda \cdot e^{-\lambda(1+1/\theta)} \, d\lambda.$$

Integrating by parts, we obtain

$$\left[\begin{array}{c|c} u = \lambda & du = d\lambda \\ dv = e^{-\lambda(1+1/\theta)}\, d\lambda & v = -\frac{\theta}{1+\theta}e^{-\lambda(1+1/\theta)} \end{array} \right].$$

Hence,

$$\mathbf{P}\left(N=1\right) = -\frac{\lambda}{1+\theta}e^{-\lambda(1+1/\theta)}\Big|_0^\infty + \frac{1}{1+\theta}\int_0^\infty e^{-\lambda(1+1/\theta)} \, d\lambda =$$

$$= \frac{1}{1+\theta}\int_0^\infty e^{-\lambda(1+1/\theta)} \, d\lambda = -\frac{\theta}{(1+\theta)^2}e^{-\lambda(1+1/\theta)}\Big|_0^\infty = \frac{\theta}{(1+\theta)^2} =$$

$$= \frac{10}{121} = 0.08264.$$

Therefore,

$$\mathbf{P}\left(N=0\right) + \mathbf{P}\left(N=1\right) = \frac{1}{11} + \frac{10}{121} = \frac{21}{121} = 0.1736.$$

Hence, the the probability of two or more losses is

$$\mathbf{P}\left(N \geq 2\right) = 1 - \left(\mathbf{P}\left(N=0\right) + \mathbf{P}\left(N=1\right)\right) = 1 - \frac{21}{121} = \frac{100}{121} = \mathbf{0.8264}.$$

2.7. Let λ be the rate per hour. Then, $\tilde{\lambda} = \lambda/4$ is the rate per 15 minutes:

$$\mathbf{E}[\tilde{\lambda}] = \frac{1}{4}\mathbf{E}[\lambda] = \frac{20}{4} = 5, \ \mathbf{Var}(\tilde{\lambda}) = \frac{1}{16}\mathbf{Var}(\lambda) = \frac{35}{16} = 2.1875$$

Let α and θ be the distribution parameters of $\tilde{\lambda}$. Then,

$$\alpha\theta = 5 \text{ and } \alpha\theta^2 = 2.1875.$$

Solving this system, we have

$$\theta = \frac{2.1875}{5} = 0.4375, \ \alpha = \frac{5}{0.4375} = 11.4286.$$

Therefore,

$$N \sim \mathbf{NB}[r = \alpha = 11.4286, \beta = \theta = 0.4375] \Rightarrow$$

Calculating the probability of four claims, we obtain

$$
p_4 = \frac{r(r+1)(r+2)(r+3)}{4!} \left(\frac{\beta}{1+\beta}\right)^4 \left(\frac{1}{1+\beta}\right)^r =
$$
$$
= \frac{11.4286 \cdot 12.4286 \cdot 13.4286 \cdot 14.4286}{24} \left(\frac{0.4375}{1.4375}\right)^4 \left(\frac{1}{1.4375}\right)^{11.4286} =
$$
$$
= \mathbf{0.1555}.
$$

2.8. Since λ varies by minute, we can represent the total number of claims arriving in 2 minutes as $N = N_1 + N_2$, where N_i is the number of claims arriving in i-th minute, $N_i \sim \mathbf{NB}[r = 1, \beta = 4]$.

Since each $N_i \sim \mathbf{NB}[r = 1, \beta = 4]$, the sum

$$
N = N_1 + N_2 \sim \mathbf{NB}[r = 1 + 1 = 2, \beta = 4].
$$

Therefore,

$$
p_3 = \frac{r(r+1)(r+2)\beta^3}{3!(1+\beta)^{r+3}} = \frac{2 \cdot 3 \cdot 4 \cdot 4^3}{6 \cdot 5^5} = \mathbf{0.08192}.
$$

2.9. Let I indicate a class of insured.

We are given $(N|I) \sim \mathbf{Poi}[\lambda]$, $\lambda \sim \mathbf{Gamma}[\alpha = 5, \theta = 0.25]$,

$X \sim \mathbf{LN}[\mu = 9, \sigma = 2.3]$, $d = 9 \cdot 10^5$, $\mathbf{P}(\tilde{N} = 2)$, where $\tilde{N} = (N|X > d)$.

Thus,

$$
v = \mathbf{P}(X > 9 \cdot 10^5) = 1 - \Phi(z), \ z = \frac{\ln 9 \cdot 10^5 - 9}{2.3} = 2.0479,
$$
$$
\Phi(2.0479) = 0.9797 \Rightarrow v = 1 - 0.9797 = 0.0203 \Rightarrow
$$
$$
\tilde{N} \sim \mathbf{NB}[r = \alpha = 5, \beta = v\theta = 0.0203 \cdot 0.25 = 0.00507]
$$
$$
p_2 = \frac{r(r+1)\beta^2}{2(1+\beta)^{r+2}} = \frac{5 \cdot 6 \cdot 0.00507^2}{2 \cdot 1.00507^7} = \mathbf{0.0003724}.
$$

2.10. Calculating the **joint** probability distribution of the pair, (N, X), using the product of marginal probability for N and conditional probability for $(X | N = n)$, we have

$$
\mathbf{P}\left[(N = n) \bigcap (X = k)\right] = \mathbf{P}[N = n] \cdot \mathbf{P}[X = k | N = n] =
$$
$$
= \left[\frac{\lambda^n}{n!} \cdot e^{-\lambda}\right] \cdot \frac{n!}{k!(n-k)!} q^k (1-q)^{n-k}
$$

for all integer values $n \geq 0$ and for all integer values $0 \leq k \leq n$.

(a) Calculating the **marginal** distribution of X, which can be found by means of the **double expectation** formula, we have

$$\mathbf{P}\left[X = k\right] = \mathbf{E}\left[\mathbf{P}\left[X = k \,|\, N\right]\right] = \sum_{n=0}^{\infty} \mathbf{P}\left[N = n\right] \cdot \mathbf{P}\left[X = k \,|\, N = n\right],$$

and since $0 \le k \le n$, we need to take the sum over $n \ge k$, which leads to the following expression:

$$\mathbf{P}\left[X = k\right] = \sum_{n=k}^{\infty} \frac{\lambda^n}{n!} \cdot e^{-\lambda} \cdot \frac{n!}{k! \cdot (n-k)!} \cdot q^k \cdot (1-q)^{n-k} =$$

$$= \left(e^{-\lambda}\right) \frac{(\lambda q)^k}{k!} \cdot \sum_{n=k}^{\infty} \frac{\left(\lambda\left(1-q\right)\right)^{n-k}}{(n-k)!}$$

The last sum can be simplified using the substitution, $m = n - k$, as follows:

$$\sum_{n=k}^{\infty} \frac{\left(\lambda\left(1-q\right)\right)^{n-k}}{(n-k)!} = \sum_{m=0}^{\infty} \frac{\left(\lambda\left(1-q\right)\right)^{m}}{m!} = e^{\lambda(1-q)}$$

Therefore, for **any** natural k, we obtain

$$\mathbf{P}\left[X = k\right] = \frac{(\lambda q)^k}{k!} \cdot e^{-\lambda q},$$

which implies that the marginal distribution of X is Poisson, with the intensity

$$\tilde{\lambda} = \lambda q = 10 \cdot 0.2 = 2.$$

(b) The marginal expected value of X is $\mathbf{E}\left[X\right] = \tilde{\lambda} = 2$.

(c) The marginal variance of X is $\mathbf{Var}\left[X\right] = \tilde{\lambda} = 2$.

2.11. (a) Calculating the **conditional** distribution of N, given $X = k$, $0 \le k \le n$, we have

$$\mathbf{P}\left[N = n \,|\, X = k\right] = \mathbf{P}\left[(N = n) \bigcap (X = k)\right] \div \mathbf{P}\left[X = k\right] =$$

$$= \left[\frac{\lambda^n}{n!} \cdot e^{-\lambda}\right] \cdot \frac{n!}{k! \, (n-k)!} q^k \, (1-q)^{n-k} \div \frac{(\lambda q)^k}{k!} e^{-\lambda q} =$$

$$= \frac{\left(\lambda\left(1-q\right)\right)^{n-k}}{(n-k)!} \cdot e^{-\lambda(1-q)}, \; n \ge k.$$

(b) The **conditional** distribution of $N - X$, given $X = k$, is the same as Poisson with the intensity $\lambda\left(1 - q\right)$, using the same substitution, $m = n - k$, as before. It does not depend on $X = k$. Thus, $N - X$ and X are **independent**.

(c) Since these two random variables are independent, their marginal covariance (with no N given) is **zero**.

2.12. Note that λ is the reciprocal to the expected value; that is, $\lambda = \theta^{-1}$, where $\theta = \mathbf{E}[X]$. Also, since X and Y are both distributed according to the gamma distribution, with parameters $\alpha = 1$ and $\theta = \lambda^{-1}$, their sum T has gamma distribution, with parameters $\alpha = 2$ and $\theta = \lambda^{-1}$.

(a) The **joint** density of (X, T) is derived as follows:

$$f_{X,T}(x,t) = f_X(x) \cdot f_{T|X}(t|x) = f_X(x) \cdot f_Y(t-x), \quad 0 < x < t. \qquad (2.14)$$

Indeed, the joint CDF for (X, T), $T = X + Y$ is

$$F_{X,T}(x,t) = \mathbf{P}[(X \le x) \bigcap (T \le t)] = \mathbf{E}\left[\mathbf{P}\left[\left((X \le x) \bigcap (X + Y \le t)\right) | X\right]\right] =$$

$$= \mathbf{E}\left[\mathbf{P}\left[\left((X \le x) \bigcap (Y \le t - x)\right) | X\right]\right] = \mathbf{E}\left[\mathbf{P}\left[(Y \le t - x) | X\right]\right],$$

which, upon differentiation, implies identity (2.14).

Hence, using (2.10),

$$f_{X,T}(x,t) = \lambda e^{-\lambda x} \cdot \lambda e^{-\lambda(t-x)} = \lambda^2 e^{-\lambda t}, \quad 0 < x < t.$$

(b) Using (2.9), the **conditional** density of T, given $X = x$, is the ratio:

$$f_{T|X}(t|x) = \frac{f_{X,T}(x,t)}{f_X(x)} = f_Y(t-x) = \lambda \cdot e^{-\lambda(t-x)}, \quad 0 < x < t.$$

(c) Using (2.11), the **conditional** density of X, given $T = t$, is also a ratio

$$f_{X|T}(x|t) = \frac{f_{X,T}(x,t)}{f_T(t)} = \lambda^2 e^{-\lambda t} \div \lambda^2 t \cdot e^{-\lambda t} = \frac{1}{t}, \quad 0 < x < t$$

Thus, $(X|T = t)$ is uniformly-distributed over the interval $(0 < x < t)$.

2.13. Recall relationships between beta-integrals and gamma-integrals introduced by Leonard Euler as

$$\mathbf{B}(a,b) = \int_0^1 q^{a-1}(1-q)^{b-1}\,dq = \frac{\Gamma(a)\,\Gamma(b)}{\Gamma(a+b)},$$

where

$$\Gamma(a) = \int_0^\infty u^{a-1} e^{-u}\,du,$$

and for any $a > 0$, the equation $\Gamma(a+1) = a \cdot \Gamma(a)$ holds. In particular, for any natural a, this results in $\Gamma(a) = (a-1)!$

By definition, a continuous random variable Q that follows a beta distribution, with parameters $a > 0$ and $b > 0$, has a density function defined on the unit interval $(0, 1)$ as

$$g(q|a,b) = \frac{\Gamma(a+b)}{\Gamma(a) \cdot \Gamma(b)} q^{a-1}(1-q)^{b-1}.$$

For $a = 3$ and $b = 4$,

$$g(q) = \frac{\Gamma(7)}{\Gamma(3) \cdot \Gamma(4)} q^2(1-q)^3 = 60q^2(1-q)^3.$$

Note that the first two moments of the beta-distributed random variable can be evaluated as

$$\mathbf{E}[Q] = \frac{a}{a+b} \quad \text{and} \quad \mathbf{E}[Q^2] = \frac{a\,(a+1)}{(a+b)\,(a+b+1)}.$$

Also, by definition of a binimially distributed random variable, with parameters $m = 5$ and q,

$$\mathbf{P}[X = k\,|Q = q] = \frac{5!}{k!\,(5-k)!}\,q^k \cdot (1-q)^{5-k}$$

for integer values k, $0 \le k \le 5$.

Calculating **conditional** moments of X, given $Q = q$, we have

$$\mathbf{E}\left[X\,|Q = q\right] = 5q \quad \text{and} \quad \mathbf{E}\left[X^2\,|Q = q\right] = 5q(1-q) + (5q)^2 = 20q^2 + 5q.$$

(a) By the **double expectation** theorem, the **marginal** expectation of X is

$$\mathbf{E}\left[X\right] = \mathbf{E}\left[\mathbf{E}\left[X\,|Q\right]\right] = \mathbf{E}\left[5Q\right] = 5\mathbf{E}\left[Q\right] = 5 \cdot \frac{a}{a+b} = 5 \cdot \frac{3}{3+4} = \frac{15}{7}.$$

(b) The **marginal** variance of X is

$$\mathbf{Var}[X] = \mathbf{E}[X^2] - (\mathbf{E}[X])^2.$$

By the **double expectation** theorem, the **marginal** second moment of X is

$$\mathbf{E}[X^2] = \mathbf{E}\left[\mathbf{E}\left[X^2\,|Q\right]\right] = \mathbf{E}\left[20Q^2 + 5Q\right] = 20\mathbf{E}\left[Q^2\right] + 5\mathbf{E}\left[Q\right] =$$

$$= 20 \cdot \frac{a\,(a+1)}{(a+b)\,(a+b+1)} + 5 \cdot \frac{a}{a+b} = 20 \cdot \frac{3 \cdot 4}{7 \cdot 8} + 5 \cdot \frac{3}{7} = 10 \cdot \frac{3}{7} + 5 \cdot \frac{3}{7} = \frac{45}{7}.$$

Therefore,

$$\mathbf{Var}[X] = \frac{45}{7} - \left(\frac{15}{7}\right)^2 = \frac{90}{49}.$$

(c) Given $X = k$, the **conditional** expectation $\mathbf{E}[Q\,|X = k]$ can be found using the **joint** probability for a mixed pair (Q, X), where the first component is continuous and the second is discrete.

The **conditional** (or **posterior**) density at q, of Q, given $X = k$, can be presented as ratio of the joint probability function of the pair (Q, X) to the marginal probability mass function for X at $X = k$; that is,

$$g_{Q|X}\left(q\,|k\right) = \frac{g_{Q,X}(q, k)}{g_X(k)}.$$

The joint probability function of the pair (Q, X) can be represented as follows:

$$g_{Q,X}(u, k) = g_{X|Q}\left(k\,|q\right) \cdot g_Q(q) = \frac{5!}{k!\,(5-k)!}\,q^k \cdot (1-q)^{5-k} \cdot 60q^2(1-q)^3 =$$

$$= \frac{5! \cdot 60}{k!\,(5-k)!} \cdot q^{k+2}(1-q)^{8-k}$$

Therefore,

$$g_{Q|X}(u\,|k) = \frac{5! \cdot 60}{k!\,(5-k)!} \cdot q^{k+2}(1-q)^{8-k} \div g^X(k) = c \cdot q^{k+2}(1-q)^{8-k},$$

where $c = \dfrac{5! \cdot 60}{k!\,(5-k)! \cdot g^X(k)}.$

The probability density function of the conditional random variable $(Q\,|X)$ is proportional to $q^{k+2}(1-q)^{8-k}$. This is a beta density, with parameters

$$a' = 3+k, \; b' = 9-k.$$

Thus, the posterior density of Q, given $X = k$, is

$$g_{Q|X}(q\,|k) = \frac{\Gamma(12)}{\Gamma(3+k) \cdot \Gamma(9-k)} \cdot q^{k+2}(1-q)^{8-k} \; \text{for} \; 0 \le q \le 1, \; k = 1, \ldots 5.$$

The conditional expectation of Q, given $X = k$, therefore is the expected value under the posterior density; that is,

$$\mathbf{E}[Q\,|X = k] = \frac{a'}{a'+b'} = \frac{3+k}{12}.$$

2.14. Since Λ follows a gamma distribution, with parameters $\alpha = 1$ and $\theta = 1/4$, its density is defined as

$$f(u) = 4e^{-4u}, \; u > 0.$$

Thus, Λ has exponential distribution with mean $\theta = 1/4$.

(a) The **marginal** expectation of X can be found using the **double expectation** theorem:

$$\mathbf{E}[X] = \mathbf{E}[\mathbf{E}[X|\Lambda]] = \mathbf{E}[\Lambda] = \frac{1}{4}$$

(b) The **marginal** variance of X is

$$\mathbf{Var}[X] = \mathbf{E}[X^2] - (\mathbf{E}[X])^2.$$

By the **double expectation** theorem, the **marginal** second moment of X is

$$\mathbf{E}[X^2] = \mathbf{E}\left[\mathbf{E}\left[X^2\,|\Lambda\right]\right] = \mathbf{E}\left[\mathbf{Var}\left[X\,|\Lambda\right] + \mathbf{E}\left[X\,|\Lambda\right]^2\right] = \mathbf{E}\left[\Lambda + \Lambda^2\right] =$$
$$= \mathbf{E}\left[\Lambda\right] + \mathbf{E}\left[\Lambda^2\right].$$

For an exponentially-distributed random variable,

$$\mathbf{E}[\Lambda^k] = \theta^k \cdot k!$$

Hence,

$$\mathbf{E}\left[\Lambda^2\right] = 2\theta^2 = 2 \cdot \left(\frac{1}{4}\right)^2 = 2 \cdot \frac{1}{16} = \frac{1}{8}.$$

Thus,

$$\mathbf{E}[X^2] = \frac{1}{4} + \frac{1}{8} = \frac{3}{8} \; \text{and} \; \mathbf{Var}[X] = \frac{3}{8} - \left(\frac{1}{4}\right)^2 = \frac{3}{8} - \frac{1}{16} = \frac{5}{16}.$$

(c) The **conditional** (or **posterior**) density at u of Λ, given $X = k$, can be presented as ratio of the joint probability function of the pair (Λ, X) to the marginal probability mass function for X at $X = k$; that is,

$$g_{\Lambda|X}(u\,|k) = \frac{g_{\Lambda,X}(u,k)}{g_X(k)}.$$

The joint probability function of the pair (Λ, X) can be represented as follows:

$$g_{\Lambda,X}(u,k) = g_{X|\Lambda}(k\,|u) \cdot g_{\Lambda}(u) = e^{-u} \cdot \frac{u^k}{k!} \cdot 4e^{-4u} = 4e^{-5u} \cdot \frac{u^k}{k!}$$

Therefore,

$$g_{\Lambda|X}(u\,|k) = 4e^{-5u} \cdot \frac{u^k}{k!} \div g^X(k) = c \cdot e^{-5u} \cdot u^k, \text{ where } c = \frac{4}{k! \cdot g^X(k)}.$$

The probability density function of the conditional random variable $(\Lambda\,|X)$ is proportional to $u^k \cdot e^{-5u}$. This is a gamma density, with parameters

$$\alpha' = k + 1, \ \theta' = \frac{1}{5}.$$

Thus, the posterior density of Λ, given $X = k$ is

$$g_{\Lambda|X}(u\,|k) = \frac{5^{k+1}}{k!} u^k e^{-5u} \text{ for } u > 0.$$

2.15. (a) Let $\{A_1, A_2, A_3\}$ be the three events corresponding to the three types of policies. Then,

$$\mathbf{E}[X\,|A_1] = \theta_1 = 10 \text{ and } \mathbf{Var}[X\,|A_1] = \theta_1^2 = 100, \text{ with } \mathbf{P}[A_1] = w_1 = 0.1,$$

$$\mathbf{E}[X\,|A_2] = \theta_2 = 5 \text{ and } \mathbf{Var}[X\,|A_2] = \theta_2^2 = 25, \text{ with } \mathbf{P}[A_2] = w_2 = 0.4,$$

$$\mathbf{E}[X\,|A_3] = \theta_3 = 4 \text{ and } \mathbf{Var}[X\,|A_3] = \theta_3^2 = 16, \text{ with } \mathbf{P}[A_3] = w_3 = 0.5.$$

Therefore, by the double expectation theorem,

$$\mathbf{E}[X] = \sum_{i=1}^{3} \mathbf{E}[X\,|A_i] \cdot \mathbf{P}[A_i] = 0.1 \cdot 10 + 0.4 \cdot 5 + 0.5 \cdot 4 = 1 + 2 + 2 = 5.$$

(b) To calculate the variance of the size of the claim, recall the conditional variance formula:
$$\mathbf{Var}[X] = \mathbf{E}[\mathbf{Var}[X\,|A]] + \mathbf{Var}[\mathbf{E}[X\,|A]],$$

where A indicates the type of variable, which corresponds to one of the events $\{A_1, A_2, A_3\}$.

Calculating $\mathbf{Var}[\mathbf{E}[X\,|A]]$, we obtain

$$\mathbf{Var}(\mathbf{E}[X\,|A]) = \mathbf{E}\left[\mathbf{E}[X\,|A]^2\right] - \mathbf{E}[\mathbf{E}[X\,|A]]^2 =$$
$$= 10^2 \cdot 0.1 + 5^2 \cdot 0.4 + 4^2 \cdot 0.5 - 5^2 = 10 + 10 + 8 - 25 = 3.$$

Calculating $\mathbf{E}\left[\mathbf{Var}\left[X\,|A\right]\right]$, we obtain

$$\mathbf{E}\left[\mathbf{Var}\left[X\,|A\right]\right] = 100 \cdot 0.1 + 25 \cdot 0.4 + 16 \cdot 0.5 = 10 + 10 + 8 = 28.$$

Thus,

$$\mathbf{Var}\left[X\right] = 28 + 3 = \mathbf{31}.$$

Alternatively,

$$\mathbf{E}[X^2] = \mathbf{E}\left[\mathbf{E}\left[X^2\,|A\right]\right] = 2 \cdot \left[10^2 \cdot 0.1 + 5^2 \cdot 0.4 + 4^2 \cdot 0.5\right] = 56.$$

By definition of the variance,

$$\mathbf{Var}[X] = \mathbf{E}[X^2] - \mathbf{E}[X]^2 = 56 - 5^2 = 56 - 25 = \mathbf{31}.$$

2.16. By the law of total probability, if B_i is a set of exhaustive (i.e., $\mathbf{P}(\cup_i B_i) = 1$) and mutually exclusive (i.e., $\mathbf{P}(B_i \cap B_j) = 0$ for $i \neq j$) events, then for any event A,

$$\mathbf{P}(A) = \sum_i \mathbf{P}(A \cap B_i) = \sum_i \mathbf{P}(A|B_i)\mathbf{P}(B_i).$$

Therefore,

$$\mathbf{P}\left[D = 1\right] = \mathbf{P}\left[D = 1\,\middle|\,G = \frac{1}{3}\right] \cdot \mathbf{P}\left[G = \frac{1}{3}\right] + \mathbf{P}\left[D = 1\,\middle|\,G = \frac{2}{5}\right] \cdot \mathbf{P}\left[G = \frac{2}{5}\right] =$$

$$= \frac{2}{3} \cdot \frac{2}{5} + \frac{3}{5} \cdot \frac{3}{5} = \frac{4}{15} + \frac{9}{25} = \frac{20 + 27}{75} = \frac{47}{75}.$$

By Bayes' theorem,

$$\mathbf{P}(A|B) = \frac{\mathbf{P}(B|A)\mathbf{P}(A)}{\mathbf{P}(B)}.$$

Therefore,

$$\mathbf{P}\left[G = \frac{1}{3}\,\middle|\,D = 1\right] = \frac{\mathbf{P}\left[D = 1\,\middle|\,G = \frac{1}{3}\right] \cdot \mathbf{P}\left[G = \frac{1}{3}\right]}{\mathbf{P}\left[D = 1\right]} = \frac{2}{3} \cdot \frac{2}{5} \div \frac{47}{75} =$$

$$= \frac{4}{15} \div \frac{47}{75} = \frac{20}{47}.$$

2.17. Since the random variable $(X|N = n)$ is beta-distributed, with parameters $a = n$ and $b = 1$, its expected value is

$$\mathbf{E}[X|N = n] = \frac{\Gamma(a + b)\Gamma(a + 1)}{\Gamma(a)\Gamma(a + b + 1)} = \frac{\Gamma(n + 1)\Gamma(n + 1)}{\Gamma(n)\Gamma(n + 2)}.$$

Since

$$\Gamma(n + 1) = n\Gamma(n),$$

we have

$$\mathbf{E}[X|N = n] = \frac{n\Gamma(n) \cdot n\Gamma(n)}{\Gamma(n) \cdot (n + 1)n\Gamma(n)} = \frac{n}{n + 1} = 1 - \frac{1}{n + 1}.$$

Therefore,

$$\mathbf{E}[X] = \mathbf{E}\left[\mathbf{E}[X\,|\,N = n]\right] = \mathbf{E}\left[1 - \frac{1}{N+1}\right] = 1 - \mathbf{E}\left[\frac{1}{N+1}\right] = 1 - \mathbf{E}[Y],$$

where $Y = \dfrac{1}{N+1}$.

By the double expectation theorem, the expected value of Y is

$$\mathbf{E}[Y] = \mathbf{E}\left[\frac{1}{N+1}\right] = \sum_{n=0}^{\infty} \frac{1}{n+1} \cdot \mathbf{P}[N = n] = \sum_{n=0}^{\infty} \frac{1}{n+1} \cdot \frac{\lambda^n}{n!}\, e^{-\lambda}.$$

Notice that the denominator is $(n+1) \cdot n! = (n+1)!$, and since $\lambda^n = \lambda^{n+1} \cdot \lambda^{-1}$, we can carry out $\lambda^{-1} \cdot e^{-\lambda}$ from the sum, thus obtaining

$$\mathbf{E}[Y] = \frac{1}{\lambda} \cdot e^{-\lambda} \sum_{n=0}^{\infty} \frac{\lambda^{n+1}}{(n+1)!}.$$

Making a substitution $m = n + 1$, we have

$$\mathbf{E}[Y] = \frac{1}{\lambda} \cdot e^{-\lambda} \sum_{m=1}^{\infty} \frac{\lambda^m}{m!} = \frac{1}{\lambda} \cdot e^{-\lambda} \left(e^{\lambda} - 1\right) = \frac{(1 - e^{-\lambda})}{\lambda}.$$

Hence,

$$\mathbf{E}[X] = 1 - \mathbf{E}[Y] = 1 - \frac{(1 - e^{-\lambda})}{\lambda}.$$

Since $\lambda = 2$, we obtain

$$\mathbf{E}[X] = 1 - \frac{1}{2}(1 - e^{-2}) = \frac{1}{2}(1 + e^{-2}) \approx \mathbf{0.5677}.$$

Chapter 3

Bayesian Framework for Credibility

In this chapter we will discuss prior and posterior probabilities and expectations through the Bayesian framework.

The goals of this chapter include the following:

1. Describe general techniques aimed at deriving credibility based on a given **model** and prior distribution.

2. Combine the model and prior distributions to **estimate** what should be expected after having observed a sample described by the specified model.

3. Discuss **conjugate** pairs, which are model and prior distributions connected through a posterior distribution of a structure similar to the prior.

Exercises will further deepen and develop readers' knowledge of the material presented in this chapter.

3.1 Bayes' Theorem and Credibility Theory

Recall that Bayes' theorem describes the probability of an event, based on prior knowledge of conditions that might be related to the event. It states that

$$\mathbf{P}[A|B] = \frac{\mathbf{P}[B|A]\mathbf{P}[A]}{\mathbf{P}[B]}.$$

In Bayesian statistics a posterior probability is the revised or updated probability of an event occurring after taking into consideration new information. Posterior probability is calculated by updating the prior probability using Bayes' theorem.

Credibility theory, developed by Thomas Bayes, is a form of statistical inference used to forecast an uncertain future event.

In this chapter we will discuss credibility using the Bayesian approach.

3.2   Bayesian Framework

Under the standard Bayesian framework, the following information is given:

1. **Model**

    The observed values $\mathbf{X} = \{X_i,\ i = 1, 2, \ldots, n\}$ are independent identically distributed (iid) random variables with the common **pmf** for discrete data or common **pdf**, $f(x \mid \theta)$, where θ is the unknown parameter.

2. **Prior distribution**

    It is assumed that the prior distribution of the unknown parameter θ is given by its specified **pdf** or **pmf**, denoted by $\pi(\theta)$.

3.3   Bayesian Approach

The main objectives of Bayesian analysis can be described as follows:

1. Determine the **posterior** distribution, $\pi(\theta \mid \mathbf{X})$ of the parameter viewed as a random variable Θ.

2. If $Y = X_{n+1}$ represents the future observation, the distribution of $(Y \mid \mathbf{X})$ is known as the **predictive** distribution. It can be evaluated by using the posterior distribution of Θ.

3. Finally, the **credibility premium** for the new observation, $Y = X_{n+1}$, is the expectation evaluated via the posterior distribution of Θ as follows:

$$\mathbf{E}[Y \mid \mathbf{X}] = \tilde{\mathbf{E}}[Y \mid \Theta], \tag{3.1}$$

    where the symbol $\tilde{\mathbf{E}}$ is used to emphasize that the expectation is taken with respect to the posterior distribution of Θ, given $\mathbf{X}$.

In the case of a discrete prior, the function $\pi(\theta)$ is the prior **pmf** of Θ, while in the continuous case the same notation will be used for the **pdf** of Θ.

The Bayesian estimate of the **credibility premium** is then defined via the **posterior** distribution of Θ, given $\mathbf{X} = \mathbf{x}$, or $(\Theta \mid \mathbf{X})$. It can be expressed in terms of the model and prior distributions.

3.4   Bayesian Credibility: Continuous Prior

Suppose that

$$\mathbf{X} = \{X_i\},\ i = 1, 2, \ldots, n$$

is a sample of iid observations sharing the same common **pdf** or **pmf**, denoted as $f(x \mid \theta)$. Here, θ is the unknown parameter viewed as a value of the continuous random variable Θ, with the **pdf**, denoted as $\pi(\theta)$.

3.4.1 Posterior Distribution of Parameters

The posterior **pdf** of Θ, given $\mathbf{X} = \mathbf{x}$, is the ratio

$$\pi(\theta \,|\, \mathbf{X} = \mathbf{x}) = \frac{f(\mathbf{x} \,|\, \theta) \cdot \pi(\theta)}{f(\mathbf{x})}, \qquad (3.2)$$

where

$$f(\mathbf{x} \,|\, \theta) = \prod_{i=1}^{n} f(x_i \,|\, \theta)$$

and

$$f(\mathbf{x}) = \int_{-\infty}^{\infty} f(\mathbf{x} \,|\, \theta) \cdot \pi(\theta) \, d\theta$$

is either **joint marginal pdf** or **joint marginal pmf** of $\mathbf{X}$ at $\mathbf{x}$.

3.4.2 Predictive Distribution of a New Observation

The predictive distribution of $Y = X_{n+1}$ at y is determined as

$$f(y|\mathbf{x}) = \tilde{\mathbf{E}}[f(y|\Theta)] = \int_{-\infty}^{\infty} f(y|\theta) \cdot \pi(\theta|\mathbf{x}) \, d\theta, \qquad (3.3)$$

where $\pi(\theta|\mathbf{x})$ was defined in (3.2).

3.4.3 Credibility Premium

The credibility premium is defined by the formula

$$\mathbf{E}[Y|\mathbf{X}] = \tilde{\mathbf{E}}[Y|\Theta] = \int_{-\infty}^{\infty} \mathbf{E}[Y|\theta] \cdot \pi(\theta|\mathbf{x}) \, d\theta. \qquad (3.4)$$

Thus, the expectation is evaluated with respect to the posterior distribution of $(\Theta|\mathbf{X} = \mathbf{x})$.

3.5 Conjugate Families of Distributions

In Bayesian theory, if the posterior distributions $\pi(\theta|x)$ are in the same probability distribution family as the prior probability distribution $\pi(\theta)$, the prior and posterior are called **conjugate distributions**, and the prior is called a **conjugate prior** for the likelihood function.

In the following sections we will consider special models and helpful formulae for several conjugate priors.

3.6 Beta Prior and Geometric Model

Assume that the time when the first claim X occurs has the geometric distribution **Geom** $[q]$, where the parameter q is treated as a random variable, Q, with the prior **Beta** $[\alpha, \beta]$ distribution defined by its density:

$$\pi(q) = \frac{\Gamma(\alpha + \beta)}{\Gamma(\alpha) \cdot \Gamma(\beta)} \cdot q^{\alpha-1} \cdot (1 - q)^{\beta-1}, \; 0 < q < 1 \qquad (3.5)$$

Then the model is described by

$$f(x\,|q) = (1-q)^x \cdot q \quad \text{for} \quad x = 0, 1, 2, \ldots. \tag{3.6}$$

The **conditional** expectation and variance of X are

$$\mathbf{E}[X\,|Q] = \frac{1-Q}{Q} \quad \text{and} \quad \mathbf{Var}[X\,|Q] = \frac{1-Q}{Q^2}.$$

The joint probability mass function of $X|Q$ at $\mathbf{x}$ is the product

$$f(\mathbf{x}|q) = \prod_{i=1}^{n} f(x_i|q) = \prod_{i=1}^{n} (1-q)^{x_i} \cdot q = q^n (1-q)^w, \tag{3.7}$$

where $W = \sum_{i=1}^{n} X_i$ with the current value $w = \sum_{i=1}^{n} x_i$.

Integrating (3.7) in q and using (1.28), we calculate the joint marginal probability function:

$$f(\mathbf{x}) = \int_0^1 f(\mathbf{x}|q)\,\pi(q)\,dq = \int_0^1 q^n (1-q)^w \cdot \frac{\Gamma(\alpha+\beta)}{\Gamma(\alpha)\cdot\Gamma(\beta)} \cdot q^{\alpha-1} \cdot (1-q)^{\beta-1}\,dq =$$

$$= \frac{\Gamma(\alpha+\beta)}{\Gamma(\alpha)\cdot\Gamma(\beta)} \int_0^1 q^{n+\alpha-1}(1-q)^{w+\beta-1}\,dq =$$

$$= \frac{\Gamma(\alpha+\beta)}{\Gamma(\alpha)\cdot\Gamma(\beta)} \cdot B(n+\alpha, w+\beta) = \frac{\Gamma(\alpha+\beta)}{\Gamma(\alpha)\cdot\Gamma(\beta)} \cdot \frac{\Gamma(n+\alpha)\cdot\Gamma(w+\beta)}{\Gamma(n+\alpha+w+\beta)}$$

Thus,

$$f(\mathbf{x}) = \frac{\Gamma(\alpha+\beta)}{\Gamma(\alpha)\cdot\Gamma(\beta)} \cdot \frac{\Gamma(n+\alpha)\cdot\Gamma(w+\beta)}{\Gamma(n+\alpha+w+\beta)}. \tag{3.8}$$

Focusing on the three main objectives of the Bayesian approach, let us calculate the posterior and predictive distribution and the credibility premium in this model.

3.6.1 Posterior Distribution of Q

The posterior density is defined as a ratio:

$$\pi(q|\mathbf{x}) = \frac{f(\mathbf{x}|q)\cdot\pi(q)}{f(\mathbf{x})},$$

where the numerator is the product of $f(\mathbf{x}|q)$ defined by (3.7) and the prior density described in (3.5), with the denominator $f(\mathbf{x})$ defined in (3.8).

Evaluating, we have

$$\pi(q|\mathbf{x}) = \frac{\Gamma(n+\alpha+w+\beta)}{\Gamma(n+\alpha)\cdot\Gamma(w+\beta)} \cdot q^n(1-q)^w \cdot q^{\alpha-1}\cdot(1-q)^{\beta-1} =$$

$$= \frac{\Gamma(n+\alpha+w+\beta)}{\Gamma(n+\alpha)\cdot\Gamma(w+\beta)} \cdot q^{n+\alpha-1}(1-q)^{w+\beta-1}.$$

Thus,

$$\pi(q|\mathbf{x}) = \frac{\Gamma(n+\alpha+w+\beta)}{\Gamma(n+\alpha)\cdot\Gamma(w+\beta)} \cdot q^{n+\alpha-1}(1-q)^{w+\beta-1}. \tag{3.9}$$

Note that the posterior density of Q, given $\mathbf{X} = \mathbf{x}$, belongs to the family of beta densities, with parameters:

$$\alpha' = n + \alpha \quad \text{and} \quad \beta' = w + \beta. \tag{3.10}$$

Since the posterior and the prior distributions are of similar structure, beta distribution is the conjugate prior for the given geometric model.

3.6.2 Predictive Distribution of Y

Recall that $Y = X_{n+1}$ is a future observation, which follows the same model. The predictive distribution of Y is its conditional distribution, given $\mathbf{X}$. This distribution can be obtained by taking the expectation of the model, similar to (3.7), with $y = x_{n+1}$ with respect to the **posterior** defined in (3.9):

$$
\begin{aligned}
\mathbf{P}\left[Y = y | \mathbf{X} = \mathbf{x}\right] &= \int_0^1 f\left(y|q\right) \pi(q|\mathbf{x}) \, dq = \\
&= \int_0^1 (1-q)^y \cdot q \cdot \frac{\Gamma(n+\alpha+w+\beta)}{\Gamma(n+\alpha) \cdot \Gamma(w+\beta)} \cdot q^{n+\alpha-1}(1-q)^{w+\beta-1} \, dq = \\
&= \frac{\Gamma(n+\alpha+w+\beta)}{\Gamma(n+\alpha) \cdot \Gamma(w+\beta)} \int_0^1 q^{n+\alpha}(1-q)^{w+\beta+y-1} \, dq = \\
&= \frac{\Gamma(n+\alpha+w+\beta)}{\Gamma(n+\alpha) \cdot \Gamma(w+\beta)} \cdot B\left(n+\alpha+1, w+\beta+y\right) = \\
&= \frac{\Gamma(n+\alpha+w+\beta)}{\Gamma(n+\alpha) \cdot \Gamma(w+\beta)} \cdot \frac{\Gamma(n+\alpha+1) \cdot \Gamma(w+\beta+y)}{\Gamma(n+\alpha+w+\beta+y+1)} = \\
&= (n+\alpha) \cdot \frac{\Gamma(n+\alpha+w+\beta) \cdot \Gamma(w+\beta+y)}{\Gamma(w+\beta) \cdot \Gamma(n+\alpha+w+\beta+y+1)}
\end{aligned}
$$

Thus,

$$\mathbf{P}\left[Y = y | \mathbf{X} = \mathbf{x}\right] = (n+\alpha) \cdot \frac{\Gamma(n+\alpha+w+\beta) \cdot \Gamma(w+\beta+y)}{\Gamma(w+\beta) \cdot \Gamma(n+\alpha+w+\beta+y+1)}. \tag{3.11}$$

3.6.3 Credibility Premium

Let us now calculate the Bayesian credibility, or premium, $\mathbf{E}[Y|\mathbf{X} = \mathbf{x}]$. Using (3.4), we have

$$
\begin{aligned}
\mathbf{E}[Y|\mathbf{X} = \mathbf{x}] &= \mathbf{E}[Y|W = w] = \tilde{\mathbf{E}}[Y|Q] = \int_0^1 \mathbf{E}[Y|q] \cdot \pi(q|\mathbf{x}) \, dq = \\
&= \int_0^1 \frac{1-q}{q} \cdot \pi(q|\mathbf{x}) \, dq = \frac{\Gamma(n+\alpha+w+\beta)}{\Gamma(n+\alpha) \cdot \Gamma(w+\beta)} \int_0^1 \frac{1-q}{q} \cdot q^{n+\alpha-1}(1-q)^{w+\beta-1} \, dq = \\
&= \frac{\Gamma(n+\alpha+w+\beta)}{\Gamma(n+\alpha) \cdot \Gamma(w+\beta)} \int_0^1 q^{n+\alpha-2}(1-q)^{w+\beta} \, dq = \\
&= \frac{\Gamma(n+\alpha+w+\beta)}{\Gamma(n+\alpha) \cdot \Gamma(w+\beta)} \cdot B\left(n+\alpha-1, w+\beta+1\right) = \\
&= \frac{\Gamma(n+\alpha+w+\beta)}{\Gamma(n+\alpha) \cdot \Gamma(w+\beta)} \cdot \frac{\Gamma(n+\alpha-1) \cdot \Gamma(w+\beta+1)}{\Gamma(n+\alpha+w+\beta)} = \frac{w+\beta}{n+\alpha-1}.
\end{aligned}
$$

Thus,

$$\mathbf{E}[Y|\mathbf{X} = \mathbf{x}] = \mathbf{E}[Y|W = w] = \frac{w + \beta}{n + \alpha - 1}. \tag{3.12}$$

The following lemma will be used to calculate the marginal expected value and variance of X.

Lemma 3.6.1 *If Q has distribution **Beta** $[\alpha, \beta]$, then for $\alpha > 2$,*

$$E\left[\frac{1-Q}{Q}\right] = \frac{\beta}{\alpha - 1}, \ E\left[\left(\frac{1-Q}{Q}\right)^2\right] = \frac{\beta(\beta+1)}{(\alpha-1)(\alpha-2)} \ and$$

$$Var\left[\frac{1-Q}{Q}\right] = \frac{\beta(\alpha+\beta-1)}{(\alpha-1)^2(\alpha-2)}, \ E\left[\frac{1-Q}{Q^2}\right] = \frac{\beta(\alpha+\beta-1)}{(\alpha-1)(\alpha-2)}.$$

Proof. Note that

$$\mathbf{Var}\left[\frac{1-Q}{Q}\right] = \mathbf{E}\left[\left(\frac{1-Q}{Q}\right)^2\right] - \left(\mathbf{E}\left[\frac{1-Q}{Q}\right]\right)^2.$$

If $\alpha > 1$, we have

$$\mathbf{E}\left[\frac{1-Q}{Q}\right] = \frac{\Gamma(\alpha+\beta)}{\Gamma(\alpha) \cdot \Gamma(\beta)} \int_0^1 \frac{1-q}{q} \cdot q^{\alpha-1} \cdot (1-q)^{\beta-1} \ dq =$$

$$= \frac{\Gamma(\alpha+\beta)}{\Gamma(\alpha) \cdot \Gamma(\beta)} \int_0^1 q^{\alpha-2} \cdot (1-q)^{\beta} \ dq = \frac{\Gamma(\alpha+\beta)}{\Gamma(\alpha) \cdot \Gamma(\beta)} \cdot B(\alpha-1, \beta+1) =$$

$$= \frac{\Gamma(\alpha+\beta)}{\Gamma(\alpha) \cdot \Gamma(\beta)} \cdot \frac{\Gamma(\alpha-1) \cdot \Gamma(\beta+1)}{\Gamma(\alpha+\beta)} = \frac{\Gamma(\alpha-1)\beta\Gamma(\beta)}{(\alpha-1)\Gamma(\alpha-1) \cdot \Gamma(\beta)} = \frac{\beta}{\alpha-1}.$$

Similarly, if $\alpha > 2$, we have

$$\mathbf{E}\left[\left(\frac{1-Q}{Q}\right)^2\right] = \frac{\Gamma(\alpha+\beta)}{\Gamma(\alpha) \cdot \Gamma(\beta)} \int_0^1 \left(\frac{1-q}{q}\right)^2 \cdot q^{\alpha-1} \cdot (1-q)^{\beta-1} \ dq =$$

$$= \frac{\Gamma(\alpha+\beta)}{\Gamma(\alpha) \cdot \Gamma(\beta)} \int_0^1 q^{\alpha-3} \cdot (1-q)^{\beta+1} \ dq = \frac{\Gamma(\alpha+\beta)}{\Gamma(\alpha) \cdot \Gamma(\beta)} \cdot B(\alpha-2, \beta+2) =$$

$$\frac{\Gamma(\alpha+\beta)}{\Gamma(\alpha) \cdot \Gamma(\beta)} \cdot \frac{\Gamma(\alpha-2) \cdot \Gamma(\beta+2)}{\Gamma(\alpha+\beta)} = \frac{\beta(\beta+1)}{(\alpha-1)(\alpha-2)}.$$

Note that

$$\mathbf{Var}\left[\frac{1-Q}{Q}\right] = \mathbf{Var}\left[\frac{1}{Q} - 1\right] = \mathbf{Var}\left[\frac{1}{Q}\right].$$

Therefore,

$$\mathbf{Var}\left[\frac{1-Q}{Q}\right] = \mathbf{Var}\left[\frac{1}{Q}\right] = \frac{\beta(\beta+1)}{(\alpha-1)(\alpha-2)} - \left(\frac{\beta}{\alpha-1}\right)^2 =$$

$$= \frac{\beta}{\alpha-1}\left(\frac{\beta+1}{\alpha-2} - \frac{\beta}{\alpha-1}\right) = \frac{\beta(\beta\alpha - \beta + \alpha - 1 - \beta\alpha + 2\beta)}{(\alpha-1)^2(\alpha-2)} =$$

$$= \frac{\beta(\alpha+\beta-1)}{(\alpha-1)^2(\alpha-2)}.$$

Finally,

$$
\mathbf{E}\left[\frac{1-Q}{Q^2}\right] = \frac{\Gamma(\alpha+\beta)}{\Gamma(\alpha)\cdot\Gamma(\beta)} \int_0^1 \frac{1-q}{q^2} \cdot q^{\alpha-1} \cdot (1-q)^{\beta-1} \, dq =
$$

$$
= \frac{\Gamma(\alpha+\beta)}{\Gamma(\alpha)\cdot\Gamma(\beta)} \int_0^1 q^{\alpha-3} \cdot (1-q)^{\beta} \, dq = \frac{\Gamma(\alpha+\beta)}{\Gamma(\alpha)\cdot\Gamma(\beta)} \cdot B(\alpha-2, \beta+1) =
$$

$$
= \frac{\Gamma(\alpha+\beta)}{\Gamma(\alpha)\cdot\Gamma(\beta)} \cdot \frac{\Gamma(\alpha-2)\cdot\Gamma(\beta+1)}{\Gamma(\alpha+\beta-1)} = \frac{\beta(\alpha+\beta-1)}{(\alpha-1)(\alpha-2)}.
$$

Lemma 3.6.2 *If Q has distribution $\boldsymbol{Beta}\,[\alpha,\beta]$, and the model $(X|Q)$ has a geometric distribution with parameter Q, then for $\alpha > 2$ the unconditional expectation and variance of X are*

$$
\boldsymbol{E}[X] = \frac{\beta}{\alpha-1}, \quad \boldsymbol{Var}(X) = \frac{\alpha\beta(\alpha+\beta-1)}{(\alpha-1)^2(\alpha-2)}.
$$

Proof. By the double expectation rule, using lemma 3.6.1,

$$
\mathbf{E}[X] = \mathbf{E}\left[\mathbf{E}[X|Q]\right] = \mathbf{E}\left[\frac{1-Q}{Q}\right] = \frac{\beta}{\alpha-1}.
$$

By the formula for the unconditional expectation,

$$
\mathbf{Var}(X) = \mathbf{Var}\left(\mathbf{E}[X|Q]\right) + \mathbf{E}[\mathbf{Var}(X|Q)] = \mathbf{Var}\left(\frac{1-Q}{Q}\right) + \mathbf{E}\left[\frac{1-Q}{Q^2}\right] =
$$

$$
= \frac{\beta(\alpha+\beta-1)}{(\alpha-1)^2(\alpha-2)} + \frac{\beta(\alpha+\beta-1)}{(\alpha-1)(\alpha-2)} = \frac{\beta(\alpha+\beta-1)}{(\alpha-1)(\alpha-2)}\left(1 + \frac{1}{\alpha-1}\right) =
$$

$$
= \frac{\alpha\beta(\alpha+\beta-1)}{(\alpha-1)^2(\alpha-2)}.
$$

3.7 Gamma Prior and Poisson Model

Suppose that the sample $(\mathbf{X}|\Lambda)=\{(X_i|\Lambda)\}$, $i = 1, 2, \ldots, n$ represents independent Poisson-distributed observations. The unknown common intensity λ is treated as a random variable Λ with the prior distribution $\mathbf{Gamma}[r,\theta]$, where $r \geq 1$ is a given integer value and $\theta > 0$ is a specified scale parameter. Thus, the prior density of Λ is

$$
\pi(\lambda) = \frac{1}{\Gamma(r)\cdot\theta^r} \, \lambda^{r-1} \, e^{-\lambda/\theta} \quad \text{for} \ \ \lambda > 0. \tag{3.13}
$$

The **model** describes the conditional distribution of x_i given λ as Poisson:

$$
f(x_i|\lambda) = \mathbf{P}[X_i = x_i|\lambda] = \frac{\lambda^{x_i}}{x_i!} \cdot e^{-\lambda}.
$$

The joint probability mass function of $X|\Lambda$ at $\mathbf{x}$ is the product

$$
f(\mathbf{x}|\lambda) = \prod_{i=1}^{n} f(x_i|\lambda) = \prod_{i=1}^{n} \frac{\lambda^{x_i}}{x_i!} \cdot e^{-\lambda} = C \cdot \lambda^{w} \cdot e^{-n\lambda}, \tag{3.14}
$$

where $W = \sum_{i=1}^{n} X_i$ with the current value $w = \sum_{i=1}^{n} x_i$, and

$$C = \prod_{i=1}^{n} \frac{1}{x_i!}.$$

Integrating (3.14) in λ and using (1.26) we obtain the joint marginal probability function:

$$f(\mathbf{x}) = \int_0^\infty f(\mathbf{x}|\lambda)\,\pi(\lambda)\,d\lambda = \int_0^\infty C\lambda^w \cdot e^{-n\lambda} \cdot \frac{1}{\Gamma(r) \cdot \theta^r} \lambda^{r-1} e^{-\lambda/\theta}\,d\lambda =$$

$$= \frac{C}{\Gamma(r)\theta^r} \int_0^\infty \lambda^{w+r-1} \cdot e^{-\lambda(n+1/\theta)}\,d\lambda = \frac{C}{\Gamma(r)\theta^r} \cdot \frac{\Gamma(w+r)}{(n+1/\theta)^{w+r}}$$

Thus,

$$f(\mathbf{x}) = \frac{C}{\Gamma(r)\theta^r} \cdot \frac{\Gamma(w+r)}{(n+1/\theta)^{w+r}}. \tag{3.15}$$

Focusing on the three main objectives of the Bayesian approach, let us calculate the posterior and predictive distribution and the credibility premium in this model.

3.7.1 Posterior Distribution of Λ

The posterior density is defined as a ratio:

$$\pi(\lambda|\mathbf{x}) = \frac{f(\mathbf{x}|\lambda) \cdot \pi(\lambda)}{f(\mathbf{x})},$$

where the numerator is the product of $f(\mathbf{x}|\lambda)$ defined by (3.14) and the prior density described in (3.13), with the denominator $f(\mathbf{x})$ defined in (3.15).

Evaluating, we have

$$\pi(\lambda|\mathbf{x}) = \frac{C \cdot \lambda^{w+r-1} \cdot e^{-\lambda(n+1/\theta)}}{\Gamma(r)\theta^r} \cdot \frac{\Gamma(r)\theta^r}{C} \cdot \frac{(n+1/\theta)^{w+r}}{\Gamma(w+r)} =$$

$$= \frac{(n+1/\theta)^{w+r}}{\Gamma(w+r)} \cdot \lambda^{w+r-1} \cdot e^{-\lambda(n+1/\theta)}.$$

Thus,

$$\pi(\lambda|\mathbf{x}) = \tilde{C}\lambda^{w+r-1} \cdot e^{-\lambda(n+1/\theta)}, \quad \text{where } \tilde{C} = \frac{(n+1/\theta)^{w+r}}{\Gamma(w+r)}. \tag{3.16}$$

Note that the posterior density of Λ, given $\mathbf{X} = \mathbf{x}$, belongs to the family of gamma densities, with parameters

$$r^* = w + r = \sum_{i=1}^{n} x_i + r \quad \text{and} \quad \theta^* = \left(n + \frac{1}{\theta}\right)^{-1} = \frac{\theta}{n\theta + 1}. \tag{3.17}$$

Therefore, gamma distribution is the conjugate prior for the given model.

3.7.2 Predictive Distribution of Y

Recall that $Y = X_{n+1}$ is a future observation, which follows the same model. The predictive distribution of Y is its conditional distribution, given $\mathbf{X}$. This distribution can be obtained by taking the expectation of the model, similar to (3.14), with $y = x_{n+1}$, with respect to the **posterior** defined in (3.16), which leads to the following equation:

$$\mathbf{P}\left[Y = y | \mathbf{X} = \mathbf{x}\right] = \int_0^\infty f\left(y | \lambda\right) \pi(\lambda | \mathbf{x})\, d\lambda =$$

$$= \int_0^\infty \frac{\lambda^y}{y!} e^{-\lambda} \cdot \frac{(n + 1/\theta)^{w+r}}{\Gamma(w + r)} \lambda^{w+r-1} \cdot e^{-\lambda(n+1/\theta)}\, d\lambda =$$

$$= \frac{(n + 1/\theta)^{w+r}}{\Gamma(w + r)y!} \int_0^\infty \lambda^{w+r+y-1} \cdot e^{-\lambda(n+1/\theta+1)}\, d\lambda =$$

$$= \frac{\Gamma(w + r + y)}{\Gamma(w + r)y!} \cdot \frac{(n + 1/\theta)^{w+r}}{(n + 1/\theta + 1)^{w+r+y}} =$$

$$= \frac{\Gamma(w + r + y)}{\Gamma(w + r)y!} \cdot \left(\frac{n\theta + 1}{\theta}\right)^{w+r} \cdot \left(\frac{\theta}{n\theta + \theta + 1}\right)^{w+r+y} =$$

$$= \frac{\Gamma(w + r + y)}{\Gamma(w + r)y!} \cdot \left(\frac{n\theta + 1}{n\theta + 1 + \theta}\right)^{w+r} \cdot \left(\frac{\theta}{n\theta + \theta + 1}\right)^{y}.$$

Thus,

$$\mathbf{P}\left[Y = y | \mathbf{X} = \mathbf{x}\right] = \frac{\Gamma(w + r + y)}{\Gamma(w + r)y!} \cdot \left(\frac{n\theta + 1}{n\theta + 1 + \theta}\right)^{w+r} \cdot \left(\frac{\theta}{n\theta + \theta + 1}\right)^{y}. \tag{3.18}$$

Recall that the negative binomial distribution describes the probability of having a given number of y failures before the rth success occurs, as follows:

$$\mathbf{P}[Y = y] = \frac{(r + y - 1)!}{(r - 1)! \cdot y!} \cdot q^r (1 - q)^y = \frac{\Gamma(r + y)}{\Gamma(r)} \cdot q^r (1 - q)^y,$$

where $y = 0, 1, \ldots$ and $0 < q < 1$ is the success rate.

Thus, Y, given $\mathbf{X} = \mathbf{x}$, or, equivalently, given $W = w$, has the negative binomial distribution with the parameters $r^* = w + r$ and

$$q^* = \frac{n\theta + 1}{n\theta + 1 + \theta}.$$

3.7.3 Credibility Premium

Let us now calculate the Bayesian credibility, or premium, $\mathbf{E}[Y | \mathbf{X} = \mathbf{x}]$. Since $(Y | X)$ is negative binomial with parameters r^* and q^*, its expectation is

$$\mathbf{E}[Y | \mathbf{X} = \mathbf{x}] = \mathbf{E}[Y | W = w] = r^* \cdot \frac{1 - q^*}{q^*} =$$

$$= (w + r) \cdot \frac{n\theta + 1 + \theta}{n\theta + 1} \cdot \frac{\theta}{n\theta + \theta + 1} = (w + r) \cdot \frac{\theta}{n\theta + 1}. \tag{3.19}$$

3.8 Normal Prior and Normal Model

Suppose that the sample $(\mathbf{X}|\Lambda) = \{(X_i|\Lambda)\}$, $i = 1, 2, \ldots, n$ represents independent normally-distributed observations with the common density

$$f(x|\lambda) = \frac{1}{\sigma\sqrt{2\pi}} e^{-(x-\lambda)^2/(2\sigma^2)}, \tag{3.20}$$

where σ^2 is given and λ is unknown. The unknown parameter is viewed as a random variable Λ with the prior normal distribution $\mathbf{N}(\mu, \tau^2)$. Thus, the prior density is

$$\pi(\lambda) = \frac{1}{\tau\sqrt{2\pi}} e^{-(\lambda-\mu)^2/(2\tau^2)}, \tag{3.21}$$

with parameters μ and τ^2 specified.

Let $W = \sum_{i=1}^{n} X_i$ with the current value $w = \sum_{i=1}^{n} x_i$.

Focusing on the three main objectives of the Bayesian approach, we will state the posterior and predictive distribution and the credibility premium in this model.

3.8.1 Posterior Distribution of Λ

The **posterior density** of Λ, given $\mathbf{X} = \mathbf{x}$, is normal with the mean

$$\mu^* = \left(\frac{w}{\sigma^2} + \frac{\mu}{\tau^2}\right) \bigg/ \left(\frac{n}{\sigma^2} + \frac{1}{\tau^2}\right) = \frac{w\tau^2 + \mu\sigma^2}{n\tau^2 + \sigma^2} \tag{3.22}$$

and variance

$$(\sigma^*)^2 = \left(\frac{n}{\sigma^2} + \frac{1}{\tau^2}\right)^{-1} = \frac{\sigma^2 \cdot \tau^2}{n\tau^2 + \sigma^2}. \tag{3.23}$$

3.8.2 Predictive Distribution of Y

The random variable Y, given $\mathbf{X} = \mathbf{x}$, or, equivalently, given $W = w$, has the normal distribution, with parameters μ^* and $(\sigma^*)^2 + \sigma^2$.

3.8.3 Credibility Premium

Since $(Y|X)$ is normal, its expected value, and, by definition, the credibility premium, is

$$\mathbf{E}[Y|\mathbf{X}] = \mu^* = \frac{w\tau^2 + \mu\sigma^2}{n\tau^2 + \sigma^2}. \tag{3.24}$$

3.9 Beta Prior and Bernoulli Model

Suppose that a zero-one variable $(X|Q)$ has a Bernoulli distribution,

$$\mathbf{P}[X = x|Q = q] = q^x(1-q)^{1-x}, \quad \text{for } x = 0, 1, \tag{3.25}$$

where the parameter q is unknown and thus treated as a random variable Q.

The prior density of Q is **Beta**$[a, b]$, defined as follows:

$$\pi(q) = \frac{\Gamma(a+b)}{\Gamma(a) \cdot \Gamma(b)} \cdot q^{a-1} \cdot (1-q)^{b-1}, \quad \text{for } 0 < q < 1, \ a > 0, \ b > 0 \tag{3.26}$$

Having observed n conditionally independent records of X, or a sample

$$\mathbf{X} = \{X_i : \ i = 1, 2, \ldots, n\},$$

given $Q = q$, the joint conditional probability mass function of $\mathbf{X}$ at $\mathbf{x}$ is

$$\mathbf{P}[\mathbf{X} = \mathbf{x}|Q = q] = f(\mathbf{x}|q) = \prod_{i=1}^{n} f(x_i|q) = q^w \cdot (1-q)^{n-w},$$

where $w = \sum_{i=1}^{n} x_i$ is the value of the random variable $W = \sum_{i=1}^{n} X_i$.

In statistics, a statistic is **sufficient** with respect to a statistical model and its associated unknown parameter if "no other statistic that can be calculated from the same sample provides any additional information as to the value of the parameter[7]."

It is known that W is a sufficient statistic for q and thus all conclusions about the posterior distribution of $(Q|\mathbf{X})$ will be based on W.

Focusing on the three main objectives of the Bayesian approach, let us calculate the posterior and predictive distributions, as well as the credibility premium in this model.

3.9.1   Posterior Distribution of Q

The posterior density of $(Q|\mathbf{X} = \mathbf{x})$ is obtained as the ratio

$$\pi(q|\mathbf{x}) = \frac{f(\mathbf{x}|q)\pi(q)}{f(\mathbf{x})} = C \cdot q^{w+a-1} \cdot (1-q)^{n+b-w-1}, \tag{3.27}$$

where $C = C(\mathbf{x}, a, b)$ does not depend on q and depends on observations and on parameters of the prior distribution, and where the denominator in (3.27) can be found by integrating the joint conditional probability function $f(\mathbf{x}|q)$ in q.

Indeed, calculating the numerator of $\pi(q|\mathbf{x})$ in (3.27), we have

$$f(\mathbf{x}|q)\pi(q) = q^w \cdot (1-q)^{n-w} \cdot \frac{\Gamma(a+b)}{\Gamma(a) \cdot \Gamma(b)} \cdot q^{a-1} \cdot (1-q)^{b-1} =$$

$$= \frac{\Gamma(a+b)}{\Gamma(a) \cdot \Gamma(b)} q^{w+a-1} \cdot (1-q)^{n+b-w-1}.$$

For the denominator of $\pi(q|\mathbf{x})$ in (3.27), we have

$$f(\mathbf{x}) = \int_0^1 f(\mathbf{x}|q)\pi(q)\, dq = \int_0^1 \frac{\Gamma(a+b)}{\Gamma(a) \cdot \Gamma(b)} \cdot q^{w+a-1} \cdot (1-q)^{n+b-w-1}\, dq =$$

$$= \frac{\Gamma(a+b)}{\Gamma(a) \cdot \Gamma(b)} \int_0^1 q^{w+a-1} \cdot (1-q)^{n+b-w-1}\, dq =$$

$$= \frac{\Gamma(a+b)}{\Gamma(a) \cdot \Gamma(b)} \cdot B(w+a, n+b-w) = \frac{\Gamma(a+b)}{\Gamma(a) \cdot \Gamma(b)} \cdot \frac{\Gamma(w+a) \cdot \Gamma(n+b-w)}{\Gamma(n+a+b)}.$$

Hence,

$$
\begin{aligned}
\pi(q|\mathbf{x}) &= \frac{\Gamma(a+b)}{\Gamma(a) \cdot \Gamma(b)} \cdot q^{w+a-1} \cdot (1-q)^{n+b-w-1} \cdot \frac{\Gamma(a)\Gamma(b)}{\Gamma(a+b)} \cdot \\
&\cdot \frac{\Gamma(n+a+b)}{\Gamma(w+a) \cdot \Gamma(n+b-w)} = \frac{\Gamma(n+a+b)}{\Gamma(w+a) \cdot \Gamma(n+b-w)} \cdot q^{w+a-1} \cdot \\
&\cdot (1-q)^{n+b-w-1} = C \cdot q^{w+a-1} \cdot (1-q)^{n+b-w-1},
\end{aligned}
$$

where

$$
C = C(\mathbf{x}, a, b) = \frac{\Gamma(n+a+b)}{\Gamma(w+a) \cdot \Gamma(n+b-w)}.
$$

Thus, the posterior density also has the form of beta distribution, with parameters

$$
a^* = w + a \quad \text{and} \quad b^* = n - w + b. \tag{3.28}
$$

3.9.2   Predictive Distribution of Y

If $Y = X_{n+1}$ is a future observation, then, conditionally, given $Q = q$, it has the same Bernoulli distribution (3.25). The predictive distribution of Y can be obtained by integrating in q, with respect to the posterior density from (3.27), as follows: By definition of the predictive distribution of $Y = X_{n+1}$, defined by (3.3), we have

$$
\begin{aligned}
\mathbf{P}[Y = y|\mathbf{X}] &= \mathbf{P}[Y = y|W = w] = \int_0^1 f(y|q) \cdot \pi(q|\mathbf{x}) \, dq = \\
&= \frac{\Gamma(n+a+b)}{\Gamma(w+a) \cdot \Gamma(n+b-w)} \int_0^1 q^{w+a+y-1} \cdot (1-q)^{n-w+b+1-y-1} \, dq = \\
&= \frac{\Gamma(n+a+b)}{\Gamma(w+a) \cdot \Gamma(n-w+b)} \cdot \frac{\Gamma(w+a+y) \cdot \Gamma(n-w+b+1-y)}{\Gamma(n+a+b+1)} = \\
&= \frac{1}{\Gamma(w+a) \cdot \Gamma(n-w+b)} \cdot \frac{\Gamma(w+a+y) \cdot \Gamma(n-w+b+1-y)}{n+a+b}.
\end{aligned}
$$

Thus,

$$
\begin{aligned}
\mathbf{P}[Y = y|\mathbf{X}] &= \frac{1}{\Gamma(w+a) \cdot \Gamma(n-w+b)} \times \\
&\times \frac{\Gamma(w+a+y) \cdot \Gamma(n-w+b+1-y)}{n+a+b},
\end{aligned} \tag{3.29}
$$

where $y = 0$ or $y = 1$.

If $y = 0$, the predicting probability is

$$
\begin{aligned}
\mathbf{P}[Y = 0|\mathbf{X}] &= \frac{1}{\Gamma(w+a) \cdot \Gamma(n-w+b)} \cdot \frac{\Gamma(w+a) \cdot \Gamma(n-w+b+1)}{n+a+b} = \\
&= \frac{n-w+b}{n+a+b}.
\end{aligned}
$$

If $y = 1$, the predicting probability is

$$\mathbf{P}[Y = 1|\mathbf{X}] = \frac{1}{\Gamma(w + a) \cdot \Gamma(n - w + b)} \cdot \frac{\Gamma(w + a + 1) \cdot \Gamma(n - w + b)}{n + a + b} =$$

$$= \frac{w + a}{n + a + b}.$$

Note that if

$$q^* = \frac{w + a}{n + a + b},$$

then

$$\frac{n - w + b}{n + a + b} = 1 - q^*.$$

Thus, $(Y|\mathbf{X})$ is Bernoulli, with $q^* = (w + a)/(n + a + b)$.

3.9.3 Credibility Premium

Since $(Y|\mathbf{X})$ is Bernoulli, with $q^* = (w + a)/(n + a + b)$, its expectation is

$$\tilde{\mathbf{E}}[Y|\mathbf{X} = \mathbf{x}] = q^* = \frac{w + a}{n + a + b} = \frac{a^*}{a^* + b^*}, \tag{3.30}$$

where $a^* = w + a$ and $b^* = n - w + b$.

3.10 Beta Prior and Binomial Model

Suppose that a random variable $(X|Q)$ has a binomial distribution,

$$\mathbf{P}[X = x|Q = q] = \binom{m}{x} q^x (1 - q)^{1-x}, \quad \text{for } x = 0, 1, ..., m, \tag{3.31}$$

where the parameter q is unknown and thus treated as a random variable Q.

The prior density of Q is again $\mathbf{Beta}[a, b]$ defined in (3.26):

$$\pi(q) = \frac{\Gamma(a + b)}{\Gamma(a) \cdot \Gamma(b)} \cdot q^{a-1} \cdot (1 - q)^{b-1},$$

where $0 < q < 1$ and parameters of the density function are positive: $a > 0$ and $b > 0$.
Having observed n conditionally independent records of X, or a sample,

$$\mathbf{X} = \{X_i : i = 1, 2, \ldots, n\},$$

given $Q = q$, the joint conditional probability mass function of $\mathbf{X}$ at $\mathbf{x}$ is

$$\mathbf{P}[\mathbf{X} = \mathbf{x}|Q = q] = f(\mathbf{x}|q) = \prod_{i=1}^{n} f(x_i|q) = \prod_{i=1}^{n} \binom{m}{x_i} \cdot q^w (1 - q)^{nm-w},$$

where $w = \sum_{i=1}^{n} x_i$ is the value of the random variable $W = \sum_{i=1}^{n} X_i$.

Focusing on the three main objectives of the Bayesian approach, let us calculate the posterior and predictive distributions, as well as the credibility premium in this model.

3.10.1 Posterior Distribution of Q

The posterior density of $(Q|\mathbf{X} = \mathbf{x})$ is obtained as the ratio

$$\pi(q|\mathbf{x}) = \frac{f(\mathbf{x}|q)\pi(q)}{f(\mathbf{x})} = C \cdot q^{w+a-1} \cdot (1-q)^{nm+b-w-1}, \qquad (3.32)$$

where $C = C(\mathbf{x}, a, b)$ does not depend on q and depends on observations and on parameters of the prior distribution and the denominator in (3.32) can be found by integrating the joint conditional probability function $f(\mathbf{x}|q)$ in q.

Indeed, calculating the numerator of $\pi(q|\mathbf{x})$ in (3.32), we have

$$f(\mathbf{x}|q)\pi(q) = K\, q^w \cdot (1-q)^{nm-w} \cdot q^{a-1} \cdot (1-q)^{b-1} =$$

$$= K\, q^{w+a-1} \cdot (1-q)^{nm+b-w-1}, \; K = \prod_{i=1}^n \binom{m}{x_i} \times \frac{\Gamma(a+b)}{\Gamma(a) \cdot \Gamma(b)}.$$

For the denominator of $\pi(q|\mathbf{x})$ in (3.32), we have

$$f(\mathbf{x}) = \int_0^1 f(\mathbf{x}|q)\pi(q)\, dq = K \int_0^1 q^{w+a-1} \cdot (1-q)^{nm+b-w-1}\, dq =$$

$$= K\, B(w+a, nm+b-w) = K\, \frac{\Gamma(w+a) \cdot \Gamma(nm+b-w)}{\Gamma(nm+a+b)}.$$

Hence,

$$\pi(q|\mathbf{x}) = \frac{\Gamma(nm+a+b)}{\Gamma(w+a) \cdot \Gamma(nm+b-w)} q^{w+a-1} \cdot (1-q)^{nm+b-w-1}.$$

Thus, the posterior density also has the form of beta distribution, with parameters

$$a^* = w + a \quad \text{and} \quad b^* = nm - w + b. \qquad (3.33)$$

3.10.2 Predictive Distribution of Y

If $Y = X_{n+1}$ is a future observation, then, conditionally, given $Q = q$, it has the same binomial distribution (3.31). The predictive distribution of Y can be obtained by integrating in q with respect to the posterior density from (3.32). By definition of the predictive distribution of $Y = X_{n+1}$, defined by (3.3), we have

$$\mathbf{P}[Y = y|\mathbf{X}] = \mathbf{P}[Y = y|W = w] = \int_0^1 f(y|q) \cdot \pi(q|\mathbf{x})\, dq =$$

$$= \binom{m}{y} \frac{\Gamma(nm+a+b)}{\Gamma(w+a) \cdot \Gamma(nm+b-w)} \int_0^1 q^{w+a+y-1} \cdot (1-q)^{nm-w+b+m-y-1}\, dq =$$

$$= \binom{m}{y} \frac{\Gamma(nm+a+b)}{\Gamma(w+a) \cdot \Gamma(nm+b-w)} B(w+a+y, m-y+nm-w+b) =$$

$$= \binom{m}{y} \frac{\Gamma(nm+a+b)}{\Gamma(w+a) \cdot \Gamma(nm+b-w)} \cdot \frac{\Gamma(w+a+y)\Gamma(m-y+nm-w+b)}{\Gamma(nm+a+b+m)} =$$

$$= \binom{m}{y} \frac{B(a^*+y, m-y+b^*)}{B(a^*, b^*)},$$

where a^* and b^* are defined in (3.33).

Thus, for $y = 0, 1, \ldots, m$, we have

$$\mathbf{P}[Y = y|\mathbf{X}] = \binom{m}{y} \frac{B(a^* + y, m - y + b^*)}{B(a^*, b^*)}. \tag{3.34}$$

This is a beta-binomial distribution.

Note that for $m = 1$ we obtain the results in the Beta-Bernoulli case described in section 3.9 with

$$\mathbf{P}[Y = 0|\mathbf{X}] = \frac{n - w + b}{n + a + b}, \quad \mathbf{P}[Y = 1|\mathbf{X}] = \frac{w + a}{n + a + b} \quad \text{and}$$

$$\mathbf{P}[Y = 0|\mathbf{X}] + \mathbf{P}[Y = 1|\mathbf{X}] = \frac{n - w + b}{n + a + b} + \frac{w + a}{n + a + b} = 1.$$

Consider the case of $m = 2$.

If $y = 0$, the predicting probability is

$$\mathbf{P}[Y = 0|\mathbf{X}] = \frac{\Gamma(2n + a + b)}{\Gamma(w + a) \cdot \Gamma(2n - w + b)} \cdot \frac{\Gamma(w + a)\Gamma(2n - w + b + 2)}{\Gamma(2n + a + b + 2)} =$$

$$= \frac{(2n - w + b + 1)(2n - w + b)}{(2n + a + b + 1)(2n + a + b)}.$$

If $y = 1$, the predicting probability is

$$\mathbf{P}[Y = 1|\mathbf{X}] = 2 \cdot \frac{\Gamma(2n + a + b)}{\Gamma(w + a) \cdot \Gamma(2n - w + b)} \cdot \frac{\Gamma(w + a + 1)\Gamma(2n - w + b + 1)}{\Gamma(2n + a + b + 2)} =$$

$$= \frac{2(w + a)(2n - w + b)}{(2n + a + b + 1)(2n + a + b)}.$$

If $y = 2$, the predicting probability is

$$\mathbf{P}[Y = 2|\mathbf{X}] = \frac{\Gamma(2n + a + b)}{\Gamma(w + a) \cdot \Gamma(2n - w + b)} \cdot \frac{\Gamma(w + a + 2)\Gamma(2n - w + b)}{\Gamma(2n + a + b + 2)} =$$

$$= \frac{(w + a)(w + a + 1)}{(2n + a + b + 1)(2n + a + b)}.$$

Adding these probabilities, we obtain

$$\mathbf{P}[Y = 0|\mathbf{X}] + \mathbf{P}[Y = 1|\mathbf{X}] + \mathbf{P}[Y = 2|\mathbf{X}] =$$

$$= \frac{(2n - w + b + 1)(2n - w + b) + 2(w + a)(2n - w + b) + (w + a)(w + a + 1)}{(2n + a + b + 1)(2n + a + b)} = 1.$$

Indeed, considering the numerator of this fraction, we have

$$(2n - w + b + 1)(2n - w + b) + 2(w + a)(2n - w + b) + (w + a)(w + a + 1) =$$
$$= (2n - w + b + 1)(2n - w + b) + (w + a)(2n - w + b) +$$
$$+ (w + a)(2n - w + b) + (w + a)(w + a + 1) =$$
$$= (2n - w + b)[2n - w + b + 1 + w + a] + (w + a)[2n - w + b + w + a + 1] =$$
$$= (2n - w + b)[2n + a + b + 1] + (w + a)[2n + a + b + 1] =$$
$$= (2n + a + b + 1)(2n + a + b).$$

3.10.3 Credibility Premium

Since $(Y|\mathbf{X})$ is beta-binomial, its expectation is

$$\tilde{\mathbf{E}}[Y|\mathbf{X} = \mathbf{x}] = \frac{ma^*}{a^* + b^*} = \frac{m(w + a)}{w + a + nm - w + b} = \frac{m(w + a)}{nm + a + b}. \tag{3.35}$$

3.11 Inverse Gamma Prior and Exponential Model

Suppose that $(\mathbf{X}|\Theta) = \{(X_i|\Theta)\}$, $i = 1, 2, \ldots, n$, are independent exponentially-distributed random variables, with the common density

$$f(x|\theta) = \frac{1}{\theta} e^{-x/\theta} \text{ for } x > 0 \text{ and } f(x|\theta) = 0 \text{ elsewhere.} \tag{3.36}$$

The unknown parameter θ is viewed as a random variable Θ that follows the **inverse gamma** distribution, with parameters (a, b). Equivalently, $\Theta^{-1} = \Lambda$ has the gamma distribution, with parameters (a, b^{-1}), so its density is

$$\pi(\lambda) = \frac{b^a}{\Gamma(a)} \lambda^{a-1} \cdot e^{-\lambda b} \text{ for } \lambda > 0 \text{ and } \pi(\lambda) = 0 \text{ elsewhere.} \tag{3.37}$$

It can be validated by looking at the prior density $g(\theta)$ of the original parameter Θ, which is defined as

$$g(\theta) = \frac{1}{\theta^2} \cdot \pi\left(\frac{1}{\theta}\right).$$

It is more convenient to include the change of variable to avoid operations with a more complicated prior density $g(\theta)$.

Therefore, in terms of $\Lambda = \Theta^{-1}$, the model (3.36) can be written as

$$f(x|\lambda) = \lambda e^{-\lambda x}, \ x > 0.$$

The joint conditional density of $(\mathbf{X}|\Lambda = \lambda)$ is

$$f(\mathbf{x}|\lambda) = \prod_{i=1}^{n} f(x_i|\lambda) = \lambda^n \cdot e^{-\lambda w},$$

where $w = \sum_{i=1}^{n} x_i$ is the value of the sufficient statistic $W = \sum_{i=1}^{n} X_i$ that carries out all information about the parameter.

Calculating the marginal probability function, we have

$$f(\mathbf{x}) = \int_0^\infty f(x|\lambda)\pi(\lambda) \, d\lambda = \int_0^\infty \lambda^n \cdot e^{-\lambda w} \cdot \frac{b^a}{\Gamma(a)} \cdot \lambda^{a-1} \cdot e^{-\lambda b} \, d\lambda =$$

$$= \frac{b^a}{\Gamma(a)} \int_0^\infty \lambda^{n+a-1} \cdot e^{-(w+b)\lambda} \, d\lambda = \frac{b^a}{\Gamma(a)} \cdot \frac{\Gamma(n + a)}{(w + b)^{n+a}}.$$

Focusing on the three main objectives of the Bayesian approach, let us calculate the posterior and predictive distribution and the credibility premium in this model.

3.11.1 Posterior Distribution of Λ

By definition of the posterior density,

$$\pi(\lambda|\mathbf{x}) = \frac{f(x|\lambda)\pi(\lambda)}{f(\mathbf{x})} = \frac{b^a}{\Gamma(a)}\lambda^{n+a-1} \cdot e^{-(w+b)\lambda} \cdot \frac{\Gamma(a)}{b^a} \cdot \frac{(w+b)^{n+a}}{\Gamma(n+a)} =$$

$$= \frac{(w+b)^{n+a}}{\Gamma(n+a)}\lambda^{n+a-1} \cdot e^{-(w+b)\lambda}.$$

Thus, in terms of w, the posterior density of Λ, given $\mathbf{X} = \mathbf{x}$, can be written as follows:

$$\pi(\lambda|\mathbf{x}) = \pi(\lambda|W = w) = C \cdot \lambda^{n+a-1} \cdot e^{-(w+b)\lambda} \quad \text{for} \quad \lambda > 0, \tag{3.38}$$

where

$$C = \frac{(w+b)^{n+a}}{\Gamma(n+a)}.$$

This implies that the posterior density of $(\Lambda|\mathbf{X})$ also is a gamma density, with parameters

$$a^* = n + a \quad \text{and} \quad b^* = (w+b)^{-1}.$$

3.11.2 Predictive Distribution of Y

Conditionally, given $\Lambda = \lambda$, the distribution of Y is exponential with parameter λ. Therefore, the predictive distribution of $(Y|\mathbf{X} = \mathbf{x})$ is obtained by integrating this function with respect to the posterior density of $(\Lambda|\mathbf{X})$, which leads to

$$\mathbf{P}\left[Y = y|X = \mathbf{x}\right] = \int_0^\infty f(y|\lambda)\pi(\lambda|\mathbf{x})\,d\lambda =$$

$$= \frac{(w+b)^{n+a}}{\Gamma(n+a)}\int_0^\infty \lambda e^{-\lambda y}\lambda^{n+a-1} \cdot e^{-(w+b)\lambda}\,d\lambda =$$

$$= \frac{(w+b)^{n+a}}{\Gamma(n+a)} \cdot \int_0^\infty \lambda^{n+a} \cdot e^{-\lambda(w+b+y)}\,d\lambda = \frac{(w+b)^{n+a}}{\Gamma(n+a)} \cdot \frac{\Gamma(n+a+1)}{(w+b+y)^{n+a+1}} =$$

$$= \left(\frac{w+b}{w+b+y}\right)^{n+a} \cdot \frac{n+a}{w+b+y} = \frac{(n+a)(w+b)^{n+a}}{(y+w+b)^{n+a+1}}.$$

Thus,

$$f_{Y|W}(y|w) = \mathbf{P}\left[Y = y|X = \mathbf{x}\right] = \frac{(n+a)(w+b)^{n+a}}{(y+w+b)^{n+a+1}}. \tag{3.39}$$

This is Pareto distribution, with parameters

$$\alpha^* = n + a \text{ and } \theta^* = w + b.$$

Note that since W is a sufficient statistic, all conditioning evaluations, given $\mathbf{X}$, can be expressed in terms of the current value $W = w$.

3.11.3 Credibility Premium

Let us now calculate the posterior mean of the new observation, $Y = X_{n+1}$, given $\mathbf{X} = \mathbf{x}$. Since $(Y|\mathbf{X})$ is Pareto, with parameters α^* and θ^*, its expected value is

$$\mathbf{E}\left[Y|\mathbf{X}\right] = \frac{\theta^*}{\alpha^* - 1} = \frac{w+b}{n+a-1}. \tag{3.40}$$

3.12 Gamma Prior and Exponential Model

Assume that the conditional claim severity $(Y|\Lambda)$ is exponentially-distributed with the density

$$f(y|\lambda) = \lambda \cdot e^{-\lambda \cdot y}, \; y > 0.$$

The unknown parameter is treated as a random variable Λ with the prior density **Gamma** $[\alpha, \beta]$, defined as

$$\pi(\lambda) = \frac{1}{\Gamma(\alpha) \cdot \beta^\alpha} \cdot \lambda^{\alpha-1} \cdot e^{-\lambda/\beta}, \; \lambda > 0. \tag{3.41}$$

In this situation, observable severity Y has the conditional expectation and variance,

$$\mathbf{E}[Y|\Lambda] = \frac{1}{\Lambda} \text{ and } \mathbf{Var}[Y|\Lambda] = \frac{1}{\Lambda^2}.$$

Lemma 3.12.1 *If $(Y|\Lambda)$ is exponentially-distributed, with parameter*

$$\Lambda \sim \boldsymbol{Gamma}\,[\alpha, \beta]\,,$$

then

$$\boldsymbol{E}[Y] = \frac{1}{(\alpha-1)\beta} \quad and$$

$$\boldsymbol{Var}\,(Y) = \frac{\alpha}{\beta^2(\alpha-1)^2(\alpha-2)}, \; \alpha > 2.$$

Proof. Let us first show that

$$\mathbf{E}\left[\Lambda^{-1}\right] = \frac{1}{(\alpha-1)\beta} \text{ and } \mathbf{E}\left[\Lambda^{-2}\right] = \frac{1}{(\alpha-1)(\alpha-2)\beta^2}, \; \alpha > 2. \tag{3.42}$$

For the first inverse moment we have

$$\mathbf{E}\left[\Lambda^{-1}\right] = \int_0^\infty \frac{1}{\Gamma(\alpha) \cdot \beta^\alpha} \cdot \frac{1}{\lambda} \cdot \lambda^{\alpha-1} \cdot e^{-\lambda/\beta}\, d\lambda = \frac{1}{\Gamma(\alpha) \cdot \beta^\alpha} \int_0^\infty \lambda^{\alpha-2} \cdot e^{-\lambda/\beta}\, d\lambda.$$

Recall that the **gamma function** is a special function defined by

$$\Gamma(x) = \int_0^\infty t^{x-1} e^{-t}\, dt, \text{ for } x > 0.$$

It follows that

$$\int_0^\infty t^{x-1} e^{-\delta t}\, dt = \frac{\Gamma(x)}{\delta^x}.$$

Therefore,

$$\mathbf{E}\left[\Lambda^{-1}\right] = \frac{1}{\Gamma(\alpha) \cdot \beta^\alpha} \cdot \frac{\Gamma(\alpha-1)}{1/\beta^{\alpha-1}} = \frac{\Gamma(\alpha-1)\beta^{\alpha-1}}{(\alpha-1)\Gamma(\alpha-1)\beta^\alpha} = \frac{1}{(\alpha-1)\beta}.$$

Similarly, for the second inverse moment we have

$$\mathbf{E}\left[\Lambda^{-2}\right] = \int_0^\infty \frac{1}{\Gamma(\alpha) \cdot \beta^\alpha} \cdot \frac{1}{\lambda^2} \cdot \lambda^{\alpha-1} \cdot e^{-\lambda/\beta}\, d\lambda = \frac{1}{\Gamma(\alpha) \cdot \beta^\alpha} \int_0^\infty \lambda^{\alpha-3} \cdot e^{-\lambda/\beta}\, d\lambda =$$

$$= \frac{1}{\Gamma(\alpha) \cdot \beta^\alpha} \cdot \frac{\Gamma(\alpha-2)}{1/\beta^{\alpha-2}} = \frac{\Gamma(\alpha-2)\beta^{\alpha-2}}{(\alpha-1)(\alpha-2)\Gamma(\alpha-2)\beta^\alpha} = \frac{1}{(\alpha-1)(\alpha-2)\beta^2}.$$

By the double expectation theorem,

$$\mathbf{E}\left[Y\right] = \mathbf{E}\left[\mathbf{E}\left[Y|\Lambda\right]\right] = \mathbf{E}\left[\Lambda^{-1}\right] = \frac{1}{(\alpha - 1)\beta}.$$

By the double conditional variance formula,

$$\begin{aligned}
\mathbf{Var}\left(Y\right) &= \mathbf{E}\left[\mathbf{Var}\left(Y|\Lambda\right)\right] + \mathbf{Var}\left(\mathbf{E}\left[Y|\Lambda\right]\right) = \mathbf{E}\left[\Lambda^{-2}\right] + \mathbf{Var}\left(\Lambda^{-1}\right) = \\
&= \mathbf{E}\left[\Lambda^{-2}\right] + \mathbf{E}\left[\Lambda^{-2}\right] - \mathbf{E}\left[\Lambda^{-1}\right]^2 = 2\mathbf{E}\left[\Lambda^{-2}\right] - \mathbf{E}\left[\Lambda^{-1}\right]^2 = \\
&= \frac{2}{(\alpha - 1)(\alpha - 2)\beta^2} - \frac{1}{(\alpha - 1)^2\beta^2} = \frac{1}{(\alpha - 1)\beta^2}\left[\frac{2}{\alpha - 2} - \frac{1}{\alpha - 1}\right] = \\
&= \frac{2\alpha - 2 - \alpha + 2}{\beta^2(\alpha - 1)^2(\alpha - 2)} = \frac{\alpha}{\beta^2(\alpha - 1)^2(\alpha - 2)}.
\end{aligned}$$

3.13   Inverse Gamma Prior and Gamma Model

Suppose that $(\mathbf{X}|\Theta) = \{(X_i|\Theta)\}$, $i = 1, 2, \ldots, n$, are independent gamma-distributed random variables with the common parameters α and θ:

$$f(x|\theta) = \frac{x^{\alpha-1}}{\theta^\alpha\Gamma(\alpha)}\, e^{-x/\theta} \quad \text{for} \quad x > 0 \quad \text{and} \quad f(x|\theta) = 0 \quad \text{elsewhere.}$$

The unknown parameter θ is viewed as a random variable Θ that follows the **inverse gamma** distribution, with parameters (a, b). Equivalently, $\Theta^{-1} = \Lambda$ has the gamma distribution, with parameters, (a, b^{-1}), so its density is

$$\pi(\lambda) = \frac{b^a}{\Gamma(a)}\, \lambda^{a-1} \cdot e^{-\lambda b} \quad \text{for} \quad \lambda > 0 \quad \text{and} \quad \pi(\lambda) = 0 \quad \text{elsewhere.}$$

Therefore, in terms of $\Lambda = \Theta^{-1}$, the model $(\mathbf{X}|\Theta)$ can be written as

$$f(x|\lambda) = \frac{x^{\alpha-1}\lambda^\alpha}{\Gamma(\alpha)}e^{-\lambda x}, \ x > 0.$$

The joint conditional density of $(\mathbf{X}|\Lambda = \lambda)$ is

$$f(\mathbf{x}|\lambda) = \prod_{i=1}^{n} f(x_i|\lambda) = \frac{\lambda^{n\alpha}}{\Gamma(\alpha)^n}\prod_{i=1}^{n} x_i^{\alpha-1} \cdot e^{-\lambda w},$$

where $w = \sum_{i=1}^{n} x_i$ is the value of the sufficient statistic $W = \sum_{i=1}^{n} X_i$ that carries all information about the parameter.

Calculating the marginal probability function, we have

$$\begin{aligned}
f(\mathbf{x}) &= \int_0^\infty f(x|\lambda)\pi(\lambda)\, d\lambda = \int_0^\infty \frac{\lambda^{n\alpha}}{\Gamma(\alpha)^n}\prod_{i=1}^{n} x_i^{\alpha-1} \cdot e^{-\lambda w} \cdot \frac{b^a}{\Gamma(a)} \cdot \lambda^{a-1} \cdot e^{-\lambda b}\, d\lambda = \\
&= \prod_{i=1}^{n} x_i^{\alpha-1} \cdot \frac{b^a}{\Gamma(\alpha)^n \cdot \Gamma(a)}\int_0^\infty \lambda^{n\alpha+a-1} \cdot e^{-(w+b)\lambda}\, d\lambda = \\
&= \prod_{i=1}^{n} x_i^{\alpha-1} \cdot \frac{b^a}{\Gamma(\alpha)^n \cdot \Gamma(a)} \cdot \frac{\Gamma(n\alpha + a)}{(w + b)^{n\alpha+a}}.
\end{aligned}$$

Focusing on the three main objectives of the Bayesian approach, let us calculate the posterior and predictive distribution and the credibility premium in this model.

3.13.1 Posterior Distribution of Λ

By definition of the posterior density,

$$\pi(\lambda|\mathbf{x}) = \frac{f(x|\lambda)\pi(\lambda)}{f(\mathbf{x})} =$$

$$= \frac{\lambda^{n\alpha}}{\Gamma(\alpha)^n} \prod_{i=1}^{n} x_i^{\alpha-1} \cdot e^{-\lambda w} \cdot \frac{b^a}{\Gamma(a)} \lambda^{a-1} \cdot e^{-\lambda b} \cdot \frac{\Gamma(\alpha)^n \cdot \Gamma(a)}{\prod_{i=1}^{n} x_i^{\alpha-1} \cdot b^a} \cdot \frac{(w+b)^{n\alpha+a}}{\Gamma(n\alpha+a)} =$$

$$= \frac{(w+b)^{n\alpha+a}}{\Gamma(n\alpha+a)} \lambda^{n\alpha+a-1} \cdot e^{-(w+b)\lambda}.$$

Thus, in terms of w, the posterior density of Λ, given $\mathbf{X} = \mathbf{x}$, can be written as follows:

$$\pi(\lambda|\mathbf{x}) = \pi(\lambda|W = w) = C \cdot \lambda^{n\alpha+a-1} \cdot e^{-(w+b)\lambda} \quad \text{for} \quad \lambda > 0,$$

where

$$C = \frac{(w+b)^{n\alpha+a}}{\Gamma(n\alpha+a)}.$$

This implies that the posterior density of $(\Lambda|\mathbf{X})$ also is a gamma density, with parameters

$$a^* = n\alpha + a \quad \text{and} \quad b^* = (w+b)^{-1}. \tag{3.43}$$

3.13.2 Predictive Distribution of Y

Conditionally, given $\Lambda = \lambda$, the distribution of Y is gamma, with parameters α and λ. Therefore, the predictive distribution of $(Y|\mathbf{X} = \mathbf{x})$ is obtained by integrating this function with respect to the posterior density of $(\Lambda|\mathbf{X})$, which leads to

$$\mathbf{P}[Y = y|X = \mathbf{x}] = \int_0^\infty f(y|\lambda)\pi(\lambda|\mathbf{x}) \, d\lambda =$$

$$= \frac{(w+b)^{n\alpha+a} \cdot y^{\alpha-1}}{\Gamma(n\alpha+a)\Gamma(\alpha)} \int_0^\infty \lambda^\alpha e^{-\lambda y} \lambda^{n\alpha+a-1} \cdot e^{-(w+b)\lambda} \, d\lambda =$$

$$= \frac{(w+b)^{n\alpha+a} \cdot y^{\alpha-1}}{\Gamma(n\alpha+a)\Gamma(\alpha)} \cdot \int_0^\infty \lambda^{(n+1)\alpha+a-1} \cdot e^{-\lambda(w+b+y)} \, d\lambda =$$

$$= \frac{\Gamma((n+1)\alpha+a)}{\Gamma(n\alpha+a)\Gamma(\alpha)} \cdot \frac{(w+b)^{n\alpha+a} \cdot y^{\alpha-1}}{(w+b+y)^{(n+1)\alpha+a}}.$$

Thus,

$$f_{Y|W}(y|w) = \mathbf{P}[Y = y|X = \mathbf{x}] = \frac{\Gamma((n+1)\alpha+a)}{\Gamma(n\alpha+a)\Gamma(\alpha)} \cdot \frac{(w+b)^{n\alpha+a} \cdot y^{\alpha-1}}{(w+b+y)^{(n+1)\alpha+a}}. \tag{3.44}$$

This is generalized Pareto (beta of the second kind) distribution, with parameters

$$\alpha^* = n\alpha + a, \quad \theta^* = w + b \quad \text{and} \quad \tau = \alpha.$$

Note that since W is a sufficient statistic, all conditioning evaluations, given $\mathbf{X}$, can be expressed in terms of the current value $W = w$.

3.13.3   Credibility Premium

Let us now calculate the posterior mean of the new observation, $Y = X_{n+1}$, given $\mathbf{X} = \mathbf{x}$. Since $(Y|\mathbf{X})$ is generalized Pareto, with parameters α^*, θ^* and τ, its expected value is

$$\mathbf{E}\left[Y|\mathbf{X}\right] = \frac{\theta^*\Gamma(\tau+1)\Gamma(\alpha^*-1)}{\Gamma(\alpha^*)\Gamma(\tau)} = \frac{\theta^* \cdot \tau}{\alpha^*-1} = \frac{(w+b)\alpha}{n\alpha+a-1}. \tag{3.45}$$

Conclusion

This chapter was mainly focused on situations when prior distribution of an unknown parameter and model describing the probability function related to observations form a **conjugate** pair. Informally, dependence of the prior and model on the parameter operates with similar formulas. Recognition of conjugate pairs allows one to reduce the volume of calculations when the posterior expected value, known as credibility, is derived. Readers are advised to practice with exercises, most of which present conjugate pairs.

Basic principles learned in this chapter will prepare readers for the more sophisticated situations described in the next chapter.

Exercises

3.1. Posterior Probability for a Portfolio of Policies

You are given the following information about a portfolio containing three groups of policies:

(i) The claims generation process for each policy is Poisson.

(ii) The first group includes 50% of the population and each individual is expected to generate one claim per year.

(iii) The second group contains 40% of the population and each individual is expected to generate two claims per year.

(iv) The third group contains 10% of the population and each individual is expected to generate four claims per year.

A certain insured has one claim in year 1.

Calculate the **posterior** probability that the individual was from group k for $k = 1, 2, 3$.

3.2. Marginal Moments of a Random Variable Using the Double Expectation Rule

Suppose that claim frequency, N, is Poisson-distributed, with rate Θ viewed as a random variable such that

$$\mathbf{P}\left[\Theta = 10\right] = 0.3, \quad \mathbf{P}\left[\Theta = 5\right] = 0.6, \quad \text{and} \quad \mathbf{P}\left[\Theta = 2\right] = 0.1.$$

Calculate the following:

(a) $\mathbf{E}\left[N\right]$, the expectation of N

(b) $\mathbf{Var}\left[N\right]$, the variance of N

3.3. Marginal Moments of a Random Variable Using the Double Expectation Rule

Suppose that claim frequency, N, is Poisson-distributed with rate Λ, viewed as a random variable with the prior gamma distribution, with parameters $\alpha = 5$ and $\theta = 1/2$.

Calculate the following:

(a) $\mathbf{E}\left[N\right]$, the unconditional expectation of N

(b) $\mathbf{Var}\left[N\right]$, the unconditional variance of N

3.4. Projecting the Number of Claims in the Second Year with a Discrete Prior

Let N_t be the random variable for number of claims in year t.

Suppose that claim frequency values (N_1, N_2) are independent Poisson-distributed, with rate Θ, that is viewed as a random variable such that

$$\mathbf{P}\left[\Theta = 10\right] = 0.3, \quad \mathbf{P}\left[\Theta = 5\right] = 0.6, \quad \text{and} \quad \mathbf{P}\left[\Theta = 2\right] = 0.1.$$

Suppose the observed number of claims N_1 on a randomly selected policy in the first year is 1.

We would like to project the claim frequency N_2 for the next year.

(a) Derive the posterior distribution of $(\Theta | N_1 = 1)$.

(b) Determine conditional probability, $\mathbf{P}[N_2 = 1 | N_1 = 1]$.

(c) Calculate the Bayesian credibility premium, $\mathbf{E}[N_2 | N_1 = 1]$.

3.5. Projecting the Number of Claims in the Second Year with a Gamma Prior

Suppose that claim frequency N is Poisson-distributed, with rate Λ viewed as a random variable with the prior gamma distribution, with parameters $\alpha = 5$ and $\theta = 1/2$.

Let N_t be the random variable for number of claims in year t.

(a) Derive the posterior distribution of $(\Lambda | N_1 = 1)$.

(b) Determine conditional probability, $\mathbf{P}[N_2 = 1 | N_1 = 1]$.

(c) Calculate the Bayesian credibility premium, $\mathbf{E}[N_2 | N_1 = 1]$.

3.6. Projecting the Number of Claims in the Second Year with a Discrete Prior

Let N_t be the random variable for number of claims in year t.

Suppose that claim frequency is Bernoulli-distributed, with unknown parameter q. Prior distribution of Q is such that

$$\mathbf{P}[Q = 0.2] = \pi(0.2) = 0.4 \quad \text{and} \quad \mathbf{P}[Q = 0.6] = \pi(0.6) = 0.6.$$

Suppose the observed number of claims, N_1, on a randomly selected policy in the first year is 1.

We would like to project the claim frequency, N_2, for the next year.

(a) Determine posterior distribution of $(Q | N_1 = 1)$.

(b) Evaluate conditional probabilities:

$$\mathbf{P}[N_2 = 1 | N_1 = 1] \quad \text{and} \quad \mathbf{P}[N_2 = 0 | N_1 = 1]$$

(c) Determine conditional expectation of N_2, given that $N_1 = 1$.

3.7. Projecting the Number of Years before the First Claim with a Beta Prior

Suppose that a random variable N indicates number of years before the first claim occurs. The distribution of the conditional random variable $(N|Q)$ is geometric, with parameter q. Prior distribution of the corresponding random variable Q is beta, with parameters $a = 5$, $b = 3$.

Suppose that (N_1, N_2) are two observable components that are conditionally independent, given $Q = q$. You are given that the observed value $N_1 > 0$.

(a) Derive the posterior density of $(Q|N_1 > 0)$.

(b) Evaluate the conditional probability, $\mathbf{P}[N_2 = 0 | N_1 > 0]$.

(c) Determine the Bayesian credibility premium, $\mathbf{E}[N_2 | N_1 > 0]$.

3.8. Binomial Model and Beta Prior

A group insurance plan includes five policies. The annual number of claims N has binomial distribution $\mathbf{Bin}[5, q]$, based on the assumption that only one claim per policy will be accepted and that individual claim counts are independent Bernoulli-distributed.

Parameter q is unknown, and the corresponding random variable Q has prior beta distribution, with parameters $(a = 3, b = 2)$.

Suppose that in the first year there were no claims: $N_1 = 0$.

(a) Determine marginal probability that $N_1 = 0$.

(b) Find **posterior** density of Q, given $N_1 = 0$.

(c) Derive the Bayesian credibility for next year, $\mathbf{E}[N_2 | N_1 = 0]$.

3.9. Binomial Model and Beta Prior

Suppose that a random variable, Q, has a prior density function

$$\pi(q) = 2(1 - q) \quad \text{for} \quad 0 < q < 1 \quad \text{and} \quad \pi(q) = 0 \text{ elsewhere.}$$

Given $Q = q$, a random variable X, is a Bernoulli random variable, with conditional probabilities:

$$\mathbf{P}[X = 0 | Q = q] = q \quad \text{and} \quad \mathbf{P}[X = 1 | Q = q] = 1 - q, \tag{3.46}$$

where $X = 0$ means no loss claimed per a given year, and $X = 1$ indicates one claim.

Suppose that for the last **six** years, there was no loss in either of those years.

Determine the posterior probability that there will be a loss for the **seventh** year.

3.10. Calculating Moments of an Inverse Beta

A random variable, Q, has a beta distribution, with parameters $a = 6$ and $b = 3$.
Consider $T = Q^{-1}$.

Calculate the following:

(a) $\mathbf{E}[T]$, the expected value of T
(b) $\mathbf{E}[T^2]$, the second moment of T
(c) $\mathbf{Var}(T)$, the variance of T

3.11. Geometric Model and Beta Prior

Let N be the number of years with no claim. Suppose that N, given $Q = q$, has a
geometric distribution with parameter q. Let the prior distribution of Q be beta,
with parameters $a = 6$ and $b = 3$.

a) Determine $\mathbf{E}[N]$, the marginal expectation of N.
b) Evaluate $\mathbf{Var}[N]$, the variance of N.
c) Given that there was no claim for **three** consecutive years, calculate the conditional probability of having no claim in year **four**.

3.12. Credibility for Poisson Model and Gamma Prior

Claim frequency for a portfolio of insurance policies is Poisson-distributed, with
unknown rate λ. The random variable Λ follows a gamma distribution, with
parameters $\alpha = 4$ and $\theta = 1$.

Let N_t be the number of claims in the year t. Suppose that in the three consecutive
years the claim counts are

$$N_1 = 1, \ N_2 = 3, \ N_3 = 0.$$

(a) Evaluate a posterior density,

$$\pi(\lambda | N_1 = 1, \ N_2 = 3, \ N_3 = 0).$$

(b) Calculate conditional probability of having at least one claim in the **fourth** year.

(c) Determine Bayesian credibility, $\mathbf{E}[N_4 | N_1 = 1, \ N_2 = 3, \ N_3 = 0]$.

3.13. Bayesian Credibility for Gamma Model and Gamma Prior

Suppose that losses on a policy for two consecutive years (X_1, X_2) are independent
gamma-distributed, with parameters $\alpha = 3$ and $\theta = 1/\beta$, where β is the unknown
parameter.

The prior distribution of B is gamma, with parameters $\alpha' = 4$ and $\theta' = 1$.

(a) Derive **marginal** density of X_1.

(b) Determine the **posterior** density of B, given X.

(c) Evaluate **Bayesian credibility**, $\mathbf{E}\left[X_2|X_1\right]$, for next year, given $X_1 = x$.

3.14. Poisson Model and Truncated Exponential Prior

You are given the following information about a conditional and prior distribution of the number of observed claims:

(i) The number of claims observed in a one-year period has a Poisson distribution with the mean λ.

(ii) Prior density has a truncated exponential distribution, defined as

$$\pi(\lambda) = \frac{e^{-\lambda}}{1 - e^{-k}} \quad \text{for} \ \ 0 < \lambda < k \ \text{and} \ \pi(\lambda) = 0 \ \text{elsewhere}.$$

Suppose that the unconditional probability of observing **at least** one claim in a year is 0.23.

Calculate k.

3.15. Bayesian Credibility for Poisson Model and Gamma Prior

Suppose that an individual car policy has an annual claim frequency X that follows a Poisson distribution with unknown rate λ.

Two actuaries, Tom and Jerry, want to derive Bayesian credibility.

(i) Tom assumes that Λ has prior distribution **Gamma** $\left[4, \frac{1}{4}\right]$.

(ii) Jerry also believes in gamma prior for Λ with the same mean, but with the **variance twice as large** compared to Tom.

Suppose that in the last three years there was one claim on the policy.

(a) Determine the parameters of the prior distribution for Jerry.

(b) Evaluate Bayesian credibility for each actuary.

3.16. Bayesian Credibility for Poisson Model and Gamma Prior

Suppose that claim frequency is Poisson-distributed with unknown rate λ.

The corresponding random variable Λ has gamma distribution, with parameters α and θ, which are unknown.

Claim frequencies for two consecutive years (N_1, N_2), have been observed.

You are given the following information about the Bayesian credibilities:

(i)
$$\mathbf{E}[N_3|N_1 = N_2 = 0] = 2.8$$

(ii)
$$\mathbf{E}[N_3|(N_1 = 2)\bigcap(N_2 = 4)] = 5.6$$

Calculate the Bayesian credibility:

$$\mathbf{E}[N_3|(N_1 = 4)\bigcap(N_2 = 5)]$$

3.17. Bayesian Credibility for Geometric Model and Beta Prior

A portfolio of insurance policies is analyzed.

A random variable Y indicates a number of years before the first claim occurs.

A sample of $m = 4$ policies was collected and values $\{Y_1 = 1, Y_2 = 3, Y_3 = Y_4 = 0\}$ were recorded.

You are given the following information about conditional and prime random variables:

(i) Given $Q = q$, random variables $(Y_j|Q)$ are independent and identically distributed with probability mass function

$$\mathbf{P}[Y = k|Q = q] = (1 - q)^k \cdot q, \ \ k \geq 0.$$

(ii) Parameter q is considered a random variable Q with prior density

$$\pi(q) = 6q^5 \ \text{ for } \ 0 < q < 1 \ \ \text{ and } \ \pi(q) = 0 \ \text{ elsewhere.}$$

Let B be the following event:

$$B = (Y_1 = 1)\bigcap(Y_2 = 3)\bigcap(Y_3 = 0)\bigcap(Y_4 = 0)$$

Evaluate Bayesian credibility:
$$\mathbf{E}[Y_5|B]$$

3.18. Posterior Probability for Poisson Model and Beta Prior

You are given the following information about conditional and prime random variables:

(i) The annual number of claims N for each policyholder has a Poisson distribution with $q = \mathbf{P}[N = 0]$, treated as an unknown parameter.

(ii) The **prior** density of Q is beta, with parameters $a = 6$ and $b = 1$.

A randomly selected policyholder is known to have no claims for **three** consecutive years.

Determine the **posterior** probability that this policyholder will have no claims in the **fourth** year.

3.19. Posterior Expectation for Exponential Model and Inverse Gamma Prior

Suppose that, conditionally, given $\Theta = \theta$, individual losses $\mathbf{X} = \{X_i\}_{i=1}^n$ are independent and exponentially-distributed with mean θ.

Suppose that parameter Θ has **inverse gamma** distribution such that

$$\mathbf{E}[\Theta] = 20 \quad \text{and} \quad \mathbf{Var}[\Theta] = 100.$$

The following losses are observed for the **five** consecutive time periods:

$$X_1 = 100, \; X_2 = 400, \; X_3 = 250, \; X_4 = 350, \; X_5 = 100.$$

(a) Determine the parameters of the prior distribution.
(b) Derive the expected loss for the **sixth** year.

3.20. Credibility for Exponential Model and Inverse Gamma Prior

For an automotive property damage liability coverage, claim sizes are exponentially-distributed with density

$$f(x|\lambda) = \lambda \cdot e^{-\lambda x} \text{ for } x > 0.$$

Parameter λ is viewed as a random variable that is gamma-distributed, with parameters $\alpha = 6$ and $\beta = 10^{-3}$.

A particular insured submitted $n = 10$ claims. Given the amount of these losses, the posterior mean claim size for this insured was derived as 360.

Determine the average amount of ten claim sizes.

3.21. Credibility for Gamma Model and Inverse Gamma Prior

Suppose that, conditionally, given $\Lambda = \lambda$, individual losses $\mathbf{X} = \{X_i\}_{i=1}^n$ are independent and gamma-distributed, with parameters $\alpha = 2$ and $\theta = 1/\lambda$.

Suppose that parameter Λ has prior **inverse gamma** distribution such that for its reciprocal, $\Theta = \Lambda^{-1}$, mean and variance are

$$\mathbf{E}[\Theta] = 0.06 \quad \text{and} \quad \mathbf{Var}[\Theta] = 0.0006.$$

There are $n = 5$ exposures with the total loss of $w = 3500$.

Consider projected loss $Y = X_6$ for the **sixth** year.

(a) Determine the parameters of the prior density for Λ.

(b) Evaluate expected loss, $\mathbf{E}[Y|W = 3500]$.

3.22. Marginal Density for Exponential Model and Gamma Prior

The amount of an individual claim, Y, is exponentially-distributed with mean $1/\lambda$ and density

$$f(y|\lambda) = \lambda e^{-\lambda y} \text{ for } y > 0.$$

Prior density for Λ is gamma-distributed, with parameters $\alpha = 3$ and $\theta = 1/6$.

(a) Determine posterior distribution of Λ, given $Y = y$.

(b) Evaluate the expected loss for the next year, given the current year loss as $Y = 9$.

(c) Calculate the value of a marginal density for Y at $y = 9$.

3.23. Uniform Model and Single Parameter Pareto Prior

Suppose that an individual loss on the policy is uniformly-distributed over the interval $(0, w)$ with unknown parameter w.

Suppose that the prior density of W is single-parameter Pareto, with parameters $\alpha = 5$ and $\theta = 1$.

(a) Determine marginal distribution of X at $x > 1$.

(b) Derive posterior density of $(W|X = x)$.

(c) Given that this year's loss was $w = 1500$, calculate the expected loss for the next year, that is, $\mathbf{E}[X_2|X_1 = 1500]$.

3.24. Normal Model and Normal Prior

Suppose that individual losses are independent normally-distributed, with parameters θ and $\sigma^2 = 25,000$.

Parameter θ is unknown and is normally-distributed, with parameters $\mu = 1000$ and $\tau^2 = 10,000$.

Suppose that n claims resulted in the posterior variance $(\sigma')^2 = 2000$.

Determine the number of claims n.

3.25. Normal Model and Normal Prior

Suppose that claim sizes are normally-distributed with unknown mean θ and variance $v = 120$.

Suppose that parameter θ is viewed as normally-distributed random variables, with mean $\mu = 9$ and variance $a = 12$.

A policy holder submits $n = 5$ claims with sum equal to w.

The posterior expected value of Θ is $\mu' = 38$.

Calculate the value of w.

3.26. Poisson Model and Gamma Prior

Suppose that the number of claims (X) during one year has a Poisson distribution with a random parameter (Λ).

The random variable Λ has a prior **gamma** distribution, with the coefficient of variation equal to 0.0625.

Calculate the coefficient of variation for a **posterior** distribution after having observed $X = 144$ exposures.

Solutions

3.1. Let N be the number of claims in year 1 and let T be a random variable that indicates belonging of a random individual to a group. Then,

$$\mathbf{P}\,[T = 1] = 0.5, \; \mathbf{P}\,[T = 2] = 0.4, \; \text{ and } \mathbf{P}\,[T = 3] = 0.1.$$

By the law of total probability, the **marginal** probability that $X = 1$ is

$$\mathbf{P}\,[N = 1] = \sum_{i=1}^{3} \mathbf{P}\,[T = i] \cdot \mathbf{P}\,[N = 1 | T] = 0.5 \cdot \frac{1^1}{1!} \cdot e^{-1} + 0.4 \cdot \frac{2^1}{1!} \cdot e^{-2} +$$

$$+\, 0.1 \cdot \frac{4^1}{1!} \cdot e^{-4} \approx \mathbf{0.2995}.$$

Therefore, by Bayes' theorem, **posterior** probability distribution of T is obtained directly from the definition of the conditional probability:

$$\mathbf{P}\,[T = 1 | N = 1] = \frac{\mathbf{P}\,[T = 1] \cdot \mathbf{P}\,[N = 1 | T = 1]}{\mathbf{P}\,[N = 1]} = 0.5 \cdot \frac{1^1}{1!} \cdot e^{-1} \div 0.2995 \approx$$

$$\approx \mathbf{0.6141}$$

$$\mathbf{P}\,[T = 2 | N = 1] = \frac{\mathbf{P}\,[T = 2] \cdot \mathbf{P}\,[N = 1 | T = 2]}{\mathbf{P}\,[N = 1]} = 0.4 \cdot \frac{2^1}{1!} \cdot e^{-2} \div 0.2995 \approx$$

$$\approx \mathbf{0.3615}$$

$$\mathbf{P}\,[T = 3 | N = 1] = \frac{\mathbf{P}\,[T = 3] \cdot \mathbf{P}\,[N = 1 | T = 3]}{\mathbf{P}\,[N = 1]} = 0.1 \cdot \frac{4^1}{1!} \cdot e^{-4} \div 0.2995 \approx$$

$$\approx \mathbf{0.02446}$$

3.2. Since the conditional random variable $(N | \Theta)$ is Poisson-distributed,

$$\mathbf{E}[N | \Theta] = \mathbf{Var}[N | \Theta] = \Theta.$$

(a) By the **double expectation rule**, we have

$$\mathbf{E}[N] = \mathbf{E}[\mathbf{E}[N | \Theta]] = \mathbf{E}[\Theta] = (10)(0.3) + (5)(0.6) + (2)(0.1) = \mathbf{6.2}.$$

(b) Using the conditional variance formula,

$$\mathbf{Var}[N] = \mathbf{E}[\mathbf{Var}[N | \Theta]] + \mathbf{Var}[\mathbf{E}[N | \Theta]] = \mathbf{E}[\Theta] + \mathbf{Var}[\Theta].$$

Calculating the second raw moment of Θ, we have

$$\mathbf{E}[\Theta^2] = (10^2)(0.3) + (5^2)(0.6) + (2^2)(0.1) = 30 + 15 + 0.4 = \mathbf{45.4}.$$

Therefore,

$$\mathbf{Var}[\Theta] = 45.4 - (6.2)^2 = \mathbf{6.96}.$$

Thus,

$$\mathbf{Var}[N] = 6.2 + 6.96 = \mathbf{13.16}.$$

3.3. Since Λ is gamma-distributed, with parameters $\alpha = 5$ and $\theta = 1/2$, its **pdf** is of the form

$$\pi_\Lambda(\lambda) = \frac{(\lambda/\theta)^\alpha \, e^{-\lambda/\theta}}{\lambda \Gamma(\alpha)} = \frac{2^5}{\Gamma(5)} \lambda^4 \cdot e^{-2\lambda}, \ \lambda > 0.$$

The expected value and the variance of a gamma-distributed random variable are

$$\mathbf{E}[\Lambda] = \frac{\theta\Gamma(\alpha+1)}{\Gamma(\alpha)} = \frac{\theta\alpha\Gamma(\alpha)}{\Gamma(\alpha)} = \theta\alpha$$

$$\mathbf{E}[\Lambda^2] = \frac{\theta^2\Gamma(\alpha+2)}{\Gamma(\alpha)} = \frac{\theta^2(\alpha+1)\alpha\Gamma(\alpha)}{\Gamma(\alpha)} = \theta^2(\alpha+1)\alpha$$

$$\mathbf{Var}(\Lambda) = \mathbf{E}[\Lambda^2] - \mathbf{E}[\Lambda]^2 = \theta^2(\alpha+1)\alpha - \theta^2\alpha^2 = \theta^2\alpha(\alpha+1-\alpha) = \theta^2\alpha.$$

Since the conditional random variable $(N|\Lambda)$ is Poisson-distributed,

$$\mathbf{E}[N|\Lambda] = \mathbf{Var}[N|\Lambda] = \Lambda.$$

(a) By the **double expectation rule**, we have

$$\mathbf{E}[N] = \mathbf{E}[\mathbf{E}[N|\Lambda]] = \mathbf{E}[\Lambda] = \theta\alpha = \frac{1}{2} \cdot 5 = \mathbf{2.5}.$$

Also,

$$\mathbf{Var}[N|\Lambda] = \theta^2\alpha = \left(\frac{1}{2}\right)^2 \cdot 5 = \frac{5}{4} = 1.25.$$

(b) Using the conditional variance formula

$$\mathbf{Var}[N] = \mathbf{E}[\mathbf{Var}[N|\Lambda]] + \mathbf{Var}[\mathbf{E}[N|\Lambda]] = \mathbf{E}[\Lambda] + \mathbf{Var}[\Lambda] =$$
$$= 2.5 + 1.25 = \mathbf{3.75}.$$

3.4. Since the conditional random variable $(N|\Theta)$ is Poisson, the conditional mass density function is of the following form:

$$f(n|\theta) = f_{N|\Theta}(n|\theta) = \mathbf{P}[N = n|\Theta = \theta] = \frac{\theta^n}{n!} \cdot e^{-\theta},$$

where $n = 0, 1, \dots$.

Thus,

$$\mathbf{P}[N = 1|\Theta = \theta] = \theta \cdot e^{-\theta}.$$

By the law of total probability, the **marginal** probability that $N_1 = 1$ is

$$\mathbf{P}[N_1 = 1] = \sum_\Theta \mathbf{P}[\Theta] \cdot \mathbf{P}[N_1 = 1|\Theta] = \mathbf{E}[\Theta \cdot e^{-\Theta}] =$$
$$= 10 \cdot e^{-10} \cdot 0.3 + 5 \cdot e^{-5} \cdot 0.6 + 2 \cdot e^{-2} \cdot 0.1 \approx$$
$$\approx 0.000136 + 0.020214 + 0.0270671 = \mathbf{0.04742}.$$

(a) To calculate the posterior distribution of $(\Theta|N_1 = 1)$, note that

$$\pi(\theta|N_1 = 1) = \mathbf{P}[\Theta = \theta|N_1 = 1] = \frac{\mathbf{P}[N_1 = 1|\Theta = \theta]\mathbf{P}[\Theta = \theta]}{\mathbf{P}[N_1 = 1]} =$$

$$= \frac{\theta \cdot e^{-\theta} \cdot \mathbf{P}[\Theta = \theta]}{\mathbf{P}[N_1 = 1]}.$$

Calculating $\pi(\theta|N_1 = 1)$ for each value of Θ, we obtain

$$\pi(\Theta = 10|N_1 = 1) = \frac{0.000136}{0.047417} \approx 0.002872 \approx \mathbf{0.0029}$$

$$\pi(\Theta = 5|N_1 = 1) = \frac{0.020214}{0.291021} \approx 0.426299 \approx \mathbf{0.4263}$$

$$\pi(\Theta = 2|N_1 = 1) = \frac{0.270671}{0.291021} \approx 0.5708290 \approx \mathbf{0.5708}.$$

(b) Conditional probability $\mathbf{P}[N_2 = 1|N_1 = 1]$ can be found either using the posterior distribution of $(\Theta|N_1)$, or in a straightforward way, using the following formula:

$$\mathbf{P}[N_2 = 1|N_1 = 1] = \frac{\mathbf{P}[(N_1 = 1)\bigcap(N_2 = 1)]}{\mathbf{P}[N_1 = 1]}$$

Since (N_1, N_2) are conditionally independent,

$$\mathbf{P}[(N_1 = 1)\bigcap(N_2 = 1)] = \mathbf{E}[\mathbf{P}[N_1 = 1|\Theta] \cdot \mathbf{P}[N_2 = 1|\Theta]] =$$

$$= \mathbf{E}[\Theta^2 \cdot e^{-2\Theta}] = (10)^2 \cdot e^{-20}(0.3) + (5)^2 \cdot e^{-10}(0.6) + (2)^2 \cdot e^{-4}(0.1) =$$

$$= 30 \cdot e^{-20} + 15 \cdot e^{-10} + 0.4 \cdot e^{-4} \approx \mathbf{0.008007}.$$

Therefore,

$$\mathbf{P}[N_2 = 1|N_1 = 1] = \frac{0.008007}{0.04742} \approx \mathbf{0.1689}.$$

(c) Bayesian credibility premium equals the posterior mean of N_2, and since N_1 and N_2 are conditionally independent,

$$\mathbf{E}[N_2|N_1 = 1] = \tilde{\mathbf{E}}[\Theta|N_1 = 1] = \sum_{\Theta} \Theta \cdot \mathbf{P}[\Theta|N_1 = 1] =$$

$$= 10 \cdot \mathbf{P}[\Theta = 10|N_1 = 1] + 5 \cdot \mathbf{P}[\Theta = 5|N_1 = 1] + 2 \cdot \mathbf{P}[\Theta = 2|N_1 = 1].$$

Using the results from part (a), we have

$$\mathbf{E}[N_2|N_1 = 1] \approx 10 \cdot 0.002872 + 5 \cdot 0.4263 + 2 \cdot 0.5708 =$$

$$= 0.02872 + 2.131495 + 1.141658 \approx \mathbf{3.3019}.$$

3.5. Since Λ is gamma-distributed, with parameters $\alpha = 5$ and $\theta = 1/2$, its **pdf** is of the form

$$\pi_\Lambda(\lambda) = \frac{(\lambda/\theta)^\alpha e^{-\lambda/\theta}}{\lambda\Gamma(\alpha)} = \frac{2^5}{\Gamma(5)}\lambda^4 \cdot e^{-2\lambda}, \; \lambda > 0$$

Since the conditional random variable $(N|\Theta)$ is Poisson, the conditional mass density function is of the following form:

$$f(n|\lambda) = f_{N|\Lambda}(n|\lambda) = \mathbf{P}[N = n|\Lambda = \lambda] = \frac{\lambda^n}{n!} \cdot e^{-\lambda}.$$

By the law of total probability, the **marginal** probability that $N = n$ is

$$\mathbf{P}[N = n] = \int_0^\infty f(n|\lambda) \cdot \pi(\lambda)\, d\lambda.$$

Therefore, using (1.26), we have

$$\mathbf{P}[N_1 = 1] = \int_0^\infty f(N_1 = 1|\lambda) \cdot \pi(\lambda)\, d\lambda = \frac{2^5}{\Gamma(5)} \int_0^\infty \left(\lambda \cdot e^{-\lambda}\right) \cdot \left(\lambda^4 \cdot e^{-2\lambda}\right) d\lambda$$

$$= \frac{2^5}{\Gamma(5)} \int_0^\infty \lambda^5 \cdot e^{-3\lambda}\, d\lambda = \frac{2^5}{\Gamma(5)} \cdot \frac{\Gamma(6)}{3^6} = \frac{5!}{4! \cdot 3} \left(\frac{2}{3}\right)^5 = \frac{5}{3} \left(\frac{2}{3}\right)^5 \approx \mathbf{0.2195}.$$

(a) Calculating posterior density of $(\Lambda|N_1 = 1)$, we have

$$\pi(\lambda|N_1 = 1) = \frac{\pi(\lambda) \cdot \mathbf{P}[N_1 = 1|\Lambda = \lambda]}{\mathbf{P}[N_1 = 1]} = \frac{2^5}{\Gamma(5)} \lambda^4 \cdot e^{-2\lambda} \cdot \lambda \cdot e^{-\lambda} \cdot \frac{1}{0.2195} =$$

$$= C \cdot \lambda^5 \cdot e^{-3\lambda}, \text{ where } C = \frac{2^5}{0.2195 \cdot \Gamma(5)}.$$

Thus, the posterior density $\pi(\lambda|N_1 = 1)$ is proportional to

$$\lambda^5 \cdot e^{-3\lambda}.$$

Recall that if Λ is gamma-distributed, with parameters α and θ, its **pdf** is of the form

$$\pi_\Lambda(\lambda) = \frac{(\lambda/\theta)^\alpha e^{-\lambda/\theta}}{\lambda \Gamma(\alpha)} = \frac{\lambda^{\alpha-1} e^{-\lambda/\theta}}{\theta^\alpha \Gamma(\alpha)}.$$

Thus the posterior distribution of $(\Lambda|N_1 = 1)$ is gamma with parameters $\alpha' = 6$ and $\theta' = 1/3$.

(b) Conditional probability, $\mathbf{P}[N_2 = 1|N_1 = 1]$, can be evaluated using the same reasoning as in the previous problem:

$$\mathbf{P}[N_2 = 1|N_1 = 1] = \frac{\mathbf{P}[(N_1 = 1) \bigcap (N_2 = 1)]}{\mathbf{P}[N_1 = 1]}$$

Since N_1 and N_2 are conditionally independent,

$$\mathbf{P}[(N_1 = 1) \bigcap (N_2 = 1)|\Lambda = \lambda] = f(1|\lambda) \cdot f(1|\lambda) = (f(1|\lambda))^2 = \lambda^2 \cdot e^{-2\lambda}.$$

Therefore, the marginal joint probability is

$$\mathbf{P}[(N_1 = 1) \bigcap (N_2 = 1)] = \int_0^\infty \lambda^2 \cdot e^{-\lambda} \pi(\lambda)\, d\lambda =$$

$$= \frac{2^5}{\Gamma(5)} \int_0^\infty \left(\lambda^2 e^{-2\lambda}\right)\left(\lambda^4 e^{-2\lambda}\right) d\lambda = \frac{2^5}{\Gamma(5)} \int_0^\infty \lambda^6 \cdot e^{-4\lambda}\, d\lambda.$$

Applying formula (1.26) again, we have

$$\mathbf{P}[(N_1 = 1) \cap (N_2 = 1)] = \frac{2^5}{\Gamma(5)} \cdot \frac{\Gamma(7)}{4^7} = \frac{6!}{4^2 \cdot 4!} \left(\frac{1}{2}\right)^5 = \frac{30}{16} \left(\frac{1}{2}\right)^5 =$$

$$= \frac{15}{8} \left(\frac{1}{2}\right)^5 \approx \mathbf{0.05859}.$$

Finally, the desired conditional probability is

$$\mathbf{P}[N_2 = 1 | N_1 = 1] = \frac{0.05859}{0.2195} \approx \mathbf{0.2670}.$$

(c) Bayesian credibility premium equals the posterior mean of N_2, and since N_1 and N_2 are conditionally independent,

$$\mathbf{E}[N_2 | N_1 = 1] = \tilde{\mathbf{E}}[\Lambda | N_1 = 1].$$

Since the posterior distribution of $(\Lambda | N_1 = 1)$ is gamma, with parameters $\alpha' = 6$ and $\theta' = 1/3$, calculating the expected value, we have

$$\tilde{\mathbf{E}}[\Lambda | N_1 = 1] = \alpha' \cdot \theta' = \frac{6}{3} = \mathbf{2}.$$

3.6. Since the conditional random variable $(N|Q)$ is Bernoulli, the conditional mass density function is of the following form:

$$f_{N|Q}(1|q) = \mathbf{P}[N = 1 | Q = q] = q, \quad f_{N|Q}(0|q) = \mathbf{P}[N = 0 | Q = q] = 1 - q$$

By the law of total probability, the **marginal** probability that $N_1 = 1$ is

$$\mathbf{P}[N_1 = 1] = \sum_Q \mathbf{P}[Q] \cdot \mathbf{P}[N_1 = 1 | Q] = \sum_Q \mathbf{P}[Q] \cdot Q =$$

$$= \pi(0.2) \cdot 0.2 + \pi(0.6) \cdot 0.6 = 0.4 \cdot 0.2 + 0.6 \cdot 0.6 = 0.08 + 0.36 = \mathbf{0.44}.$$

(a) Calculating posterior distribution of $(Q|N_1 = 1)$, we have

$$\pi(Q = 0.2 | N_1 = 1) = \frac{\mathbf{P}[N_1 = 1 | Q = 0.2] \mathbf{P}[Q = 0.2]}{\mathbf{P}[N_1 = 1]} = \frac{\pi(Q = 0.2) \cdot 0.2}{\mathbf{P}[N_1 = 1]} =$$

$$= \frac{0.4 \cdot 0.2}{0.44} = \frac{0.08}{0.44} = \frac{2}{11}.$$

The remaining probability is

$$\pi(Q = 0.6 | N_1 = 1) = \frac{\mathbf{P}[N_1 = 1 | Q = 0.6] \mathbf{P}[Q = 0.6]}{\mathbf{P}[N_1 = 1]} = \frac{\pi(Q = 0.6) \cdot 0.6}{\mathbf{P}[N_1 = 1]} =$$

$$= \frac{0.6 \cdot 0.6}{0.44} = \frac{0.36}{0.44} = \frac{9}{11}.$$

Equivalently, since Q is a binary random variable,

$$\pi(Q = 0.6 | N_1 = 1) = 1 - \frac{2}{11} = \frac{9}{11}.$$

(b) Conditional distribution of $(N_2|N_1)$ can be found directly as

$$\mathbf{P}[N_2 = 1|N_1 = 1] = \frac{\mathbf{P}[(N_1 = 1) \bigcap (N_2 = 1)]}{\mathbf{P}[N_1 = 1]}.$$

Since (N_1, N_2), conditionally, given $Q = q$, are independent,

$$\mathbf{P}[(N_1 = 1) \bigcap (N_2 = 1)|Q = q] = f(1|q) \cdot f(1|q) = q^2.$$

Therefore, the marginal joint probability is

$$\mathbf{P}[(N_1 = 1) \bigcap (N_2 = 1)] = \sum_q \mathbf{P}[q] \cdot q^2 = \mathbf{E}[Q^2] = 0.2^2 \cdot 0.4 + 0.6^2 \cdot 0.6 =$$
$$= 0.016 + 0.216 = 0.232.$$

Thus,

$$\mathbf{P}[N_2 = 1|N_1 = 1] = \frac{0.232}{0.44} = \frac{29}{55} \approx \mathbf{0.5273}.$$

Since N is a binary random variable,

$$\mathbf{P}[N_2 = 0|N_1 = 1] = 1 - \frac{29}{55} = \frac{26}{55} \approx \mathbf{0.4727}.$$

(c) Since the conditional random variable $(N_2|N_1 = 1)$ is Bernoulli, with probabilities

$$\mathbf{P}[N_2 = 1|N_1 = 1] = \frac{29}{55} \quad \text{and} \quad \mathbf{P}[N_2 = 0|N_1 = 1] = \frac{26}{55},$$

the conditional expectation is

$$\mathbf{E}[N_2|N_1 = 1] = \mathbf{P}[N_2 = 1|N_1 = 1] = \frac{29}{55} \approx \mathbf{0.5273}.$$

3.7. Since the conditional random variable $(N|Q)$ is geometric, with parameter q, its probability density is of the form

$$f(n|q) = (1 - q)^n \cdot q, \quad \text{where} \quad n = 0, 1, \dots$$

and rate q is unknown.

Since the random variable Q is beta, with parameters $a = 5$, $b = 3$, the prior density is of the form

$$\pi(q) = \frac{\Gamma(8)}{\Gamma(5)\Gamma(3)} q^4(1 - q)^2 = \frac{7!}{4!\,2!} q^4(1 - q)^2 = \frac{5 \cdot 6 \cdot 7}{2} q^4(1 - q)^2 =$$
$$= 105\, q^4(1 - q)^2, \ 0 < q < 1.$$

Since the conditional random variable $(N|Q)$ is geometric, we have

$$\mathbf{P}[N_1 = 0|Q = q] = q \ \Leftrightarrow \mathbf{P}[N_1 > 0|Q = q] = 1 - q.$$

Therefore,

$$\mathbf{P}[N_1 > 0] = \mathbf{E}[\mathbf{P}[N_1 > 0|Q]] = \mathbf{E}[1 - Q] = 1 - \mathbf{E}[Q].$$

Since Q is beta, with parameters $a = 5$, $b = 3$,

$$\mathbf{E}[Q] = \frac{a}{a+b}.$$

Hence,

$$\mathbf{P}[N_1 > 0] = \frac{5}{5+3} = \frac{3}{8} = 0.375.$$

(a) Calculating posterior density of $(Q|N_1 > 0)$, we have

$$\pi(q|N_1 > 0) = \frac{\pi(q)\mathbf{P}[N_1 > 0|Q = q]}{\mathbf{P}[N_1 > 0]} = \frac{\pi(q) \cdot (1 - q)}{0.375} =$$
$$= \frac{105 \, q^4(1-q)^2 \cdot (1-q)}{0.375} = 280q^4(1-q)^3.$$

Thus, $(Q|N_1 > 0)$ has a beta distribution, with parameters $a = 5$, $b = 4$.

(b) Calculating conditional probability, $\mathbf{P}[N_2 = 0|N_1 > 0]$, we have

$$\mathbf{P}[(N_2 = 0) \bigcap (N_1 > 0)] = \mathbf{E}[\mathbf{P}[(N_2 = 0) \bigcap (N_1 > 0)]|Q] = \mathbf{E}[Q(1 - Q)] =$$
$$= 105 \cdot \int_0^1 \left[q^4(1-q)^2\right] [q(1-q)] \, dq = 105 \cdot \int_0^1 q^5(1-q)^3 \, dq = 105 \, B(6,4).$$

Using (1.28),

$$B(a,b) = \int_0^1 t^{a-1}(1-t)^{b-1} \, dt = \frac{\Gamma(a)\Gamma(b)}{\Gamma(a+b)} \text{ for } a > 0, \, b > 0.$$

Therefore,

$$\mathbf{P}[(N_2 = 0) \bigcap (N_1 > 0)] = 105 \cdot \frac{\Gamma(6) \cdot \Gamma(4)}{\Gamma(10)} = 105 \cdot \frac{5! \cdot 3!}{9!} = \frac{105}{7 \cdot 8 \cdot 9} = \frac{5}{8 \cdot 3} = \frac{5}{24}.$$

Hence,

$$\mathbf{P}[N_2 = 0|N_1 > 0] = \frac{\mathbf{P}[(N_2 = 0) \bigcap (N_1 > 0)]}{\mathbf{P}[N_1 > 0]} = \frac{5}{24} \div \frac{3}{8} = \frac{5}{24} \times \frac{8}{3} = \frac{5}{9}.$$

(c) Recall that the Bayesian credibility premium $\mathbf{E}[N_2|N_1 > 0]$ is the posterior expectation of $(N|Q)$. Using (3.4), we have

$$\mathbf{E}[N_2|N_1 > 0] = \tilde{\mathbf{E}}[N|Q] = \int_{-\infty}^{\infty} \mathbf{E}[N|q] \cdot \pi(q|n) \, dq$$

so that the expectation is evaluated with respect to the posterior distribution of $(Q|N = n)$.

Since $(N|Q)$ is geometric, with parameter q, its expectation is

$$\mathbf{E}[N|Q] = \frac{1-Q}{Q}.$$

Since $(Q|N)$ is beta, with parameters $a=5$, $b=4$, using (1.28), we have

$$\mathbf{E}[N_2|N_1 > 0] = \frac{\Gamma(9)}{\Gamma(5)\cdot\Gamma(4)} \int_0^1 [q^4(1-q)^3] \cdot \frac{1-q}{q}\, dq =$$

$$= \frac{\Gamma(9)}{\Gamma(5)\cdot\Gamma(4)} \int_0^1 q^3(1-q)^4\, dq = \frac{\Gamma(9)}{\Gamma(5)\cdot\Gamma(4)} \cdot \frac{\Gamma(5)\cdot\Gamma(4)}{\Gamma(9)} = \mathbf{1}.$$

3.8. Note that the prior density is

$$\pi(q) = \frac{\Gamma(5)}{\Gamma(3)\cdot\Gamma(2)} \cdot q^2(1-q) = \frac{4!}{2!} \cdot q^2(1-q) = 12q^2(1-q),\ 0 < q < 1.$$

The model is described as

$$f(n|q) = \mathbf{P}[N = n|Q = q] = \frac{5!}{n!(5-n)!}\, q^n(1-q)^{5-n} \text{ for } n = 0, 1, \ldots, 5.$$

In particular, $f(0|q) = (1-q)^5$.

(a) Calculating the marginal probability that $N_1 = 0$, using (1.28), we have

$$\mathbf{P}[N_1 = 0] = \int_0^1 \mathbf{P}[N_1 = 0|Q = q]\pi(q)\, dq = \int_0^1 (1-q)^5 \pi(q)\, dq =$$

$$= \mathbf{E}[(1-Q)^5] = 12 \int_0^1 q^2(1-q) \cdot (1-q)^5\, dq =$$

$$= 12 \int_0^1 q^2(1-q)^6\, dq = 12 \cdot \frac{\Gamma(3)\cdot\Gamma(7)}{\Gamma(3+7)} = 12 \cdot \frac{2!\cdot 6!}{9!} = \frac{1}{21}.$$

(b) Calculating the posterior density of Q, given $N_1 = 0$, we have

$$\pi(q|N_1 = 0) = \frac{\mathbf{P}[N_1 = 0|Q = q]\pi(q)}{\mathbf{P}[N_1 = 0]} = 21 \cdot (1-q)^5 \cdot 12q^2(1-q) =$$

$$= 252q^2(1-q)^6,$$

which is identified as **Beta** $[a = 3,\ b = 7]$. Note that

$$\frac{\Gamma(10)}{\Gamma(3)\cdot\Gamma(7)} = \frac{9!}{2!\cdot 6!} = 252.$$

(c) Recall that the Bayesian credibility premium $\mathbf{E}[N_2|N_1 = 0]$ is the posterior expectation of $(N|Q)$. Using (3.4), we have

$$\mathbf{E}[N_2|N_1 = 0] = \tilde{\mathbf{E}}[N|Q] = \int_{-\infty}^{\infty} \mathbf{E}[N|q] \cdot \pi(q|n)\, dq$$

so that the expectation is evaluated with respect to the posterior distribution of $(Q|N = n)$.

Since $(N|Q)$ is binomial, with parameters $m = 5$ and q, its expectation is, $\mathbf{E}[N|Q] = 5Q$. Therefore,

$$\mathbf{E}[N_2|N_1 = 0] = 5\mathbf{E}[Q|N_1 = 0] = 5 \cdot \frac{3}{3+7} = \frac{15}{10} = \mathbf{1.5}.$$

3.9. Let X_j denote a zero-one variable associated with the year j so that, conditionally, given $Q = q$, variables

$$\{X_1, X_2, \ldots, X_7\}$$

are independent and identically distributed according to (3.46). We need to calculate

$$\mathbf{P}[X_7 = 1|X_1 = X_2 = \ldots = X_6 = 0].$$

Let A and B be the following events: $A = [X_1 = X_2 = \ldots = X_6 = 0]$ and $B = [X_7 = 1]$.

Recall that

$$\mathbf{P}[B|A] = \frac{\mathbf{P}[A \bigcap B]}{\mathbf{P}[A]}.$$

The numerator can be determined as

$$\mathbf{P}[A \bigcap B] = \mathbf{E}[\mathbf{P}[A \bigcap B|Q]],$$

Since, conditionally, variables $\{(X_j|Q = q)\}$ are independent, the conditional probability is $(1 - q)^6 \cdot q$. Taking the expectation with respect to the prior distribution of Q, using (1.28), we have

$$\mathbf{P}[A \bigcap B] = \int_0^1 q^6(1 - q)\, 2(1 - q)\, dq = 2 \int_0^1 q^6\, (1 - q)^2\, dq = 2 \cdot \frac{\Gamma(7) \cdot \Gamma(3)}{\Gamma(10)} =$$
$$= 2 \cdot \frac{6! \cdot 2!}{9!} = \frac{1}{126}.$$

Similarly,

$$\mathbf{P}[A] = 2 \int_0^1 q^6\, (1 - q)\, dq = 2 \cdot \frac{\Gamma(7) \cdot \Gamma(2)}{\Gamma(9)} = 2 \frac{6!}{8!} = \frac{1}{28}.$$

The required probability is

$$\mathbf{P}[B|A] = \frac{28}{126} = \frac{2}{9}.$$

3.10. Since Q has a beta distribution, with parameters $a = 6$ and $b = 3$, its **pdf** is of the form

$$\pi(q) = \frac{\Gamma(9)}{\Gamma(6) \cdot \Gamma(3)} \cdot q^5 (1 - q)^2 = \frac{8!}{5! \cdot 2!} \cdot q^5 (1 - q)^2 = \frac{6 \cdot 7 \cdot 8}{2} \cdot q^5 (1 - q)^2 =$$
$$= 21 \cdot 8 \cdot q^5 (1 - q)^2 = 168 \cdot q^5 (1 - q)^2$$

for $0 < q < 1$, and $\pi(q) = 0$ elsewhere.

(a) Calculating $\mathbf{E}[T]$, the expected value of T, using (1.28), we have

$$\mathbf{E}[T] = \int_0^1 q^{-1} \cdot \pi(q)\, dq = 168 \int_0^1 q^{-1} \cdot q^5 (1-q)^2 \, dq =$$
$$= 168 \int_0^1 q^4 (1-q)^2 \, dq = 168 \cdot \frac{\Gamma(5)\,\Gamma(3)}{\Gamma(8)} = 168 \cdot \frac{4! \cdot 2!}{7!} = \frac{8}{5} = \mathbf{1.6}.$$

(b) Similarly, calculating $\mathbf{E}[T^2]$, the second value of T, using (1.28), we have

$$\mathbf{E}[T^2] = \int_0^1 q^{-2} \cdot \pi(q)\, dq = 168 \int_0^1 q^{-2} \cdot q^5 (1-q)^2 \, dq =$$
$$= 168 \int_0^1 q^3 (1-q)^2 \, dq = 168 \cdot \frac{\Gamma(4)\,\Gamma(3)}{\Gamma(7)} = 168 \cdot \frac{3! \cdot 2!}{6!} = \mathbf{2.8}.$$

(c) Calculating $\mathbf{Var}[T]$, the variance of T, we have

$$\mathbf{Var}[T] = \frac{14}{5} - \left(\frac{8}{5}\right)^2 = \frac{14}{5} - \frac{64}{25} = \frac{70 - 64}{25} = \frac{6}{25} = \mathbf{0.24}.$$

3.11. Since, given $Q = q$, a number N of years with no claim is geometrically-distributed, its **pmf** is of the following form:

$$\mathbf{P}[N = n] = (1-q)^n q \quad \text{for} \quad n = 0, 1, 2, \dots$$

In addition, since Q has a beta distribution, with parameters $a = 6$ and $b = 3$, its **pdf** is of the form

$$\pi(q) = 168 \cdot q^5 (1-q)^2$$

for $0 < q < 1$, and $\pi(q) = 0$ elsewhere.
Therefore,

$$\mathbf{E}[N|Q = q] = \frac{1-q}{q} \quad \Rightarrow \quad \mathbf{E}[N|Q] = \frac{1-Q}{Q} = T - 1, \text{ where } T = \frac{1}{Q}.$$

a) Calculating the marginal expectation of N, we have

$$\mathbf{E}[N] = \mathbf{E}[\mathbf{E}[N|Q]] = \mathbf{E}[T-1] = 1.6 - 1 = \mathbf{0.6}.$$

b) Calculating the variance of N, we have

$$\mathbf{Var}[N] = \mathbf{Var}[\mathbf{E}[N|Q]] + \mathbf{E}[\mathbf{Var}[N|Q]] = \mathbf{Var}[T-1] + \mathbf{E}[T^2 - T] =$$
$$= \mathbf{Var}[T] + \mathbf{E}[T^2] - \mathbf{E}[T] = 0.24 + 2.8 - 1.6 = \mathbf{1.44}.$$

c) Given that there was no claim for **three** consecutive years, conditional probability of having no claim in year **four** can be evaluated as

$$\mathbf{P}[A|B] = \frac{\mathbf{P}[A \cap B]}{\mathbf{P}[B]},$$

where $A = [N_4 = 0]$ and $B = [N_1 = N_2 = N_3 = 0]$. Note that, using (1.28), we have

$$\mathbf{P}[A \cap B] = \mathbf{E}[\mathbf{P}[A \cap B | Q]] = \int_0^1 (1-q)^4 \, \pi(q) \, dq =$$

$$= 168 \int_0^1 (1-q)^4 q^5 (1-q)^2 \, dq =$$

$$= 168 \int_0^1 q^5 (1-q)^6 \, dq = 168 \cdot \frac{\Gamma(6) \cdot \Gamma(7)}{\Gamma(13)} = 168 \cdot \frac{5! \cdot 6!}{12!} = \frac{1}{33}.$$

Similarly,

$$\mathbf{P}[B] = 168 \int_0^1 (1-q)^3 \cdot q^5 (1-q)^2 \, dq = 168 \int_0^1 q^5 (1-q)^5 \, dq =$$

$$= 168 \cdot \frac{\Gamma(6) \cdot \Gamma(6)}{\Gamma(12)} = \frac{168 \cdot (5!)^2}{11!} = \frac{2}{33}.$$

Therefore,

$$\mathbf{P}[A|B] = \frac{1}{33} \cdot \frac{33}{2} = \mathbf{0.5}.$$

3.12. Since Λ follows a gamma distribution, with parameters $\alpha = 4$ and $\theta = 1$, its **pdf** is of the form

$$\pi(\lambda) = \frac{1}{6} \lambda^3 \cdot e^{-\lambda} \quad \text{for} \quad \lambda > 0, \quad \text{and} \quad \pi(\lambda) = 0 \quad \text{elsewhere.}$$

Thus,

$$\mathbf{E}[\Lambda] = \alpha \cdot \theta = 4 \quad \text{and} \quad \mathbf{Var}[\Lambda] = \alpha \cdot \theta^2 = 4.$$

Since $(N|\Lambda)$ is Poisson with parameter Λ, its **pmf** is

$$\mathbf{P}[N = n | \Lambda = \lambda] = e^{-\lambda} \cdot \frac{\lambda^n}{n!}.$$

The joint probability function for (Λ, N_1, N_2, N_3) is

$$\pi(\lambda) \cdot f(1|\lambda) \cdot f(3|\lambda) \cdot f(0|\lambda) = \frac{1}{6} \lambda^3 e^{-\lambda} \cdot \lambda e^{-\lambda} \cdot \frac{\lambda^3}{3!} e^{-\lambda} \cdot \frac{\lambda^0}{0!} e^{-\lambda} = \frac{1}{36} \lambda^7 e^{-4\lambda}.$$

Let A be an event, defined as $A = [N_1 = 1, \ N_2 = 3, \ N_3 = 0]$.

(a) Evaluating posterior density $\pi(\lambda | N_1 = 1, \ N_2 = 3, \ N_3 = 0) = \pi(\lambda|A)$, we have

$$\pi(\lambda|A) = \frac{\pi(\lambda) f(N_1, N_2, N_3|\lambda)}{\int \pi(\lambda) f(N_1, N_2, N_3|\lambda) \, d\lambda},$$

where

$$f(N_1, N_2, N_3|\lambda) = \prod_{i=1}^3 f(N_i|\lambda).$$

Thus,

$$\pi(\lambda|A) = C \cdot \lambda^7 e^{-4\lambda}, \quad \text{where } C = \frac{1}{\int \lambda^7 c^{-4\lambda} \, d\lambda}.$$

Therefore, the posterior density is gamma-distributed, with parameters $\alpha' = 8$ and $\theta' = 1/4$.

(b) Calculating conditional probability of having at least one claim in the **fourth** year, we have

$$\mathbf{P}[N_4 \geq 1|A] = \int_0^\infty \mathbf{P}[N \geq 1|\lambda]\pi(\lambda|A) \, d\lambda = \tilde{\mathbf{E}}[\mathbf{P}[N_4 \geq 1]|\Lambda],$$

where $\tilde{\mathbf{E}}$ denotes posterior expectation, given A.

Since

$$\mathbf{P}[N \geq 1|\Lambda = \lambda] = 1 - e^{-\lambda},$$

it follows, using (1.26), that

$$\mathbf{P}[N_4 \geq 1|A] = \int_0^\infty \left[1 - e^{-\lambda}\right] \cdot \pi(\lambda|A) \, d\lambda = 1 - \int_0^\infty e^{-\lambda} \cdot \pi(\lambda|A) \, d\lambda =$$

$$= 1 - \frac{4^8}{\Gamma(8)} \int_0^\infty e^{-\lambda} \cdot \lambda^7 \cdot e^{-4\lambda} \, d\lambda = 1 - \frac{4^8}{7!} \int_0^\infty \lambda^7 \cdot e^{-5\lambda} \, d\lambda =$$

$$= 1 - \frac{4^8}{7!} \cdot \frac{7!}{5^8} = 1 - \left(\frac{4}{5}\right)^8 = 1 - (0.8)^8 \approx 1 - 0.16777 = \mathbf{0.8322}.$$

(c) The Bayesian credibility premium $\mathbf{E}[N_4|N_1 = 1, \ N_2 = 3, \ N_3 = 0] = \mathbf{E}[N_4|A]$ is the posterior expectation of $(N_4|\Lambda)$. Using (3.4), we have

$$\mathbf{E}[N_4|A] = \tilde{\mathbf{E}}[N|\Lambda] = \int_0^\infty \mathbf{E}[N|\lambda] \cdot \pi(\lambda|n) \, d\lambda$$

so that the expectation is evaluated with respect to the posterior distribution of $(\Lambda|N = n)$.

Since $(N|\Lambda)$ is Poisson, with parameters Λ, its expectation is $\mathbf{E}[N|\Lambda] = \Lambda$. Also, $(\Lambda|A)$ is gamma, with parameters $\alpha' = 8$ and $\theta' = 1/4$. Therefore,

$$\mathbf{E}[N_4|A] = \frac{4^8}{\Gamma(8)} \int_0^\infty \lambda \cdot \lambda^7 \cdot e^{-4\lambda} \, d\lambda = \mathbf{E}[\Lambda|A] = \alpha' \cdot \theta' = 8 \cdot \frac{1}{4} = \mathbf{2}.$$

We can also verify that, using (1.26),

$$\mathbf{E}[N_4|A] = \frac{4^8}{\Gamma(8)} \int_0^\infty \lambda^8 \cdot e^{-4\lambda} \, d\lambda = \frac{4^8}{\Gamma(8)} \cdot \frac{\Gamma(9)}{4^9} = \frac{8!}{7! \cdot 4} = \frac{8}{4} = \mathbf{2}.$$

3.13. Since the conditional random variable $(X|B)$ is gamma-distributed, with parameters $\alpha = 3$ and $\theta = 1/\beta$, its **pdf** is of the following form:

$$f(x|\theta) = \frac{\beta^3}{2} \cdot x^2 e^{-\beta x} \quad \text{for } x > 0$$

Similarly, since the prior distribution of B is gamma, with parameters $\alpha' = 4$ and $\theta' = 1$, its **pdf** is of the following form:

$$\pi(\beta) = \frac{1}{6} \cdot \beta^3 e^{-\beta} \text{ for } \beta > 0$$

Calculating the joint distribution of (B, X) as a product of the **pdf**'s, we have

$$f(x, \beta) = \pi(\beta) f(x|\beta) = \frac{\beta^3}{2} \cdot x^2 e^{-\beta x} \cdot \frac{1}{6} \cdot \beta^3 e^{-\beta} = \frac{1}{12} \beta^6 \cdot x^2 \cdot e^{-(x+1)\beta}.$$

(a) To calculate the **marginal** density of X_1, we integrate $f(x, \beta)$ in β. Using (1.26), we obtain

$$f(x) = \frac{x^2}{12} \int_0^\infty \beta^6 \cdot e^{-(x+1)\beta} \, d\beta = \frac{6! \, x^2}{12(x+1)^7} = \frac{60x^2}{(x+1)^7}, \ x > 0.$$

(b) The **posterior** density of B, given X, is the ratio

$$\pi(\beta|x) = \frac{f(x, \beta)}{f(x)} = \frac{x^2 \cdot \beta^6 \cdot e^{-\beta(1+x)}}{12} \cdot \frac{(x+1)^7}{60x^2} = \frac{1}{720} \beta^6 (1+x)^7 e^{-\beta(1+x)}.$$

This is gamma density, with parameters $\alpha'' = 7$ and $\theta'' = (1+x)^{-1}$.

Note that $\Gamma(7) = (7-1)! = 720$.

(c) The **Bayesian credibility**, $\mathbf{E}[X_2|X_1]$, is evaluated via the posterior density. Conditionally, given $B = \beta$, the expected value of X is $\mathbf{E}[X|B] = 3B^{-1}$. Therefore, using (1.26), we have

$$\mathbf{E}[X_2|X_1 = x] = \int_0^\infty 3\beta^{-1} \cdot \pi(\beta|x) \, d\beta = \frac{3(1+x)^7}{\Gamma(7)} \int_0^\infty \beta^{-1} \cdot \beta^6 e^{-\beta(1+x)} \, d\beta =$$

$$= \frac{3(1+x)^7}{\Gamma(7)} \int_0^\infty \beta^5 e^{-\beta(1+x)} \, d\beta = \frac{3(1+x)^7}{\Gamma(7)} \cdot \frac{\Gamma(6)}{(1+x)^6} = \frac{3}{6}(1+x) = \frac{1+x}{2}.$$

3.14. Since the unconditional probability of observing at least one claim in a year is 0.23, the unconditional probability of observing zero claims in a year is

$$\mathbf{P}[N = 0] = 1 - 0.23 = 0.77.$$

Recall that

$$\mathbf{P}[N = 0] = \mathbf{E}[\mathbf{P}[N = 0|\Lambda]].$$

Since the conditional random variable $(N|\Lambda)$ is Poisson-distributed, with a parameter Λ, the conditional probability of observing no claims is

$$\mathbf{P}[N = 0|\Lambda = \lambda] = e^{-\lambda}.$$

Therefore,

$$\mathbf{P}[N = 0] = \mathbf{E}[\mathbf{P}[N = 0|\Lambda]] = \int_0^k e^{-\lambda} \cdot \pi(\lambda) \, d\lambda = \frac{1}{1 - e^{-k}} \int_0^k e^{-\lambda} \cdot e^{-\lambda} \, d\lambda =$$

$$= \frac{1}{1 - e^{-k}} \int_0^k e^{-2\lambda} \, d\lambda = \frac{1}{2(1 - e^{-k})} \left(1 - e^{-2k}\right) = \frac{1 + e^{-k}}{2} = 0.77.$$

Solving this equation for k, we obtain

$$e^{-k} = 2 \cdot 0.77 - 1 = 0.54 \Leftrightarrow k = -\ln(0.54) \approx \mathbf{0.6162}.$$

3.15. (a) Using the information for the gamma prior for Tom, we have

$$\mathbf{E}[\Lambda] = \alpha_1 \cdot \theta_1 = 4 \cdot \frac{1}{4} = 1 \quad \text{and} \quad \mathbf{Var}[\Lambda] = \alpha_1 \cdot \theta_1^2 = 4 \cdot \frac{1}{16} = \frac{1}{4}.$$

Jerry uses gamma distribution, with parameters (α_2, θ_2), such that

$$\alpha_2 \cdot \theta_2 = \alpha_1 \cdot \theta_1 = 1 \quad \text{and} \quad \alpha_2 \cdot \theta_2^2 = 2 \cdot \alpha_1 \cdot \theta_1^2 = \frac{1}{2}.$$

Therefore,

$$\theta_2 = \frac{1}{2} \quad \text{and} \quad \alpha_2 = 2.$$

(b) Let X_i be the number of claims on the policy in year i and let W be the total number of claims in n years. Then, for $n = 3$,

$$W = \sum_{i=1}^{3} X_i = 1.$$

Using (3.17), the posterior distribution of Λ, given $W = w = 1$ and $n = 3$, is **Gamma** $[a', \theta']$, where

$$a' = w + \alpha \quad \text{and} \quad \theta' = \frac{\theta}{n\theta + 1}.$$

Calculating the Bayesian credibility for Tom, the posterior distribution of Λ is gamma, with parameters:

$$\alpha_1' = w + \alpha_1 = 1 + \alpha_1 = 1 + 4 = 5 \quad \text{and}$$
$$\theta_1' = \frac{\theta_1}{3\theta_1 + 1} = \frac{1}{4} \div \left(3 \cdot \frac{1}{4} + 1 \right) = \frac{1}{4} \div \frac{7}{4} = \frac{1}{4} \cdot \frac{4}{7} = \frac{1}{7}.$$

Therefore, Bayesian credibility for Tom is

$$\mathbf{E}\left[X_4 \,|\, W = 1\right] = \tilde{\mathbf{E}}\left[X_4 \,|\, \Lambda\right] = \alpha_1' \cdot \theta_1' = 5 \cdot \frac{1}{7} = \frac{5}{7}.$$

Similarly, calculating the Bayesian credibility for Jerry, we have

$$\alpha_2' = 1 + \alpha_2 = 1 + 2 = 3 \quad \text{and}$$
$$\theta_2' = \frac{\theta_2}{3 \cdot \theta_2 + 1} = \frac{1}{2} \div \left(3 \cdot \frac{1}{2} + 1 \right) = \frac{1}{2} \div \frac{5}{2} = \frac{1}{2} \cdot \frac{2}{5} = \frac{1}{5}.$$

Therefore, Bayesian credibility for Jerry is

$$\mathbf{E}\left[X_4 \,|\, W = 1\right] = \tilde{\mathbf{E}}\left[X_4 \,|\, \Lambda\right] = \alpha_2' \cdot \theta_2' = 3 \cdot \frac{1}{5} = \frac{3}{5}.$$

3.16. Since the random variable Λ has gamma distribution, with parameters α and θ, $\Lambda \sim \textbf{Gamma}\,[\alpha,\,\theta]$, the prior density is of the following form:

$$\pi(\lambda) = \frac{1}{\theta^\alpha \cdot \Gamma(\alpha)} \cdot \lambda^{\alpha-1} \cdot e^{-\lambda/\theta}, \ \lambda > 0$$

Also, given λ, the random variable $W = N_1 + N_2$ has a Poisson distribution with parameter 2λ.

Given $W = N_1 + N_2 = w$, the posterior density is

$$\pi(\lambda|w) = \frac{\pi(\lambda) \cdot \textbf{P}[W = w|\Lambda = \lambda]}{\textbf{P}[W = w]} = \frac{1}{\textbf{P}[W = w]} \cdot \frac{1}{\theta^\alpha \cdot \Gamma(\alpha)} \cdot \lambda^{\alpha-1} \cdot e^{-\lambda/\theta} \times$$

$$\times \frac{1}{w!} \cdot (2\lambda)^w \cdot e^{-2\lambda} = A \cdot [\lambda^{\alpha+w-1} \cdot e^{-\lambda(2+1/\theta)}],$$

where the factor A does not depend on λ. Therefore,

$$(\Lambda|W = w) \sim \textbf{Gamma}\,[\alpha',\,\theta'],$$

where

$$\alpha' = \alpha + w \ \text{ and } \ \theta' = [2 + 1/\theta]^{-1} = \frac{\theta}{2\theta + 1}.$$

Using (3.4), the credibility premium is defined by the formula

$$\textbf{E}[N_3|W = w] = \tilde{\textbf{E}}[N_3|\Lambda] = \int_{-\infty}^{\infty} \textbf{E}[N_3|\lambda] \cdot \pi(\lambda|w)\,d\lambda$$

so that the expectation is evaluated with respect to the posterior distribution of $(\Lambda|W = w)$.

Note that $\textbf{E}[N|\lambda] = \lambda$. Therefore,

$$\textbf{E}[N_3|(N_1 = n_1)\textstyle\bigcap(N_2 = n_2)] = \int_0^{\infty} \lambda \cdot \pi(\lambda|w)\,d\lambda = \tilde{\textbf{E}}[\Lambda|W] = \alpha' \cdot \theta' =$$

$$= (\alpha + w) \cdot \frac{\theta}{2\theta + 1}, \ w = n_1 + n_2.$$

If $(N_1 = N_2 = 0)$, then $w = 0$, and the first equation for Bayesian credibility leads to

$$(\alpha + 0) \cdot \frac{\theta}{2\theta + 1} = 2.8.$$

Similarly, if $N_1 = 4$ and $N_2 = 2$, then $w = 4 + 2 = 6$, which results in the equation for credibility, as follows:

$$(\alpha + 6) \cdot \frac{\theta}{2\theta + 1} = 5.6.$$

Thus, we obtain the following system of equations:

$$\begin{cases} \alpha \cdot \frac{\theta}{2\theta+1} = 2.8 \\[2mm] (\alpha + 6) \cdot \frac{\theta}{2\theta+1} = 5.6 \end{cases}$$

Dividing one equation by the other, we obtain

$$\frac{\alpha + 6}{\alpha} = 2 \Leftrightarrow \alpha + 6 = 2\alpha \Leftrightarrow \alpha = \mathbf{6}.$$

Using $\alpha = 6$ in the first equation, we have

$$\frac{6\theta}{2\theta + 1} = 2.8 \Leftrightarrow \frac{\theta}{2\theta + 1} = 0.4\overline{66} \Leftrightarrow 0.9\overline{33}\theta + 0.4\overline{66} = \theta \Leftrightarrow 0.0\overline{66}\theta = 0.4\overline{66} \Leftrightarrow$$
$$\theta = 15 \cdot 0.4\overline{66} = \mathbf{7}.$$

Calculating the Bayesian credibility for $N_1 = 4$ and $N_2 = 5$, we have

$$\mathbf{E}[N_3|(N_1 = 4) \bigcap (N_2 = 5)] = \mathbf{E}[N_3|(W = 9)] = (\alpha + 9) \cdot \frac{\theta}{2\theta + 1} =$$
$$= (6 + 9) \cdot \frac{7}{2 \cdot 7 + 1} = \frac{15 \cdot 7}{15} = \mathbf{7}.$$

3.17. Note that the conditional distribution of $(Y|Q)$ is geometric, with parameter q, and the prior density is **Beta** $[6, 1]$.

Let $W = \sum_{j=1}^{4} Y_j$. The posterior distribution of $(Q|B)$ is

$$\pi(q|B) = \frac{\mathbf{P}[B|Q = q] \cdot \pi(q)}{\mathbf{P}[B]} = \frac{1}{\mathbf{P}[B]} \cdot 6q^5 \cdot [(1 - q)^4 \cdot q^4] = A \cdot q^9 \cdot (1 - q)^4,$$

where A does not depend on q.

Thus, the posterior probability is beta, with parameters $a = 10$ and $b = 5$: $(Q|B) \sim \mathbf{Beta}[10, 5]$.

Using (3.4), the credibility premium is defined by the formula

$$\mathbf{E}[Y_5|B] = \tilde{\mathbf{E}}[Y_5|Q] = \int_0^1 \mathbf{E}[Y_5|q] \cdot \pi(q|w) \, dq$$

so that the expectation is evaluated with respect to the posterior distribution of $(Q|B)$.

Note that Y_5, given $Q = q$, has geometric distribution, and its conditional expectation is

$$\mathbf{E}[Y_5|Q = q] = \frac{1 - q}{q}.$$

Therefore, Bayesian credibility will be a posterior expected value of $(1 - Q)/Q$:

$$\mathbf{E}[Y_5|B] = \frac{\Gamma(15)}{\Gamma(10) \cdot \Gamma(5)} \int_0^1 \frac{1 - q}{q} \cdot q^9 (1 - q)^4 \, dq =$$
$$= \frac{\Gamma(15)}{\Gamma(10) \cdot \Gamma(5)} \int_0^1 q^8 (1 - q)^5 \, dq =$$
$$= \frac{\Gamma(15)}{\Gamma(10) \cdot \Gamma(5)} \times \frac{\Gamma(9) \cdot \Gamma(6)}{\Gamma(15)} = \frac{5}{9}.$$

3.18. Since the random variable Q has beta distribution, with parameters $a = 6$ and $b = 1$, its **pdf** is of the form

$$\pi_Q(q) = 6q^5 \quad \text{for} \quad 0 < q < 1.$$

Let N_j be the number of claims during the year j.

We need to calculate

$$\mathbf{P}[N_4 = 0 | N_1 = N_2 = N_3 = 0].$$

Let A and B be the events, defined as

$$A = [N_4 = 0] \quad \text{and} \quad B = [N_1 = N_2 = N_3 = 0].$$

Then, conditionally, given $Q = q$, we have

$$\mathbf{P}[A \cap B | Q = q] = q^4 \quad \text{and} \quad \mathbf{P}[B | Q = q] = q^3.$$

Calculating $\mathbf{P}[A \cap B]$, we have

$$\mathbf{P}[A \cap B] = \int_0^1 \mathbf{P}[A \cap B | Q = q]\,\pi(q)\,dq = 6 \int_0^1 q^4 \cdot q^5\,dq = 6 \int_0^1 q^9\,dq = \frac{6}{10} = \frac{3}{5}.$$

Similarly,

$$\mathbf{P}[B] = \int_0^1 \mathbf{P}[B | Q = q]\,\pi(q)\,dq = 6 \int_0^1 q^3 \cdot q^5\,dq = 6 \int_0^1 q^8\,dq = \frac{6}{9} = \frac{2}{3}.$$

Therefore,

$$\mathbf{P}[A | B] = \frac{\mathbf{P}[A \cap B]}{\mathbf{P}[B]} = \frac{3}{5} \div \frac{2}{3} = \frac{3}{5} \cdot \frac{3}{2} = \frac{9}{10} = \mathbf{0.9}.$$

3.19. (a) Recall that for a random variable that has inverse gamma, with parameters (a, b), the **pdf** is of the form

$$f(\theta) = \frac{b^a}{\theta^{a+1}\Gamma(a)} e^{-b/\theta}.$$

The kth raw moment is

$$\mathbf{E}[\Theta^k] = \frac{b^k \Gamma(a - k)}{\Gamma(a)}.$$

Therefore,

$$\mathbf{E}[\Theta] = \frac{b\Gamma(a - 1)}{\Gamma(a)} = \frac{b}{a - 1}$$

and

$$\mathbf{E}[\Theta^2] = \frac{b^2 \Gamma(a - 2)}{\Gamma(a)} = \frac{b^2}{(a - 1)(a - 2)}.$$

Thus,

$$\mathbf{Var}[\Theta] = \mathbf{E}[\Theta^2] - \mathbf{E}[\Theta]^2 = \frac{b^2}{(a-1)(a-2)} - \left(\frac{b}{a-1}\right)^2 =$$

$$= \frac{b^2}{a-1}\left(\frac{1}{a-2} - \frac{1}{a-1}\right) = \frac{b^2}{a-1} \cdot \frac{a-1-a+2}{(a-1)(a-2)} = \frac{b^2}{(a-1)^2(a-2)}.$$

Therefore, we obtain the following two equations for parameters:

$$\frac{b}{a-1} = 20 \quad \text{and} \quad \frac{b^2}{(a-1)^2(a-2)} = 100$$

Squaring the first equation and using it in the second equation, we obtain

$$\frac{b^2}{(a-1)^2} = 400 \quad \text{and} \quad \frac{b^2}{(a-1)^2(a-2)} = 100.$$

Thus,

$$400 \cdot \frac{1}{a-2} = 100 \Leftrightarrow \frac{1}{a-2} = \frac{1}{4} \Leftrightarrow a = 6.$$

From the first equation,

$$\frac{b}{5} = 20 \Leftrightarrow b = 100.$$

Thus, the parameters of this inverse gamma distribution are $a = 6$ and $b = 100$.

(b) Using (3.40), the posterior mean of the new observation, $Y = X_{n+1}$, given $\mathbf{X} = \mathbf{x}$, is

$$\mathbf{E}[Y|\mathbf{X}] = \frac{w+b}{a+n-1}, \quad \text{where } w = \sum_{i=1}^{n} X_i.$$

For $n = 5$ exposures, the total loss is

$$W = \sum_{i=1}^{5} X_i = 1200, \quad a+n = 6+5-1 = 10 \quad \text{and} \quad b+w = 100+1200 = 1300.$$

Hence,

$$\mathbf{E}[Y|\mathbf{X}] = \frac{1300}{10} = \mathbf{130}.$$

3.20. Since Λ is gamma-distributed, its reciprocal, $\Theta = \Lambda^{-1}$, is inverse gamma-distributed, with parameters $(a = \alpha = 6, b = \beta^{-1} = 1000)$.

Using (3.38), the posterior distribution of Θ, given $n = 10$ exposures and

$$W = \sum_{i=1}^{10} X_i = w,$$

will also be of the same type, with parameters

$$a' = a + n = 6 + 10 = 16 \quad \text{and} \quad b' = b + w = 1000 + w.$$

Using (3.40), the posterior mean claim size is

$$\mathbf{E}[Y|W = w] = \frac{b'}{a' - 1} = \frac{b + w}{16 - 1} = \frac{1000 + w}{15} = 360.$$

Solving this equation for w, obtain $w = 4400$. Since there were $n = 10$ exposures, the average loss was

$$\bar{x} = \frac{w}{n} = \frac{4400}{10} = \mathbf{440}.$$

3.21. Since the random variable $(X|\Lambda)$ has gamma distribution, with parameters $\alpha = 2$ and $\theta = 1/\lambda$, its **pdf** is of the form

$$f(x|\lambda) = \lambda^2 x e^{-\lambda x}, \quad x > 0.$$

In addition, since Λ has inverse gamma distribution, with parameters (a, b), its reciprocal, $\Theta = \Lambda^{-1}$, has density **Gamma** $[a, b^{-1}]$.

(a) Equating its expectation and variance to their given values, we obtain

$$\frac{a}{b} = 0.06 \quad \text{and} \quad \frac{a}{b^2} = 0.0006,$$

which results in $b^{-1} = 0.01 \Rightarrow b = \mathbf{100}$ and $a = \mathbf{6}$.

(b) Notice that posterior density, $\pi(\lambda|W = w)$, is also inverse gamma, with parameters

$$a' = a + 2n = 6 + 2 \cdot 5 = \mathbf{16} \quad \text{and} \quad b' = b + w = 100 + 3500 = \mathbf{3600}.$$

Also, by (3.44), $(Y|\mathbf{X} = \mathbf{x})$ is a generalized Pareto (beta of the second kind) distribution, with parameters

$$\alpha^* = n\alpha + a, \ \theta^* = w + b \ \text{and} \ \tau = \alpha.$$

Using (3.45), the expected loss, $\mathbf{E}[Y|W = 3500]$, is evaluated by the formula:

$$\mathbf{E}[Y|W = w] = \frac{\theta^* \cdot \tau}{\alpha^* - 1} = \frac{(w + b)\alpha}{n\alpha + a - 1} = \frac{(100 + 3500)2}{16 - 1} = \mathbf{480}.$$

3.22. Since the random variable Λ is gamma-distributed, with parameters $\alpha = 3$ and $\theta = 1/6$, its **pdf** is of the form

$$\pi(\lambda) = 108 \cdot \lambda^2 \cdot e^{-6\lambda} \quad \text{for} \ \lambda > 0.$$

Note that the conditional expectation of the loss is

$$\mathbf{E}[Y|\Lambda = \lambda] = \lambda^{-1}.$$

(a) Given $Y = y$, posterior distribution of Λ is

$$\pi(\lambda|y) = \frac{\pi(\lambda) \cdot f(y|\lambda)}{f(y)} = C(\lambda^2 \cdot e^{-6\lambda}) \cdot (\lambda e^{-\lambda y}) = C\lambda^3 \cdot e^{-(y+6)\lambda},$$

where C does not depend on λ.

Thus, $(\Lambda|Y = y)$ has gamma density, with parameters $a' = 4$ and $b' = (y+6)^{-1}$.

(b) Using (3.39), the random loss for the next year, given the current year loss, is Pareto-distributed, with parameters $\alpha^* = n + a$ and $\theta^* = w + b$, where $n = 1$, $a = 3$, $w = 9$, and $b = 6$.

Using (3.40), the expected loss for the next year, given the current year loss as $Y = 9$, is

$$\mathbf{E}\,[Y|\mathbf{X}] = \frac{\theta^*}{\alpha^* - 1} = \frac{w + b}{a + n - 1} = \frac{9 + 6}{3 + 1 - 1} = \frac{15}{3} = \mathbf{5}.$$

(c) Using (1.26), the value of a marginal density for Y at y is

$$f(y) = \int_0^\infty \pi(\lambda) \cdot f(y|\lambda)\,d\lambda = 108 \int_0^\infty (\lambda^2 \cdot e^{-6\lambda}) \cdot (\lambda e^{-\lambda y})\,d\lambda =$$
$$= 108 \int_0^\infty \lambda^3 e^{-(6+y)\lambda}\,d\lambda = 108 \cdot \frac{3!}{(6+y)^4} = \frac{648}{(6+y)^4}.$$

Thus, for $y = 9$,

$$f(9) = \frac{648}{(6+y)^4} = \frac{648}{(6+9)^4} = \frac{648}{50{,}625} = \mathbf{0.0128}.$$

3.23. Since the random variable W is single-parameter Pareto, with parameters $\alpha = 5$ and $\theta = 1$, its **pdf** is of the form

$$\pi(w) = \frac{5}{w^6} \quad \text{for} \quad w > 1.$$

Since the individual loss X on the policy is uniformly-distributed over the interval $(0, w)$, the model density is

$$f(x|w) = \frac{1}{w} \quad \text{for} \quad 0 < x < w < \infty.$$

Therefore, the joint density of (W, X) is

$$\pi(w) \cdot f(x|w) = \frac{5}{w^6} \cdot \frac{1}{w} = \frac{5}{w^7} \quad \text{for} \quad 0 < x < w < \infty.$$

(a) Calculating the marginal distribution of X, we have

$$f(x) = \int_{\max(x,1)}^\infty \frac{5}{w^7}\,dw = \frac{5}{6} \cdot \frac{1}{x^6} \quad \text{for} \quad x > 1.$$

(b) The posterior density of $(W|X = x)$ is

$$\pi(w|x) = \frac{\pi(w) \cdot f(x|w)}{f(x)} = \frac{5}{w^7} \cdot \frac{6x^6}{5} = \frac{6x^6}{w^7} \quad \text{for} \quad x > 1.$$

(c) Calculating the expected loss for the next year, we have

$$\mathbf{E}[X_2|X_1 = x] = \tilde{\mathbf{E}}[X_2|W].$$

The expected value of a random variable that is uniformly-distributed on an interval $(0, W)$ is

$$\mathbf{E}[X|W] = \frac{W}{2}.$$

Therefore,

$$\mathbf{E}[X_2|X_1 = x] = \frac{1}{2} \int_x^\infty w \cdot \frac{6x^6}{w^7} \, dw = 3x^6 \int_x^\infty w^{-6} \, dw = \frac{3}{5} \cdot \frac{x^6}{x^5} = 0.6 \, x.$$

In particular, for $x = 1500$, the expected loss will be

$$\mathbf{E}[X_2|X_1 = 1500] = 0.6 \cdot 1500 = \mathbf{900}.$$

3.24. Using (3.23), the posterior variance is defined as

$$(\sigma')^2 = \left(\frac{n}{\sigma^2} + \frac{1}{\tau^2} \right)^{-1} = \frac{\sigma^2 \cdot \tau^2}{n\tau^2 + \sigma^2}.$$

Solving this equation for n, obtain:

$$(\sigma')^2 \left(n\tau^2 + \sigma^2 \right) = \sigma^2 \cdot \tau^2 \Leftrightarrow (\sigma')^2 \cdot \tau^2 \cdot n = \sigma^2 \cdot \tau^2 - (\sigma')^2 \cdot \sigma^2 \Leftrightarrow$$

$$n = \frac{\sigma^2 \cdot \left(\tau^2 - (\sigma')^2 \right)}{(\sigma')^2 \cdot \tau^2} = \frac{25{,}000 \cdot (10{,}000 - 2000)}{10{,}000 \cdot 2000} = \frac{25 \cdot 4}{10} = \mathbf{10}.$$

3.25. Using the formula (3.22) for the posterior mean, we have

$$\mu' = \frac{aw + \mu v}{na + v} \Leftrightarrow 38 = \frac{12 \cdot w + 9 \cdot 120}{5 \cdot 12 + 120} = \frac{1080 + 12w}{180} = \frac{90 + w}{15}.$$

Solving for w, we obtain

$$90 + w = 38 \cdot 15 = 570 \Leftrightarrow w = 570 - 90 = \mathbf{480}.$$

3.26. Recall that the coefficient of variation for any random variable Y is defined as the ratio

$$CV = \frac{\sqrt{\mathbf{Var}\,[Y]}}{\mathbf{E}\,[Y]}.$$

Note that if Y is gamma-distributed, $\mathbf{Gamma}[\alpha, \theta]$, then,

$$\mathbf{E}\,[Y] = \alpha \cdot \theta \quad \text{and} \quad \mathbf{Var}\,[Y] = \alpha \cdot \theta^2.$$

Hence, the coefficient of variation is

$$CV = \frac{\sqrt{\alpha} \cdot \theta}{\alpha \cdot \theta} = \frac{1}{\sqrt{\alpha}}.$$

Since $CV(\Lambda) = 0.0625$, we have

$$\frac{1}{\sqrt{\alpha}} = 0.0625 \Leftrightarrow \sqrt{\alpha} = 16 \Leftrightarrow \alpha = 16^2 = 256.$$

We have shown in section 3.7 that if the sample $(\mathbf{X}|\Lambda) = (X_i|\Lambda)_{i=1}^n$ represents independent Poisson-distributed observations and the unknown common intensity λ is treated as a random variable Λ with the prior distribution $\mathbf{Gamma}[r, \theta]$, then, by (3.17), the posterior distribution of $(\Lambda, \mathbf{X})$ is also gamma, with parameters

$$r^* = \sum_{i=1}^n x_i + r \quad \text{and} \quad \theta^* = \frac{\theta}{n\theta + 1}.$$

In our problem,

$$\sum_{i=1}^n x_i = 144 \quad \text{and} \quad r = 256.$$

Thus,

$$a' = 256 + 144 = 400.$$

Therefore, the coefficient of variation for the posterior distribution is

$$\frac{1}{\sqrt{a'}} = \frac{1}{\sqrt{400}} = \frac{1}{20} = \mathbf{0.05}.$$

Chapter 4

Bühlmann Approximation and Empirical Bayes

The purpose of this chapter is to discuss applications of the Bayesian framework that was developed in chapter 3. When the prior and the model are not **conjugate**, the Bayesian procedure becomes too time consuming and may require numerical methods. Instead, Bühlmann's approximation is aimed at deriving a simple model, usually presenting the credibility as a linear combination of the sample mean obtained from observations and expected hypothetical mean that incorporates prior distribution of the parameter.

When prior and model are conjugate, the approximation often leads to the **same** credibility premium as the initial Bayesian procedure.

Analysis becomes more complicated when a prior distribution is not specified. This situation is dealt with using the **empirical Bayes** or **non-parametric** technique approach. The advantage of this approach is that it allows one to derive statistical conclusions about the posterior moments for the parameter of interest based only on observed data.

In this chapter readers will get exposed to applications of linear regression that are essentially simplified with Bühlmann's framework. In addition, readers will observe how the empirical Bayes technique is combined with Bühlmann's approximation to develop statistical conclusions required for credibility.

Exercises will allow readers to test their knowledge and deepen their understanding of the material.

4.1   Bühlmann Approximation

In credibility theory the Bühlmann model is a random effects model (also known as **variance components model** or **hierarchical linear model**) used to determine the appropriate premium for a group of insurance contracts. The model is named after Hans Bühlmann, who first published its description in 1967[4].

Suppose that the prior distribution of parameter θ is **known** with a **pdf** or **pmf** $\pi(\theta)$ and suppose that observations $\mathbf{X} = \{X_i,\ i = 1, 2, \ldots, n\}$ are, conditionally, given $(\Theta = \theta)$, independent with the common **pdf** or **pmf** $f(x|\theta)$.

Let us define the Bühlmann approximation of the conditional expectation after observing n conditionally independent records.

4.1.1 Elements of the Bühlmann Approximation

The following elements of the Bühlmann approximation are used to estimate the credibility premium:

1. **Hypothetical mean (HM):**

$$\mu\left(\theta\right) = \mathbf{E}\left[X\,|\theta\right]$$

2. **Process variance (PV):**

$$v\left(\theta\right) = \mathbf{Var}\left(X|\theta\right)$$

3. **Expected hypothetical mean (EHM):**

$$\mu = \mathbf{E}\left[\mu\left(\Theta\right)\right]$$

4. **Expected process variance (EPV):**

$$v = \mathbf{E}\left[v\left(\Theta\right)\right]$$

5. **Variance of hypothetical mean (VHM):**

$$a = \mathbf{Var}\left[\mu\left(\Theta\right)\right]$$

Note that

$$\mathbf{Var}\left(X\right) = \mathbf{E}\left[\mathbf{Var}\left(X|\theta\right)\right] + \mathbf{Var}\left(\mathbf{E}\left[X|\theta\right]\right) = v + a. \tag{4.1}$$

4.1.2 Bühlmann Approximation of the Credibility Premium

Let **Bühlmann's k** be defined as

$$k = \frac{v}{a}.$$

Define **Bühlmann's credibility factor** as

$$Z = \frac{n}{n+k} = \frac{n}{n+v/a} = \frac{na}{na+v},$$

where n is the sample size.

Then the Bühlmann approximation for $\mathbf{E}\left[Y\,|\mathbf{X}\right]$ is defined as

$$\hat{Y} = Z \cdot \bar{X} + \left(1 - Z\right) \cdot \mu, \text{ where } \hat{Y} = X_{n+1}. \tag{4.2}$$

If $a = 0$, then set $Z = 0$ and $\hat{Y} = \mu$.

4.2   Interpretation of Bühlmann's Approximation

Suppose that a sample $\{X_i,\ i = 1, 2, \ldots, n\}$ is collected.

Its common density function (or **model**), $f(x|\theta)$, depends on a parameter θ viewed as a random variable with the specified prior distribution $\pi(\theta)$.

The expectation of a new observation, $Y = X_{n+1}$, is going to be predicted using a linear regression technique, as follows:

By the double expectation rule, $\mu = \mathbf{E}(X_i) = \mathbf{E}[\mu(\Theta)]$ is the common expectation of an observable value from the sample.

Consider a linear space spanned over the random variables

$$\mathbf{L} = \mathbf{LIN}\{\mathbf{1},\ X_1,\ X_2,\ \ldots,\ X_n\}$$

and derive the projection of $Y = X_{n+1}$ onto this space. The linear regression technique proposed by Bühlmann can be interpreted as the orthogonal projection of $Y - \mu$ onto the subspace of centered variables,

$$\{X_i - \mu;\ i = 1, 2, \ldots, n\}.$$

Such a projection always exists, as follows, from geometric considerations, even if the corresponding covariance matrix is singular. Moreover, due to the identities for covariance, the following lemma is true.

Lemma 4.2.1 *For any pair* $i \neq j$,

$$\boldsymbol{COV}[X_i, X_j] = \boldsymbol{VHM} = a. \tag{4.3}$$

In particular, this identity is true for the potentially observable $Y = X_{n+1}$.

Proof. Recall that the random variables $\{X_i,\ i = 1, 2, \ldots, n\}$ are, conditionally, given $(\Theta = \theta)$, independent with the common **pdf** or **pmf** $f(x|\theta)$. Thus,

$$\mathbf{E}\left[X_i|\Theta\right] = \mathbf{E}\left[X_j|\Theta\right] = \mu(\Theta), \quad \forall i, j.$$

By the double expectation formula we have

$$\mathbf{E}[X_i \cdot X_j] = \mathbf{E}\left[\mathbf{E}\left[X_i \cdot X_j|\Theta\right]\right].$$

Since $(X_i|\Theta)$ and $(X_j|\Theta)$ are conditionally independent, the last equality can be written as

$$\mathbf{E}\left[\mathbf{E}\left[X_i \cdot X_j|\Theta\right]\right] = \mathbf{E}\left[\mathbf{E}\left[X_i|\Theta\right] \cdot \mathbf{E}\left[X_j|\Theta\right]\right] = \mathbf{E}\left[\mu(\Theta)^2\right].$$

Similarly,

$$\mathbf{E}[X_i] \cdot \mathbf{E}[X_j] = \mathbf{E}\left[\mathbf{E}\left[X_i|\Theta\right]\right] \cdot \mathbf{E}\left[\mathbf{E}\left[X_j|\Theta\right]\right] = \mathbf{E}\left[\mu(\Theta)\right]^2.$$

By definition of the covariance,

$$\mathbf{COV}[X_i, X_j] = \mathbf{E}\left[\mathbf{E}\left[X_i \cdot X_j|\Theta\right]\right] - \mathbf{E}[X_i] \cdot \mathbf{E}[X_j] = \mathbf{E}\left[\mu(\Theta)^2\right] - \mathbf{E}\left[\mu(\Theta)\right]^2 =$$
$$= \mathbf{Var}\left[\mu\left(\Theta\right)\right] = \mathbf{VHM} = a.$$

The diagonal elements of the variance-covariance matrix coincide with the variance of X_i, which equals

$$\mathbf{Var}[X_i] = v + u, \qquad (4.4)$$

according to (4.1).

Any permutation of $\{X_i : 1 \leq i \leq n\}$ will have the same variance-covariance matrix, so the linear regression of Y onto $\mathbf{L}$ will also be invariant about permutations of observed values. This fact allows us to simplify the regression model by setting it up as

$$\hat{Y} = \alpha_0 + \alpha_1 \cdot \sum_{i=1}^{n} X_i.$$

If $\bar{X}$ is the sample mean of observed values,

$$\bar{X} = \frac{1}{n} \sum_{i=1}^{n} X_i,$$

then the model can be written as

$$\hat{Y} = \alpha_0 + \beta \cdot \bar{X}, \text{ where } \beta = n\alpha_1. \qquad (4.5)$$

Taking the expected value of both sides in equation (4.5), we have

$$\mu = \alpha_0 + \beta\mu \Rightarrow \alpha_0 = (1 - \beta)\mu.$$

It follows then, that

$$\hat{Y} = (1 - \beta)\mu + \beta \cdot \bar{X}. \qquad (4.6)$$

Such a simplified model can be obtained by means of a simple linear regression of Y onto a plane (two-dimensional subspace) spanned over $\{\mathbf{1}, \bar{X}\}$.

Taking the covariance of Y with $\bar{X}$ in (4.5), we obtain

$$\mathbf{COV}\left[Y, \bar{X}\right] = \mathbf{COV}[\alpha_0 + \beta \cdot \bar{X}, \bar{X}] = \beta\, \mathbf{Var}[\bar{X}]. \qquad (4.7)$$

Note that

$$\mathbf{COV}[Y, \bar{X}] = \mathbf{COV}[Y, X_1] = a.$$

In addition,

$$\mathbf{Var}\left[\sum_{i=1}^{n} X_i\right] = n \cdot \mathbf{Var}[X_1] + n(n-1)\mathbf{COV}[X_i, X_j] = n \cdot (v+a) + n(n-1)a = nv + n^2 a.$$

Therefore,

$$\mathbf{Var}[\bar{X}] = \frac{nv + n^2 a}{n^2} = \frac{v + na}{n}.$$

Thus, equation (4.7) can be rewritten as

$$a = \beta \cdot \frac{v + na}{n} \Rightarrow \beta = \frac{na}{na + v}.$$

In Bühlmann's notation, the coefficient β was denoted as Z and the formula in (4.6) can be written as

$$\hat{Y} = Z \cdot \bar{X} + (1 - Z) \cdot \mu. \tag{4.8}$$

Note that Z is a measure of **partial credibility** based on a sample of size n, while μ corresponds to the **full credibility** based on the **manual premium**. In other words, if $Z = 0$, which can occur if $a = 0$, then $\hat{Y} = \mu$. However, usually the covariance between distinct observations does not vanish, so formula (4.8) provides a reasonable compromise between μ as the manual premium and $\bar{X}$ as the average of observed values.

4.3   From Bayesian to Bühlmann Credibility

Chapter 3 contains numerous examples of a Bayesian approach to credibility, assuming that the prior and model form a **conjugate** pair. The Bühlmann approximation approach may be applied to these examples as well.

Assume that a sample $\mathbf{X} = \{X_i : \ 1 \leq i \leq n\}$ is described by a model, $f(x\,|\theta)$, with parameter θ viewed as a random variable having prior density, $\Theta \sim \pi(\theta)$. Let $Y = X_{n+1}$ be the next observation, so that variables, $\{\mathbf{X}, Y\}$, given $\Theta = \theta$, are independent with the same common probability function, $f(x\,|\theta)$. All examples considered in chapter 3 operated with the statistic

$$W = \sum_{i=1}^{n} X_i = n \cdot \bar{X},$$

while its observed value, $w = n \cdot \bar{x}$ was used in credibility evaluation.

Let us define the credibility premium using formula (4.8) as

$$\mathbf{E}[Y|\mathbf{X}] = Z \cdot \bar{X} + (1 - Z) \cdot \mu, \tag{4.9}$$

where the unconditional mean, $\mu = \mathbf{E}[Y]$, can be evaluated using the double expectation rule as

$$\mu = \mathbf{E}\left[\mathbf{E}\left[Y|\Theta\right]\right].$$

The following examples provide illustrations to the situations when both the Bayesian (**exact credibility**) approach and Bühlmann's approximation result in the same expression for the estimated value of a new observation, $Y = X_{n+1}$, as well as when exact calculations are either too time consuming or require numerical methods.

4.4   Examples of Bühlmann Approximation

We will start by considering a few prior and model pairs that produce the same credibility premium and finish with a couple of examples where it can be calculated with only one approach.

4.4.1   Beta Prior and Geometric Model

The conjugate pair **Beta** $[\alpha, \beta]$ prior and **Geom** $[q]$ model was studied in section 3.6. Calculating $\mu = \mathbf{E}[Y]$, we have $\mu = \beta/(\alpha - 1)$, while the credibility premium derived in section 3.6 was given by 3.12 as

$$\mathbf{E}[Y|\mathbf{X}=\mathbf{x}] = \mathbf{E}[Y|W=w] - \frac{w+\beta}{n+\alpha-1}.$$

Let the Bühlmann credibility factor be

$$Z = \frac{n}{n+\alpha-1} \Rightarrow 1-Z = \frac{\alpha-1}{n+\alpha-1}.$$

Then

$$Z \cdot \bar{x} + (1-Z) \cdot \mu = \frac{n}{n+\alpha-1} \cdot \frac{w}{n} + \frac{\alpha-1}{n+\alpha-1} \cdot \frac{\beta}{\alpha-1} =$$

$$= \frac{w}{n+\alpha-1} + \frac{\beta}{n+\alpha-1} = \frac{w+\beta}{n+\alpha-1},$$

which coincides with the credibility premium in (3.12).

4.4.2 Gamma Prior and Poisson Model

The conjugate pair **Gamma**$[r,\theta]$ prior and **Poi**$[\lambda]$ model was studied in section 3.7. Calculating $\mu = \mathbf{E}[Y]$, we have $\mu = r\theta$, while the credibility premium derived in section 3.7 was given by 3.19 as

$$\mathbf{E}[Y|\mathbf{X}=\mathbf{x}] = \mathbf{E}[Y|W=w] = (w+r) \cdot \frac{\theta}{n\theta+1}.$$

Let the Bühlmann credibility factor be

$$Z = \frac{n\theta}{n\theta+1} \Rightarrow 1-Z = \frac{1}{n\theta+1}.$$

Then

$$Z \cdot \bar{x} + (1-Z) \cdot \mu = \frac{n\theta}{n\theta+1} \cdot \frac{w}{n} + \frac{1}{n\theta+1} \cdot r\theta = (w+r) \cdot \frac{\theta}{n\theta+1},$$

which coincides with the credibility premium in 3.19.

4.4.3 Normal Prior and Normal Model

The conjugate pair $\mathbf{N}(\mu,\tau^2)$ prior and $\mathbf{N}(\lambda,\sigma^2)$ model was studied in section 3.8. Calculating $\mu = \mathbf{E}[Y]$, we have $\mu = \mu$, while the credibility premium derived in section 3.8 was given by 3.24 as

$$\mathbf{E}[Y|\mathbf{X}=\mathbf{x}] = \mathbf{E}[Y|W=w] = \frac{w\tau^2+\mu\sigma^2}{n\tau^2+\sigma^2}.$$

Let the Bühlmann credibility factor be

$$Z = \frac{n\tau^2}{n\tau^2+\sigma^2} \Rightarrow 1-Z = \frac{\sigma^2}{n\tau^2+\sigma^2}.$$

Then

$$Z \cdot \bar{x} + (1-Z) \cdot \mu = \frac{n\tau^2}{n\tau^2+\sigma^2} \cdot \frac{w}{n} + \frac{\sigma^2}{n\tau^2+\sigma^2} \cdot \mu = \frac{w\tau^2+\mu\sigma^2}{n\tau^2+\sigma^2},$$

which coincides with the credibility premium in 3.24.

4.4.4 Beta Prior and Bernoulli Model

The conjugate pair **Beta**$[a, b]$ prior and **Bin**$[1, q]$ model was studied in section 3.9. Calculating $\mu = \mathbf{E}[Y]$, we have $\mu = a/(a + b)$, while the credibility premium derived in section 3.9 was given by 3.30 as

$$\mathbf{E}[Y|\mathbf{X} = \mathbf{x}] = \mathbf{E}[Y|W = w] = \frac{w + a}{n + a + b}.$$

Let the Bühlmann credibility factor be

$$Z = \frac{n}{n + a + b} \Rightarrow 1 - Z = \frac{a + b}{n + a + b}.$$

Then

$$Z \cdot \bar{x} + (1 - Z) \cdot \mu = \frac{n}{n + a + b} \cdot \frac{w}{n} + \frac{a + b}{n + a + b} \cdot \frac{a}{a + b} = \frac{w + a}{n + a + b},$$

which coincides with the credibility premium in 3.30.

4.4.5 Beta Prior and Binomial Model

The conjugate pair **Beta**$[a, b]$ prior and **Bin**$[m, q]$ model was studied in section 3.10. Calculating $\mu = \mathbf{E}[Y]$, we have $\mu = ma/(a + b)$, while the credibility premium derived in section 3.10 was given by 3.35 as

$$\mathbf{E}[Y|\mathbf{X} = \mathbf{x}] = \mathbf{E}[Y|W = w] = \frac{m(w + a)}{nm + a + b}.$$

Let the Bühlmann credibility factor be

$$Z = \frac{mn}{mn + a + b} \Rightarrow 1 - Z = \frac{a + b}{mn + a + b}.$$

Then

$$Z \cdot \bar{x} + (1 - Z) \cdot \mu = \frac{mn}{mn + a + b} \cdot \frac{w}{n} + \frac{a + b}{mn + a + b} \cdot \frac{ma}{a + b} = \frac{m(w + a)}{nm + a + b},$$

which coincides with the credibility premium in 3.35.

4.4.6 Inverse Gamma Prior and Exponential Model

The conjugate pair **Inv Gamma**$[a, b]$ prior and **Exp**$[\theta]$ model was studied in section 3.11. Calculating $\mu = \mathbf{E}[Y]$, we have $\mu = b/(a - 1)$, while the credibility premium derived in section 3.11 was given by 3.40 as

$$\mathbf{E}[Y|\mathbf{X} = \mathbf{x}] = \mathbf{E}[Y|W = w] = \frac{w + b}{n + a - 1}.$$

Let the Bühlmann credibility factor be

$$Z = \frac{n}{n + a - 1} \Rightarrow 1 - Z = \frac{a - 1}{n + a - 1}.$$

Then

$$Z \cdot \bar{x} + (1 - Z) \cdot \mu = \frac{n}{n + a - 1} \cdot \frac{w}{n} + \frac{a - 1}{n + a - 1} \cdot \frac{b}{a - 1} = \frac{w + b}{n + a - 1},$$

which coincides with the credibility premium in 3.40.

4.4.7 Inverse Gamma Prior and Gamma Model

The conjugate pair **Gamma**$[a, b]$ prior and **Gamma**$[\alpha, \theta]$ model was studied in section 3.13. Calculating $\mu = \mathbf{E}[Y]$, we have $\mu = \alpha b/(a - 1)$, while the credibility premium derived in section 3.13 was given by 3.45 as

$$\mathbf{E}[Y|\mathbf{X} = \mathbf{x}] = \mathbf{E}[Y|W = w] = \frac{(w + b)\alpha}{n\alpha + a - 1}.$$

Let the Bühlmann credibility factor be

$$Z = \frac{n\alpha}{n\alpha + a - 1} \Rightarrow 1 - Z = \frac{a - 1}{n\alpha + a - 1}.$$

Then

$$Z \cdot \bar{x} + (1 - Z) \cdot \mu = \frac{n\alpha}{n\alpha + a - 1} \cdot \frac{w}{n} + \frac{a - 1}{n\alpha + a - 1} \cdot \frac{\alpha b}{a - 1} = \frac{(w + b)\alpha}{n\alpha + a - 1},$$

which coincides with the credibility premium in 3.45.

4.4.8 Exact Credibility versus Bühlmann: Beta and Geometric

Suppose that a random variable Q has prior distribution **Beta**$[a = 3, b = 2]$ with density

$$\pi(q) = 12q^2(1 - q),$$

and the model for the conditional random variable $(X|Q)$ is **geometric**. Thus, for each given $Q = q$, $(X|Q)$ is the number of exposures before the first claim with probability mass function

$$f(x|q) = (1 - q)^x \cdot q, \quad x = 0, 1, 2, \ldots.$$

After observing $\mathbf{X} = \{X_i : 1 \leq i \leq n\}$, let us estimate the new observation $Y = X_{n+1}$ using both the Bayesian approach and Bühlmann's approximation.

Starting with the **Bayesian credibility approach**, note that the prior and the model form a conjugate pair. By definition, if the posterior distributions $\pi(q|x)$ are in the same probability distribution family as the prior probability distribution $\pi(q)$, the prior and posterior are then called conjugate distributions and the prior is called a conjugate prior for the likelihood function.

By Bayes' theorem, the posterior distribution is

$$\pi(Q = q|\mathbf{X} = \mathbf{x}) = \frac{\pi(Q = q)f(\mathbf{X} = \mathbf{x}|Q = q)}{f(\mathbf{X} = \mathbf{x})},$$

where

$$f(\mathbf{X} = \mathbf{x}|Q = q) = \prod_{i=1}^{n} f(X_i|q) = (1 - q)^w \cdot q^n,$$

$w = \sum_{i=1}^{n} x_i$ is the value of the random variable, $W = \sum_{i=1}^{n} X_i$ and

$$f(\mathbf{X} = \mathbf{x}) = \int \pi(q)f(\mathbf{x}|q) \, dq.$$

The posterior density of $(Q|\mathbf{X})$ is proportional to

$$[(1-q)^w \cdot q^n] \cdot q^2(1-q) = q^{n+2} \cdot (1-q)^{w+1},$$

which implies $(Q|\mathbf{X})$ is $\mathbf{Beta}[a' = n+3, b' = w+2]$.

Thus, the prior and the model form a conjugate pair.

Since $(Y|Q = q)$ is geometric, the conditional expectation of $(Y|Q = q)$ is

$$\mathbf{E}[Y|Q = q] = \frac{1-q}{q}.$$

We have shown in lemma 3.6.1 of section 3.6 that if Q has the distribution $\mathbf{Beta}[a, b]$, with $a > 2$, then

$$\mathbf{E}\left[\frac{1-Q}{Q}\right] = \frac{b}{a-1} \quad \text{and} \quad \mathbf{Var}\left[\frac{1-Q}{Q}\right] = \frac{b(a+b-1)}{(a-1)^2(a-2)}. \tag{4.10}$$

Since the posterior distribution is $\mathbf{Beta}[a' = n+3, b' = w+2]$, equation (4.10) for the posterior mean yields

$$\hat{Y} = \hat{X}_{n+1} = \tilde{\mathbf{E}}[Y] = \mathbf{E}_Q[\mathbf{E}_Y[Y|Q]] = \mathbf{E}_Q\left[\frac{1-Q}{Q}\right] = \frac{b'}{a'-1} = \frac{w+2}{n+2} =$$

$$= \frac{1}{n+2} \cdot \left(\sum_{i=1}^n x_i + 2\right). \tag{4.11}$$

Estimating Y using the **Bühlmann's approximation**, we have

$$\mathbf{HM} = \mu(q) = \mathbf{E}[X|Q = q] = \frac{1-q}{q} \quad \text{and} \quad \mathbf{PV} = v(q) = \mathbf{Var}(X|Q = q) = \frac{1-q}{q^2}.$$

Since $Q \sim \mathbf{Beta}[a = 3, b = 2]$,

$$\mathbf{EHM} = \mu = \mathbf{E}[\mu(Q)] = \mathbf{E}\left[\frac{1-Q}{Q}\right] = \frac{b}{a-1} = 1.$$

Similarly,

$$\mathbf{EPV} = v = \mathbf{E}[v(Q)] = \mathbf{E}\left[\frac{1-Q}{Q^2}\right] = 12\int_0^1 \frac{1-q}{q^2} \cdot q^2(1-q)\, dq =$$

$$= 12\int_0^1 (1-q)^2\, dq = -4(1-q)^3\big|_0^1 = 4.$$

The variance of hypothetical mean is

$$a = \mathbf{VHM} = \mathbf{Var}(\mu(Q)) = \mathbf{Var}\left(\frac{1-Q}{Q}\right) = \frac{b(a+b-1)}{(a-1)^2(a-2)} = \frac{2 \cdot 4}{4} = 2.$$

Combining these values into the Bühlmann's formula, we obtain

$$k = \frac{v}{a} = \frac{4}{2} = 2 \quad \text{and} \quad Z = \frac{n}{n+k} = \frac{n}{n+2}, \quad 1-Z = \frac{2}{n+2}$$

and thus (4.8) results in

$$\hat{Y} = Z \cdot \bar{x} + (1 - Z)\mu = \frac{n}{n+2} \cdot \bar{x} + \frac{2}{n+2} \cdot 1 = \frac{1}{n+2} \left(\sum_{i=1}^{n} x_i + 2 \right).$$

This estimate is identical to the Bayesian credibility derived in equation (4.11).

4.4.9 Exact Credibility and No Bühlmann: Beta and Geometric

To provide an example when Bühlmann's approximation does not exist, consider the case similar to the previous one, when the prior density is **Beta**$[a = 2,\ b = 3]$ so that

$$\pi(q) = 12q \left(1 - q \right)^2 \quad \text{for } 0 < q < 1.$$

As before, assume that the model is geometric:

$$f(x|q) = (1 - q)^x q \quad \text{for } x = 0,\ 1,\ \dots$$

Similar to the argument in the previous example, Bayesian credibility results in posterior density $\pi(q|\mathbf{X} = \mathbf{x})$ proportional to

$$(1 - q)^w \cdot q^n \cdot q (1 - q)^2 = (1 - q)^{w+2} \cdot q^{n+1}, \quad w = \sum_{i=1}^{n} x_i,$$

which leads to the conclusion that $(Q|X)$ has beta distribution, with parameters

$$a' = n + 2 \quad \text{and} \quad b' = w + 3.$$

Thus, the Bayesian credibility becomes

$$\tilde{\mathbf{E}}[Y] = \frac{b'}{a' - 1} = \frac{w + 3}{n + 2 - 1} = \frac{w + 3}{n + 1}.$$

However, Bühlmann's method fails, because the variance of $(1 - Q)/Q$ does not exist in this case and, thus, $a =$ **VHM** cannot be calculated.

The Bühlmann's approximation becomes especially helpful when the prior distribution of Θ, expressed through $\pi(\theta)$, and the model, characterized by $f(x|\theta)$, **do not** form a conjugate pair.

4.4.10 Prior and Model Are Not Conjugate

The following example demonstrates the case when Bühlmann's technique works, but Bayesian calculations may require numerical methods.

Suppose that the prior for Q is still **Beta** $[a = 3,\ b = 2]$ so that

$$\pi(q) = 12q^2 \cdot (1 - q) \quad \text{for } 0 < q < 1.$$

The model for claim severity is exponential with the mean reciprocal to q so that

$$f(x|q) = q \cdot e^{-qx} \quad \text{for } x > 0.$$

Again, assume that the sample

$$\mathbf{X} = \{X_i : 1 \le i \le n\}$$

is collected and the objective is to approximate the expected value of $Y = X_{n+1}$, using the data and Bühlmann's technique.

Since the model is exponential, it follows that

$$\mathbf{HM} = \mu(q) = \mathbf{E}\left[X|Q = q\right] = \frac{1}{q}$$

$$\mathbf{PV} = v(q) = \mathbf{Var}\left(X|Q = q\right) = \frac{1}{q^2}$$

$$\mathbf{VHM} = a = \mathbf{Var}[\mu(Q)] = \mathbf{Var}\left[Q^{-1}\right].$$

Since by (4.10)

$$\mathbf{E}\left[\frac{1-Q}{Q}\right] = \mathbf{E}\left[\frac{1}{Q}\right] - 1,$$

it follows that

$$\mathbf{E}\left[\frac{1}{Q}\right] = \mathbf{E}\left[\frac{1-Q}{Q}\right] + 1 = \frac{b}{a-1} + 1 = \frac{a+b-1}{a-1}.$$

Similarly, by (4.10)

$$\mathbf{Var}\left[\frac{1-Q}{Q}\right] = \mathbf{Var}\left[\frac{1}{Q}\right] = \frac{b(a+b-1)}{(a-1)^2(a-2)}.$$

Calculating $\mathbf{E}\left[1/Q^2\right]$, we obtain

$$\mathbf{E}\left[\frac{1}{Q^2}\right] = \mathbf{Var}\left[\frac{1}{Q}\right] + \left(\mathbf{E}\left[\frac{1}{Q}\right]\right)^2 = \frac{b(a+b-1)}{(a-1)^2(a-2)} + \left(\frac{a+b-1}{a-1}\right)^2 =$$

$$= \frac{(a+b-1)(a+b-2)}{(a-1)(a-2)}.$$

Thus,

$$\mu = \mathbf{EHM} = \mathbf{E}[Q^{-1}] = \frac{a+b-1}{a-1} = \frac{4}{2} = 2$$

$$a = \mathbf{VHM} = \mathbf{Var}\left[Q^{-1}\right] = \frac{b(a+b-1)}{(a-1)^2(a-2)} = \frac{2\cdot 4}{4} = 2$$

$$v = \mathbf{EPV} = \mathbf{E}[Q^{-2}] = \frac{(a+b-1)(a+b-2)}{(a-1)(a-2)} = \frac{4\cdot 3}{2} = 6.$$

Calculating Bühlmann's k and credibility factor, we obtain

$$k = \frac{v}{a} = 3, \quad Z = \frac{n}{n+k} = \frac{n}{n+3} \quad \text{and} \quad 1 - Z = \frac{3}{n+3}.$$

Therefore, using (4.1), the Bühlmann's approximation for $\mathbf{E}[Y]$ is

$$\hat{Y} = \frac{n}{n+3}\cdot \bar{X} + \frac{3}{n+3}\cdot \mu = \frac{1}{n+3}\left[\sum_{i=1}^{n} X_i + 3\right].$$

Let us show that the Bayesian credibility approach proves to be challenging in this case.

Suppose that a single observation $X = x$ is given. Then the Bühlmann's approximation for $\mathbf{E}[Y]$ will be:

$$\hat{Y} = \frac{X + 3}{4}.$$

Using the Bayesian credibility approach, we calculate posterior distribution of Q as

$$\pi(q|x) = \frac{\pi(q) \cdot f(x|q)}{f(x)} = \frac{12q^2(1-q) \cdot qe^{-qx}}{f(x)} = \frac{12q^3(1-q)e^{-qx}}{f(x)},$$

where the denominator is marginal density of X:

$$f(x) = 12 \int_0^1 q^3(1-q)e^{-qx}\,dq$$

Since $\mathbf{E}[Y|Q = q] = q^{-1}$, the value of Bayesian credibility premium is expressed as posterior expectation of Y, which is

$$\tilde{\mathbf{E}}[Y] = \int_0^1 \mathbf{E}[Y|Q = q] \cdot \pi(q|x)\,dq = \frac{\int_0^1 q^2(1-q)e^{-qx}\,dq}{\int_0^1 q^3(1-q)e^{-qx}\,dq}.$$

Taking these integrals we obtain an expression that is not equal to $(x+3)/4$.

That is why Bühlmann's approximation may be a reasonable compromise that works equally well for a single observation $X = x$ and for a given sample of n records.

4.5 Empirical Bayes Approach

When the prior distribution of the parameter θ is **unknown**, the empirical Bayes approach suggested by Herbert Robbins[5] proposes to use the **empirical** distribution based on the sample $\mathbf{X}$, which, in some cases, allows one to **estimate** the posterior mean in (3.1). Instead of **specified** prior density $\pi(\theta)$ we assume that the observation X_i, given $\Theta = \theta_i$, has the distribution $f(x|\theta_i)$ with unknown parameter values, $\{\Theta_1, \Theta_2, \ldots, \Theta_n\}$, treated as independent identically distributed variables with the common **pdf** equal to $\pi(\theta)$.

4.5.1 Poisson Model with Unknown Prior Distribution

To illustrate how the empirical Bayes technique works, let X represent the counts of claims per insured (or for the same insured per given year), so that X_i is the observation associated with the individual policy i. Here, i varies from 1 to n and X_i values are integers varying from 0 to some value.

Suppose the model $(X|\Lambda)$ is Poisson with parameter Λ. Then

$$f(x|\lambda) = \frac{1}{x!} \lambda^x e^{-\lambda} \quad \text{for} \quad x = 0, 1, 2, \ldots \tag{4.12}$$

is the conditional probability of the event $[X = x|\Lambda = \lambda]$.

Suppose that the prior distribution of Λ is unknown and its density at $\lambda > 0$ is denoted as $\pi(\lambda)$.

By the law of total probability (2.2), the marginal probability of $[X = x]$ can be calculated as

$$\mathbf{P}[X = x] = \int_0^\infty f(x \,|\, \lambda) \cdot \pi(\lambda) \, d\lambda = \frac{1}{x!} \int_0^\infty \lambda^x e^{-\lambda} \pi(\lambda) \, d\lambda. \qquad (4.13)$$

Assume that the sample $\mathbf{X}$ is already summarized so that for each value x the corresponding count $n(x)$ shows how often this value appeared in the sample.

If Y represents the new record associated with the previously observed insured, for which the value $X = x$ was observed, the conditional expectation $\mathbf{E}[Y \,|\, X = x]$ can be found as follows:

$$\mathbf{E}[Y \,|\, X = x] = \frac{\int_0^\infty \lambda f(x \,|\, \lambda) \pi(\lambda) \, d\lambda}{\mathbf{P}[X = x]} = \frac{\int_0^\infty \lambda f(x \,|\, \lambda) \pi(\lambda) \, d\lambda}{\int_0^\infty f(x \,|\, \lambda) \pi(\lambda) \, d\lambda} \qquad (4.14)$$

Rewriting the numerator of (4.14), we have

$$\int_0^\infty \lambda f(x \,|\, \lambda) \pi(\lambda) \, d\lambda = \int_0^\infty \lambda \frac{1}{x!} \lambda^x e^{-\lambda} \pi(\lambda) \, d\lambda = \frac{1}{x!} \int_0^\infty \lambda^{x+1} e^{-\lambda} \pi(\lambda) \, d\lambda =$$

$$= (x+1) \cdot \frac{1}{(x+1)!} \int_0^\infty \lambda^{x+1} e^{-\lambda} \pi(\lambda) \, d\lambda = (x+1) \times \mathbf{P}[X = x+1].$$

Therefore,

$$\mathbf{E}[Y \,|\, X = x] = (x+1) \cdot \frac{\mathbf{P}[X = x+1]}{\mathbf{P}[X = x]}.$$

Had we known the prior distribution, it would be a simple task to evaluate the numerator and denominator in (4.14).

For an unknown prior distribution, Robbins[5] proposes to use the **empirical** distribution based on the sample $\mathbf{X}$.

Then the empirical Bayes formula is

$$\hat{\mathbf{E}}[Y \,|\, X = x] = (x+1) \cdot \frac{n(x+1)}{n(x)},$$

which is well defined for all x values, except for the maximal one. That is a technical difficulty that slightly limits the applicability of this method. However, as Robbins mentions, the accuracy of the empirical Bayes estimate increases as the sample size becomes large.

4.6   Empirical Bayes Estimate for Bühlmann

When the prior distribution of θ is **unknown**, we need to use the empirical Bayes approach, which in some situations can be easily adjusted for commonly used models.

4.6.1 Sample Summaries

After a sample ($\mathbf{X}$) of size n is collected, the following sums are calculated. They play an essential role in the empirical Bayes approach to the Bühlmann approximation of the Bayesian credibility.

1. **Sum and sample mean:** Let

$$A = \sum_{i=1}^{n} X_i.$$

Then the sample mean is

$$\bar{X} = \frac{1}{n} \sum_{i=1}^{n} X_i = \frac{A}{n}.$$

2. **Sum of squares and mean square:** Let

$$C = \sum_{i=1}^{n} X_i^2.$$

Then the mean square

$$B = \frac{1}{n} \sum_{i=1}^{n} X_i^2 = \overline{X^2} = \frac{C}{n}.$$

3. **Sample variance:** Let

$$S^2 = \frac{1}{n-1} \left(X_i - \bar{X} \right)^2 = \frac{1}{n-1} \left[\sum_{i=1}^{n} \left(X_i \right)^2 - n \left(\bar{X} \right)^2 \right] =$$

$$= \frac{n}{n-1} \left[B - \left(\bar{X} \right)^2 \right]. \tag{4.15}$$

4.6.2 Empirical Bayes Estimation of Bühlmann's Approximation

Since the prior distribution of the parameter θ is **unknown**, expectations in the Bühlmann formula will be replaced by their sample-based estimates. For Bühlmann factors, the "hat" - notation should be used to emphasize that they are **estimated** from the data.

The following elements of the Bühlmann approximation will now be estimated as follows:

1. **Estimated hypothetical mean (EHM):**

$$\hat{\mu} = \bar{X}$$

2. **Estimated process variance (EPV):**

$$\hat{v} = \hat{\mathbf{E}} \left[\mathbf{Var} \left(X \,|\, \theta \right) \right]$$

3. **Estimated variance of hypothetical mean (VHM):**

$$\hat{a} = S^2 - \hat{v} \tag{4.16}$$

4. **Estimated Bühlmann's** k:

$$\hat{k} = \frac{\hat{v}}{\hat{a}},$$

provided the denominator is positive.

5. **Estimated Bühlmann's credibility factor** Z:

$$\hat{Z} = \frac{m}{m + \hat{k}} = \frac{m\hat{a}}{m\hat{a} + \hat{v}},$$

where m is the number of observations.

Note that when $\hat{a} \leq 0$, the estimate for Bühlmann's Z will be set as $\hat{Z} = 0$.

6. **The empirical Bayes estimate** for the insured with record $X = x$ is

$$\hat{\mathbf{E}}[Y | X = x] = \hat{Z}x + \left(1 - \hat{Z}\right)\bar{X}. \tag{4.17}$$

4.7   Examples of Empirical Bayes Estimate

In this section we will evaluate the empirical Bayes estimate for several common distributions.

4.7.1   Empirical Bayes for Poisson Model

Suppose $(X|\Lambda)$ is Poisson with parameter Λ:

$$\mathbf{P}[X = x | \Lambda = \lambda] = \frac{1}{x!}\lambda^x e^{-\lambda}$$

Then

$$\mu(\Lambda) = \mathbf{E}[X|\Lambda] = \Lambda, \; v(\Lambda) = \mathbf{Var}(X|\Lambda) = \Lambda \Rightarrow \mu = v.$$

To estimate both μ and v, we use the same sample mean:

$$\hat{\mu} = \hat{\mathbf{E}}[\mathbf{E}[X|\Lambda]] = \hat{\mathbf{E}}[\Lambda] = \bar{X}$$

Similarly,

$$\hat{v} = \hat{\mathbf{E}}[\mathbf{Var}(X|\Lambda)] = \hat{\mathbf{E}}[\Lambda] = \bar{X}.$$

To determine $\hat{a}$, we use the relationship (4.16):

$$\hat{a} = S^2 - \hat{v} = S^2 - \bar{X}$$

Estimating **Bühlmann's k**, we have

$$\hat{k} = \frac{\hat{v}}{\hat{a}} = \frac{\bar{X}}{S^2 - \bar{X}}.$$

Estimating **Bühlmann's** credibility factor Z, we obtain

$$\hat{Z} = \frac{m}{m + \hat{k}} = \frac{n}{m + \bar{X}/\left(S^2 - \bar{X}\right)} = \frac{m\left(S^2 - \bar{X}\right)}{m\left(S^2 - \bar{X}\right) + \bar{X}}$$

$$1 - \hat{Z} = 1 - \frac{m}{m + \bar{X}/\left(S^2 - \bar{X}\right)} = \frac{\bar{X}/\left(S^2 - \bar{X}\right)}{m + \bar{X}/\left(S^2 - \bar{X}\right)} = \frac{\bar{X}}{m\left(S^2 - \bar{X}\right) + \bar{X}}.$$

Then the empirical Bayes estimate for the insured with record $X = x$ is

$$\hat{\mathbf{E}}\left[Y \,|X = x\right] = \hat{Z}x + \left(1 - \hat{Z}\right)\bar{X} = \frac{m\left(S^2 - \bar{X}\right)}{m\left(S^2 - \bar{X}\right) + \bar{X}} \cdot x + \frac{\bar{X}^2}{m\left(S^2 - \bar{X}\right) + \bar{X}}.$$

If $m = 1$, we have

$$\hat{Z} = \frac{S^2 - \bar{X}}{S^2} = 1 - \frac{\bar{X}}{S^2}, \quad 1 - \hat{Z} = \frac{\bar{X}}{S^2} \Rightarrow$$

$$\hat{\mathbf{E}}\left[Y'|X = x\right] = \hat{Z}x + \left(1 - \hat{Z}\right)\bar{X} = \left(1 - \frac{\bar{X}}{S^2}\right)x + \frac{\bar{X}^2}{S^2}.$$

4.7.2 Empirical Bayes for Geometric Distribution

Suppose $(X|Q)$ is geometric, with parameter Q:

$$\mathbf{P}\left[X = x|Q = q\right] = (1 - q)^x \cdot q, \quad x = 0, 1, 2, \ldots$$

$$\mathbf{P}\left[X \geq x|Q = q\right] = \sum_{k=x}^{\infty}(1 - q)^k \cdot q = q\sum_{k=x}^{\infty}(1 - q)^k = q \cdot \frac{(1 - q)^x}{q} = (1 - q)^x$$

The prior distribution for Q is concentrated on the unit interval, since this parameter is the unknown probability. Let $\pi(q)$ be the unknown prior density.

By the properties of the geometric distribution,

$$\mathbf{E}\left[X \,|Q\right] = \frac{1 - Q}{Q} = \frac{1}{Q} - 1 \quad \text{and} \quad \mathbf{Var}\left[X \,|Q\right] = \frac{1 - Q}{Q^2} = \frac{1}{Q}\left(\frac{1}{Q} - 1\right).$$

By (3.2), the posterior density of Q, given $X = x$, is

$$\pi\left(q \,|x\right) = \frac{f\left(\mathbf{x} \,|q\right) \cdot \pi\left(q\right)}{f\left(\mathbf{x}\right)} = \frac{(1 - q)^x \cdot q \cdot \pi\left(q\right)}{\mathbf{P}\left[X = x\right]},$$

where the marginal probability is

$$\mathbf{P}\left[X = x\right] = \int_0^1 (1 - q)^x \cdot q \cdot \pi\left(q\right) \, dq.$$

Therefore, the posterior expectation is

$$\tilde{\mathbf{E}}\left[X\right] = \tilde{\mathbf{E}}\left[\mathbf{E}\left[X \,|Q\right]\right] = \tilde{\mathbf{E}}\left[\frac{1 - Q}{Q}\right] = \int_0^1 \frac{1 - q}{q} \cdot \pi\left(q \,|x\right) \, dq =$$

$$= \frac{1}{\mathbf{P}\left[X = x\right]} \cdot \int_0^1 \frac{1 - q}{q} \cdot (1 - q)^x \cdot q \cdot \pi\left(q\right) \, dq =$$

$$= \frac{1}{\mathbf{P}\left[X = x\right]} \cdot \int_0^1 (1 - q)^{x+1} \cdot \pi\left(q\right) \, dq = \frac{\mathbf{P}\left[X \geq x + 1\right]}{\mathbf{P}\left[X = x\right]}.$$

Thus, if the prior density were known, the conditional expectation of $(Y \,|\, X = x)$ would be

$$\tilde{\mathbf{E}}\left[Y \,|\, X = x\right] = \frac{\mathbf{P}\left[X \geq (x+1)\right]}{\mathbf{P}\left[X = x\right]}. \tag{4.18}$$

Applying the empirical (or semi-parametric) Bayes approach, the conditional expectation from (4.18) can be estimated as

$$\hat{\mathbf{E}}\left[Y \,|\, X = x\right] = \frac{n - \sum_{y \leq x} n\left(y\right)}{n\left(x\right)},$$

where $n\left(x\right)$ is the count of X values equal to x, and $n = \sum_y n\left(y\right)$ represents the sample size.

Since the range of the sample is limited, the sum $\sum_{y \leq x} n\left(y\right)$ is defined only for values x smaller than the maximal recorded number.

Calculating the elements of the Bühlmann approximation, we have the following:

1. **Hypothetical mean (HM):**

$$\mu\left(Q\right) = \mathbf{E}\left[X \,|\, Q\right] = \frac{1-Q}{Q}$$

2. **Process variance (PV):**

$$v\left(Q\right) = \mathbf{Var}\left[X \,|\, Q\right] = \frac{1-Q}{Q^2}$$

3. **Expected hypothetical mean (EHM):**

$$\mu = \mathbf{E}\left[\mu\left(Q\right)\right] = \mathbf{E}\left[\frac{1-Q}{Q}\right] = \mathbf{E}\left[Q^{-1}\right] - 1$$

4. **Expected process variance (EPV):**

$$v = \mathbf{E}\left[v\left(Q\right)\right] = \mathbf{E}\left[\frac{1-Q}{Q^2}\right] = \mathbf{E}\left[Q^{-2}\right] - \mathbf{E}\left[Q^{-1}\right]$$

5. **Variance of hypothetical mean (VHM):**

$$a = \mathbf{Var}\left(\mathbf{E}\left[X \,|\, Q\right]\right) = \mathbf{Var}\left(\frac{1-Q}{Q}\right) = \mathbf{Var}\left(Q^{-1}\right)$$

6. **Hypothetical second moment:**

$$\mathbf{E}\left[X^2 \,|\, Q\right] = \mathbf{Var}\left[X \,|\, Q\right] + \mathbf{E}\left[X \,|\, Q\right]^2 = \frac{1-Q}{Q^2} + \left(\frac{1-Q}{Q}\right)^2 =$$

$$= \frac{1-Q+1-2Q+Q^2}{Q^2} = \frac{Q^2 - 3Q + 2}{Q^2} = 1 - \frac{3}{Q} + \frac{2}{Q^2}$$

Therefore,

$$\mathbf{E}\left[X^2\right] = \mathbf{E}\left[\mathbf{E}\left[X^2 \,|\, Q\right]\right] = \mathbf{E}\left[1 - \frac{3}{Q} + \frac{2}{Q^2}\right] = 1 - 3\mathbf{E}\left[Q^{-1}\right] + 2\mathbf{E}\left[Q^{-2}\right].$$

Calculating the empirical estimates of the elements of the Bühlmann's approximation, we obtain the following:

1. **Estimated EHM:**

$$\hat{\mu} = \hat{\mathbf{E}}[X] = \bar{X},$$

where $\bar{X}$ is the sample mean of all observed values of X.

2. **Estimated EPV:**

The following lemma provides convenient expressions for elements of the EPV.

Lemma 4.7.1 *For a geometrically-distributed random variable $(X|Q)$, the estimated expected process variance is*

$$\hat{v} = \frac{1}{2}\left(\bar{X} + B\right),$$

where

$$\bar{X} = \frac{1}{n}\sum_{i=1}^{n} X_i \quad and \quad B = \frac{1}{n}\sum_{i=1}^{n} (X_i)^2.$$

Proof. Note that

$$\hat{v} = \hat{\mathbf{E}}\left[Q^{-2}\right] - \hat{\mathbf{E}}\left[Q^{-1}\right].$$

Calculating $\hat{\mathbf{E}}[Q^{-1}]$, we have

$$\hat{\mu} = \bar{X} = \hat{\mathbf{E}}\left[Q^{-1} - 1\right] = \hat{\mathbf{E}}\left[Q^{-1}\right] - 1 \Rightarrow \hat{\mathbf{E}}\left[Q^{-1}\right] = \bar{X} + 1.$$

Calculating $\hat{\mathbf{E}}[Q^{-2}]$, we have

$$\hat{\mathbf{E}}\left[X^2\right] = 1 - 3\hat{\mathbf{E}}\left[Q^{-1}\right] + 2\hat{\mathbf{E}}\left[Q^{-2}\right] \Rightarrow$$
$$\hat{\mathbf{E}}\left[Q^{-2}\right] = \frac{1}{2}\left(\hat{\mathbf{E}}\left[X^2\right] - 1 + 3\hat{\mathbf{E}}\left[Q^{-1}\right]\right).$$

Note that

$$\hat{\mathbf{E}}\left[X^2\right] = \frac{1}{n}\sum_{i=1}^{n} (X_i)^2 = B.$$

Therefore,

$$\hat{\mathbf{E}}\left[Q^{-2}\right] = \frac{1}{2}\left(B - 1 + 3\left(\bar{X} + 1\right)\right) = \frac{1}{2}\left(B + 2 + 3\bar{X}\right) = \frac{3}{2}\cdot\bar{X} + \frac{1}{2}B + 1.$$

Hence,

$$\hat{v} = \hat{\mathbf{E}}\left[Q^{-2}\right] - \hat{\mathbf{E}}\left[Q^{-1}\right] = \frac{3}{2}\cdot\bar{X} + \frac{1}{2}B + 1 - \bar{X} - 1 = \frac{1}{2}\bar{X} + \frac{1}{2}B = \frac{1}{2}\left(\bar{X} + B\right).$$

3. Estimated VHM:

The following lemma provides convenient expressions for elements of the VHM.

Lemma 4.7.2 *For a geometrically-distributed random variable $(X|Q)$, the estimated variance of hypothetical mean is*

$$\hat{a} = \frac{n}{n-1}\left[B - \left(\bar{X}\right)^2\right] - \frac{1}{2}\left(B + \bar{X}\right).$$

Proof. Recall that

$$v + a = \mathbf{Var}\left(X\right).$$

Therefore,

$$\hat{v} + \hat{a} = S^2,$$

where S^2 is the sample variance:

$$S^2 = \frac{1}{n-1}\left(X_i - \bar{X}\right)^2 = \frac{1}{n-1}\left[\sum_{i=1}^{n}\left(X_i\right)^2 - n\cdot\left(\bar{X}\right)^2\right] =$$

$$= \frac{n}{n-1}\left[B - \left(\bar{X}\right)^2\right] \tag{4.19}$$

Thus,

$$\hat{a} = S^2 - \hat{v} = \frac{n}{n-1}\left[B - \left(\bar{X}\right)^2\right] - \frac{1}{2}\left(B + \bar{X}\right).$$

If $\hat{a} < 0$, we set $\hat{a} = 0$.

Estimating **Bühlmann's** k we have

$$\hat{k} = \frac{\hat{v}}{\hat{a}} = \frac{0.5\left(B + \bar{X}\right)}{n/(n-1)\cdot\left[B - \left(\bar{X}\right)^2\right] - 0.5\left(B + \bar{X}\right)}.$$

Bühlmann's credibility factor is

$$\hat{Z} = \frac{m}{m + \hat{k}}.$$

If $\hat{a} < 0$, we set $\hat{Z} = 0$.

Then the empirical Bayes estimate for the insured with record $X = x$, is

$$\hat{\mathbf{E}}\left[Y|X = x\right] = \hat{Z}x + \left(1 - \hat{Z}\right)\bar{X}.$$

4.7.3 Empirical Bayes for Binomial Model

Suppose $(X|Q)$ has binomial distribution $\mathbf{Bin}\left[m, q\right]$, with the parameters Q and m, where m is specified:

$$\mathbf{P}\left[X = x|Q = q\right] = f\left(x|q\right) = \binom{m}{x}q^x(1-q)^{m-x} = \frac{m!}{x!\,(m-x)!}\,q^x\cdot(1-q)^{m-x}$$

for $x = 0, 1, 2, \ldots$.

Suppose further that pairs $\{(X_i, Q_i) ; \ i = 1, 2, \ldots, \ n\}$ are independent, but only the X component is observed. Let $\pi(q)$ be the **pdf** for Q.

By the properties of the binomial distribution,

$$\mathbf{E}[X \,|Q] = mQ \ \text{ and } \ \mathbf{Var}[X \,|Q] = mQ(1-Q) = mQ - mQ^2.$$

By (3.2), the posterior density of Q, given $X = x$, is

$$\pi(q \,|x) = \frac{\binom{m}{x} q^x (1-q)^{m-x} \cdot \pi(q)}{\mathbf{P}[X = x]},$$

where the marginal probability is

$$\mathbf{P}[X = x] = \int_0^1 \binom{m}{x} q^x (1-q)^{m-x} \cdot \pi(q) \ dq.$$

Let Y be a new prospective observation for a random variable with $X = x$. Calculating the credibility premium, we have

$$\mathbf{E}[Y \,|X = x] = \tilde{\mathbf{E}}[Y \,|Q] = m\tilde{\mathbf{E}}[Q] = m \int_0^1 q \cdot \pi(q \,|x) \ dq =$$

$$= \frac{m}{\mathbf{P}[X = x]} \cdot \int_0^1 q \cdot \binom{m}{x} q^x (1-q)^{m-x} \cdot \pi(q) \ dq =$$

$$= \frac{m \int_0^1 q^{x+1}(1-q)^{m-x} \cdot \pi(q) \ dq}{\int_0^1 q^x (1-q)^{m-x} \cdot \pi(q) \ dq}.$$

The posterior density of Q, given $X = x$, is not easy to find. Robbins[5] makes assumptions that are hardly satisfied with actuarial data. That is the reason inferences from this model are restricted to the Bühlmann's credibility only.

Calculating the elements of the Bühlmann approximation, we have the following:

1. **Hypothetical mean (HM):**

$$\mu(Q) = \mathbf{E}[X \,|Q] = mQ$$

2. **Process variance (PV):**

$$v(Q) = \mathbf{Var}[X \,|Q] = mQ(1-Q) = mQ - mQ^2$$

3. **Expected hypothetical mean (EHM):**

$$\mu = \mathbf{E}[X] = \mathbf{E}[\mu(Q)] = \mathbf{E}[mQ] = m\mathbf{E}[Q]$$

4. **Expected process variance (EPV):**

$$v = \mathbf{E}[v(Q)] = \mathbf{E}[mQ - mQ^2] = m\mathbf{E}[Q] - m\mathbf{E}[Q^2] = \mathbf{E}[X] - m\mathbf{E}[Q^2]$$

5. **Variance of hypothetical mean (VHM):**

$$a = \mathbf{Var}\left(\mathbf{E}\left[X \mid Q\right]\right) = \mathbf{Var}\left[\mu\left(Q\right)\right] = m^2\mathbf{Var}\left[Q\right]$$

6. **Hypothetical second moment:**

$$\mathbf{E}\left[X^2 \mid Q\right] = \mathbf{Var}\left[X \mid Q\right] + \mathbf{E}\left[X \mid Q\right]^2 = mQ\left(1 - Q\right) + m^2Q^2 = mQ + \left(m^2 - m\right)Q^2$$

Therefore,

$$\mathbf{E}\left[X^2\right] = \mathbf{E}\left[\mathbf{E}\left[X^2 \mid Q\right]\right] = m\mathbf{E}\left[Q\right] + \left(m^2 - m\right)\mathbf{E}\left[Q^2\right].$$

Calculating the empirical estimates of the elements of the Bühlmann's approximation, we obtain the following:

1. **Estimated EPM:**

$$\hat{\mu} = \hat{\mathbf{E}}\left[X\right] = \bar{X},$$

　where $\bar{X}$ is the sample mean of all observed values of X.

2. **Estimated EPV:**

The following lemma provides convenient expressions for elements of the EPV.

Lemma 4.7.3 *For a binomially-distributed random variable $(X \mid Q)$, the estimated expected process variance is*

$$\hat{v} = \frac{m}{m - 1} \cdot \bar{X} - \frac{B}{m - 1},$$

where

$$\bar{X} = \frac{1}{n}\sum_{i=1}^{n} X_i \quad and \quad B = \frac{1}{n}\sum_{i=1}^{n} (X_i)^2.$$

Proof. Note that

$$\hat{v} = \hat{\mathbf{E}}\left[X\right] - m\hat{\mathbf{E}}\left[Q^2\right].$$

Since

$$\hat{\mathbf{E}}\left[X^2\right] = m\hat{\mathbf{E}}\left[Q\right] + \left(m^2 - m\right) \cdot \hat{\mathbf{E}}\left[Q^2\right],$$

it follows that

$$\hat{\mathbf{E}}\left[Q^2\right] = \frac{1}{m(m - 1)}\left(\hat{\mathbf{E}}\left[X^2\right] - m\hat{\mathbf{E}}\left[Q\right]\right).$$

Note that

$$\hat{\mathbf{E}}\left[X^2\right] = \frac{1}{n}\sum_{i=1}^{n} (X_i)^2 = B \quad \text{and} \quad m\hat{\mathbf{E}}\left[Q\right] = \hat{\mu} = \bar{X}.$$

Therefore,

$$\hat{\mathbf{E}}\left[Q^2\right] = \frac{1}{m(m - 1)}\left(B - \bar{X}\right)$$

and

$$\hat{v} = \bar{X} - \frac{1}{m - 1}\left(B - \bar{X}\right) = \frac{m}{m - 1} \cdot \bar{X} - \frac{B}{m - 1}.$$

3. **Estimated VHM:**

The following lemma provides convenient expressions for elements of the VHM.

Lemma 4.7.4 *For a binomially-distributed random variable $(X|Q)$, the estimated variance of hypothetical mean is*

$$\hat{a} = \frac{n}{n-1} \cdot \left[B - \left(\bar{X} \right)^2 \right] - \frac{m}{m-1} \cdot \bar{X} + \frac{B}{m-1}.$$

Proof. Recall that

$$v + a = \mathbf{Var}(X).$$

Therefore,

$$\hat{v} + \hat{a} = S^2,$$

where S^2 is the sample variance

$$S^2 = \frac{1}{n-1} \sum_{i=1}^{n} \left(X_i - \bar{X} \right)^2 = \frac{1}{n-1} \left[\sum_{i=1}^{n} \left(X_i \right)^2 - n \left(\bar{X} \right)^2 \right] = \frac{n}{n-1} \left[B - \left(\bar{X} \right)^2 \right].$$

Thus,

$$\hat{a} = S^2 - \hat{v} = \frac{n}{n-1} \cdot \left[B - \left(\bar{X} \right)^2 \right] - \frac{m}{m-1} \cdot \bar{X} + \frac{B}{m-1}.$$

Estimating **Bühlmann's** k we have

$$\hat{k} = \frac{\hat{v}}{\hat{a}} = \left(\frac{m}{m-1} \cdot \bar{X} - \frac{B}{m-1} \right) \div \left(\frac{n}{n-1} \cdot \left[B - \left(\bar{X} \right)^2 \right] - \frac{m}{m-1} \cdot \bar{X} + \frac{B}{m-1} \right).$$

Bühlmann's credibility factor is

$$\hat{Z} = \frac{l}{l + \hat{k}},$$

where l is the number of policies such that $X = x$.

Then the empirical Bayes estimate for the insured with record $X = x$, is

$$\hat{\mathbf{E}}[Y|X = x] = \hat{Z} \cdot x + \left(1 - \hat{Z} \right) \cdot \bar{X}.$$

4.8 Bayesian Credibility: Discrete Prior

Let $\mathbf{X} = \{X_i : i = 1, 2, \ldots, n\}$ be a sample drawn from the distribution with the common **pdf** or **pmf** $f(X|\theta)$. The parameter θ is viewed as a value of the random variable Θ with the prior **pmf** $\pi(\theta)$.

The joint probability distribution of $\mathbf{X}$ is obtained by averaging in Θ:

$$f(\mathbf{x}) = \sum_{\theta} \left[\prod_{i=1}^{n} f(x_i|\theta) \right] \cdot \pi(\theta).$$

4.8.1   Posterior Distribution of Parameter

The posterior **pmf** of Θ, given $\mathbf{X} = \mathbf{x}$, is the ratio

$$\pi(\theta|\mathbf{x}) = \mathbf{P}[\Theta = \theta|\mathbf{x}] = \frac{\pi(\theta) \cdot \prod_{i=1}^{n} f(x_i|\theta)}{f(\mathbf{x})}. \tag{4.20}$$

4.8.2   Predictive Distribution of a New Observation

The predictive distribution of $Y = X_{n+1}$ at y is determined as

$$f(y|\mathbf{x}) = \tilde{\mathbf{E}}[f(y|\Theta)] = \sum_{\theta} f(y|\theta) \cdot \pi(\theta|\mathbf{x}), \tag{4.21}$$

where $\pi(\theta|\mathbf{x})$ was defined in (4.20).

4.8.3   Credibility Premium

The credibility premium is defined by the formula:

$$\mathbf{E}[Y|\mathbf{X}] = \tilde{\mathbf{E}}[Y|\Theta] = \sum_{\theta} \mathbf{E}[Y|\theta] \cdot \pi(\theta|\mathbf{x}) \tag{4.22}$$

so that the expectation is evaluated with respect to the posterior distribution of $(\Theta|\mathbf{X} = \mathbf{x})$.

Conclusion

When the prior and model do not form a conjugate pair, direct evaluation based on the Bayesian framework becomes analytically too complicated and requires numerical methods. The method proposed by Bühlmann allows one to conduct simplified calculations that lead to an alternative solution faster. Even though it is hard to justify its accuracy, simplicity and transparency of the **Bühlmann approximation** method is attractive. The very assumption that a prior distribution of the parameter is known can be viewed as artificial. The ideas proposed by H. Robbins[5] allow for combining semi-parametric techniques and bypassing the uncertainty caused by unknown prior. Integrated with Bühlmann framework, the **empirical Bayes** method provides another alternative for developing predictive distribution and calculating credibility premium. This can be regarded as further development of the Bayesian framework.

In the following exercises readers will strengthen their understanding of the ideas developed in this chapter.

Exercises

4.1. Bühlmann's Estimates: Covariance

You are given the following information about **nine** observations, $\{X_i\}$, $i = 1, 2, \ldots, 9$:

   (i) Given $\Theta = \theta$, the observations are independent and identically distributed with parameter θ.

   (ii) The marginal expectation is $\mu = \mathbf{E}[X_i] = 3$.

   (iii) The sum of all observed values is $\sum_{i=1}^{9} X_i = 54$.

   (iv) The expected process variance is $v = 3.6$.

   (v) The numerical value of the Bühlmann's estimate is $\hat{X}_{10} = 5.4$.

Calculate the covariance between X_1 and X_2.

4.2. Bühlmann's Credibility: Binomial-Beta Model

Suppose that a number of claims for a randomly selected insured during a three-year period has a binomial distribution, $\mathbf{Bin}[3, q]$.

The parameter (q) is treated as a random variable, Q, with the prior distribution, $\mathbf{Beta}[4, 3]$.

A sample of $n = 4$ records consists of the following observations:

$$X_1 = 2, \; X_2 = 0, \; X_3 = 1, \; \text{and} \; X_4 = 1$$

Calculate the **Bühlmann's** credibility premium, $\hat{X}_5$.

4.3. Bayesian Credibility: Binomial-Beta Model

Suppose that a number of claims for a randomly selected insured during a three-year period has a binomial distribution, $\mathbf{Bin}[3, q]$.

The parameter (q) is treated as a random variable, Q, with the prior distribution, $\mathbf{Beta}[4, 3]$.

A sample of $n = 4$ records consists of the following observations:

$$X_1 = 2, \; X_2 = 0, \; X_3 = 1, \; \text{and} \; X_4 = 1$$

Determine the **Bayesian** credibility premium:

$$\mathbf{E}[X_5 \,|\, X_1 = 2, \, X_2 = 0, \, X_3 = 1, \, X_4 = 1]$$

4.4. Bühlmann's Estimates: Joint Probability

Suppose that the parameter (Θ) can take values $\Theta = 1$ and $\Theta = 2$ only.

The number of claims (X) per year can be $X = 0$, $X = 1$, or $X = 2$.

The **joint** distribution of the pair, (Θ, X) is shown in the following table:

	$\Theta = 1$	$\Theta = 2$	Total
$X = 0$	0.06	0.24	0.30
$X = 1$	0.16	0.24	0.40
$X = 2$	0.18	0.12	0.30
Total	0.40	0.60	1

(a) Derive the hypothetical mean.

(b) Evaluate the expected process variance.

(c) Determine the variance of hypothetical mean.

4.5. Bühlmann's Approximation: Joint Probability

In the previous problem let X_1 and X_2 denote the number of claims per year for two consecutive years.

(a) Determine the variance of X_1.

(b) Derive the covariance between X_1 and X_2.

(c) Derive the Bühlmann's approximation of X_2, given that there were two claims during the first year.

4.6. Bühlmann's Credibility Premium: Poisson-Gamma Model

You are given the following information about a conditional and prior distribution of the number of exposures:

(i) The number of exposures X follows the Poisson distribution with the unknown intensity λ.

(ii) The parameter λ is viewed as a random variable, Λ, with the prior gamma density distribution **Gamma[7; 5]**.

Suppose that the counts of exposures for three consecutive years are

$$X_1 = 3, \quad X_2 = 5, \quad \text{and} \quad X_3 = 1.$$

Calculate the **Bühlmann's** credibility premium for the next year, $\hat{X}_4$.

4.7. Bayesian Credibility Premium: Poisson-Gamma Model

You are given the following information about a conditional and prior distribution of the number of exposures:

(i) The number of exposures X follows the Poisson distribution with the unknown intensity λ.

(ii) The parameter λ is viewed as a random variable, Λ, with the prior gamma density distribution **Gamma**$[7; 5]$.

Suppose that the counts of exposures for three consecutive years are

$$X_1 = 3, \quad X_2 = 5, \quad \text{and} \quad X_3 = 1.$$

Calculate the **Bayesian** credibility premium for the next year.

4.8. Bühlmann's Credibility Premium

You are given the following information:

(i) Claim size, X, has the hypothetical mean

$$\mathbf{E}\left[X \,|\Theta\right] = \mu\left(\Theta\right)$$

and the expected process variance

$$v = \mathbf{E}\left[\mathbf{Var}\left[X \,|\Theta\right]\right] = 350.$$

(ii) The mean and variance of the random variable, $\mu\left(\Theta\right)$, are

$$\mu = \mathbf{E}\left[\mu\left(\Theta\right)\right] = 720 \quad \text{and} \quad a = \mathbf{Var}\left[\mu\left(\Theta\right)\right] = 70.$$

(iii) The following three claims were observed:

$$X_1 = 630, \quad X_2 = 720, \quad \text{and} \quad X_3 = 450$$

Calculate the expected size of the next claim using Bühlmann's credibility.

4.9. Bühlmann's Credibility Premium

You are given the following information:

(i) The parameter (Θ) is the probability for a randomly chosen insured to have a claim during one year.

(ii) The number of claims in one year, X, can take values 0 or 1 only, with

$$\mathbf{P}\left[X = 1 \,|\Theta\right] = \Theta = 1 - \mathbf{P}\left[X = 0 \,|\Theta\right].$$

(iii) The **overall** probability of a claim being filed by a randomly selected insured in one year is $\mu = 0.2$.

(iv) The variance of Θ is $a = 0.02$.

(v) An insured selected at random is found to have **three** claims over the past nine years, or

$$\sum_{j=1}^{9} X_j = 3.$$

Calculate the Bühlmann's credibility estimate for the next **five** years.

4.10. Bühlmann's Approximation

You are given the following information about a conditional and prior distribution of claim severities:

(i) Given $Q = q$, claim severity X has density

$$f(x|q) = \frac{3x^2}{q^3} \quad \text{for} \ \ 0 < x < q.$$

(ii) Parameter Q has prior beta distribution, with parameters $a = 3$ and $b = 2$.

After one observation period the observed loss was $X = 0.8$.

Evaluate the Bühlmann's approximation for the next year.

4.11. Bühlmann's Credibility Premium and Pure Empirical Bayes

For a group of auto policyholders, you are given the following information:

(i) The number of claims X for each policyholder has a conditional Poisson distribution, with the unknown prior distribution of the parameter Λ.

(ii) During year 1, the claim frequency data are observed and presented in the following table:

Number of Claims k	Number of Policyholders $n(k)$
0	5000
1	2000
2	1500
3	600
4	600
5	300
6 or more	0
Total	10,000

a) Estimate Bühlmann's credibility premium for **one** insured who had two claims during year 1 using the semi-parametric empirical Bayes approach.

b) Estimate $\hat{\mathbf{E}}[Y|X = 2]$, the expected number of claims for this insured for year 2, given that the insured had two claims during year 1.

4.12. Pure Empirical Bayes

You are given the following information:

(i) During a single five-year period there were 500 policies observed, and their summaries are shown in the table that follows.

(ii) The number of policy claims follows a Poisson distribution.

(iii) Each policyholder was insured for the entire five-year period and remains insured for year 6.

A randomly chosen policyholder had **two** claims for a five-year period.

Claims Frequency k	Number of Policies $n(k)$
0	300
1	180
2	120
3	80
4	70
5	50
6 or more	0
Total	800

(a) Calculate the **pure** empirical Bayes estimate for $\mathbf{E}\,[Y_6\,|X=2]$ for year 6.

(b) Using the semi-parametric empirical Bayes approach for Bühlmann approximation, estimate the expected number of claims for year 6 made by the same insured.

4.13. Bühlmann's Credibility

Losses X, given $\Theta = \theta$, are distributed according to the **model** with the density function

$$f(x|\theta) = 4 \cdot \frac{x^3}{\theta^4} \quad \text{for } 0 < x < \theta.$$

A sample of $n = 100$ observed losses consists of the following observations:

$$\sum_{i=1}^{100} X_i = 280 \quad \text{and} \quad \sum_{i=1}^{100} (X_i)^2 = 1576$$

The policyholder was observed for $m = 4$ years with the total amount of losses

$$\sum_{j=1}^{4} Y_j = 20.$$

Using the empirical Bayes approach, derive the Bühlmann credibility for losses expected by the selected policyholder in the **fifth** year.

4.14. Bühlmann's Expectation

A number (X) of claims during a one-year period has binomial distribution **Bin**$[4, q]$, with parameter q, having an unknown prior distribution.

A sample of $n = 100$ records consists of the following observations:

$$\sum_{i=1}^{100} X_i = 36 \quad \text{and} \quad \sum_{i=1}^{100} (X_i)^2 = 60$$

After observing $Y_1 = 2$ claims in one year, use the empirical Bayes approach to derive the Bühlmann estimate for the expected number of claims, Y_2, for the next year.

4.15. Bühlmann's Approximation: Gamma-Gamma Model

You are given the following information:

(i) The distribution of the claim severity for one year is described by the model

$$f(x \,|\, \lambda) = \lambda^2 \, x \, e^{-\lambda x} \quad \text{for} \ \ x > 0.$$

(ii) The unknown parameter (λ) is considered a random variable with the prior gamma density **Gamma** $[\alpha, \beta]$, such that

$$\mathbf{E}[\Lambda] = 1.2 \times 10^{-2} \quad \text{and} \quad \mathbf{Var}[\Lambda] = 2.4 \times 10^{-5}.$$

(iii) A sample of $m = 15$ consecutive years for the same insured is available, with

$$\sum_{i=1}^{15} X_i = 7500.$$

Calculate the Bühlmann's approximation of the **next year's** claim severity.

4.16. Bühlmann's Approximation

You are given the following information about claim severities:

(i) The severity of a claim has the expected value $\mu = 108$.
(ii) The sum of six observed severity values is $\sum_{i=1}^{6} X_i = 540$.
(iii) Bühlmann's approximation for predicted severity based on $m = 6$ recorded values is $\hat{Y} = 96$.
(iv) When the seventh value, X_7, was included in the sample, the Bühlmann's approximation changed to $\hat{Y} = 110.4$.

Calculate the value of X_7.

Solutions

4.1. Note that, using (4.3), the covariance between X_1 and X_2 is the same as a, the variance of hypothetical mean:

$$\mathbf{COV}[X_i, X_j] = \mathbf{VHM} = a$$

Also, Bühlmann's k can be defined as

$$k = \frac{v}{a}, \text{ where } v \text{ is the expected process variance, EPV.}$$

Thus,

$$a = \frac{v}{k}.$$

The Bühlmann's credibility factor is defined as

$$Z = \frac{n}{n + k},$$

where n is the sample size.

Therefore,

$$k = \frac{n(1 - Z)}{Z}.$$

By (4.2), the Bühlmann approximation for $\mathbf{E}[Y|\mathbf{X}]$ is defined as

$$\hat{Y} = Z \cdot \bar{X} + (1 - Z) \cdot \mu, \text{ where } \hat{Y} = X_{n+1}.$$

Hence,

$$Z = \frac{\hat{X}_{n+1} - \mu}{\bar{X} - \mu}.$$

Calculating the sample mean of nine observed values, we obtain

$$\bar{X} = \frac{54}{9} = 6.$$

Therefore,

$$Z = \frac{n}{n+k} = \frac{5.4 - 3}{6 - 3} = \frac{2.4}{3} = 0.8 \Rightarrow$$
$$k = \frac{n(1 - Z)}{Z} = \frac{9(1 - 0.8)}{0.8} = 2.25 \Rightarrow$$
$$a = \frac{v}{k} = \frac{3.6}{2.25} = \mathbf{1.6}.$$

4.2. Since the random variable Q is beta-distributed, with parameters $a = 4$ and $b = 3$, its **pdf** is of the form

$$\pi(q) = \frac{\Gamma(7)}{\Gamma(4)\,\Gamma(3)}\,q^3\,(1 - q)^2,\ 0 < q < 1.$$

Since the conditional random variable $(X|Q)$ is binomial, with parameters $m = 3$ and q, the **pmf** is

$$f(x|q) = \mathbf{P}\left[X = x \,|\, Q = q\right] = \frac{3!}{x!\,(3-x)!}\, q^x \,(1-q)^{3-x}, \;\; x = 0, 1, 2, 3.$$

Calculating the **hypothetical mean**, we have $\mu(q) = \mathbf{E}[X|Q = q] = 3q$. The expected value of Q is

$$\mathbf{E}[Q] = \frac{a}{a+b} = \frac{4}{4+3} = \frac{4}{7}.$$

Thus, the expectation is

$$\mu = \mathbf{E}[\mu(Q)] = 3 \cdot \frac{4}{7} = \frac{12}{7}.$$

Calculating the **process variance**, we have $v(q) = \mathbf{Var}[X|Q = q] = 3q(1-q)$. The expected value of Q^2 is

$$\mathbf{E}[Q^2] = \frac{a(a+1)}{(a+b)(a+b+1)} = \frac{4 \cdot 5}{7 \cdot 8} = \frac{5}{14}.$$

Thus, the **expected process variance** is

$$v = \mathbf{E}[3Q(1-Q)] = 3\mathbf{E}[Q] - 3\mathbf{E}[Q^2] = \frac{12}{7} - \frac{15}{14} = \frac{24 - 15}{14} = \frac{9}{14}.$$

Variance of Q is

$$\mathbf{Var}[Q] = \mathbf{E}[Q^2] - \mathbf{E}[Q]^2 = \frac{a(a+1)}{(a+b)(a+b+1)} - \left(\frac{a}{a+b}\right)^2 =$$
$$= \frac{ab}{(a+b)^2(a+b+1)} = \frac{4 \cdot 3}{49 \cdot 8} = \frac{3}{98}.$$

The **variance of hypothetical mean** is

$$a = \mathbf{Var}[3Q] = 9\mathbf{Var}[Q] = 9 \cdot \frac{3}{98} = \frac{27}{98}.$$

Therefore,

$$k = \frac{v}{a} = \frac{9}{14} \div \frac{27}{98} = \frac{9}{14} \cdot \frac{98}{27} = \frac{7}{3}.$$

The Bühlmann's Z is

$$Z = \frac{n}{n+k} = \frac{4}{4+7/3} = \frac{12}{19} \Rightarrow 1 - Z = \frac{7}{19}.$$

Calculating the sample mean of four observed policies, we have

$$\bar{X} = \frac{2+0+1+1}{4} - 1.$$

Hence, the Bühlmann's credibility for X_5 is

$$\hat{X}_5 = Z \cdot \bar{X} + (1-Z) \cdot \mu = \frac{12}{19} \cdot 1 + \frac{7}{19} \cdot \frac{12}{7} = \frac{12}{19} + \frac{12}{19} = \frac{24}{19} \approx 1.26315 \approx \mathbf{1.263}.$$

4.3. Let A be the following event:

$$A = (X_1 = 2) \bigcap (X_2 = 0) \bigcap (X_3 = 1) \bigcap (X_4 = 1)$$

We need to calculate $\mathbf{E}[X_5|A]$.

Since the random variable Q is beta-distributed, with parameters $a = 4$ and $b = 3$, its **pdf** is of the form

$$\pi(q) = \frac{\Gamma(7)}{\Gamma(4)\,\Gamma(3)} q^3(1-q)^2, \ 0 < q < 1.$$

Since the conditional random variable $X|Q$ is binomial, with parameters $m = 3$ and q, the **pmf** is

$$f(x|q) = \mathbf{P}[X = x \,|Q = q] = \frac{3!}{x!(3-x)!} q^x (1-q)^{3-x}, \ x = 0, 1, 2, 3.$$

Therefore,

$$f(A|q) = C \cdot q^2(1-q) \cdot (1-q)^3 \cdot q(1-q)^2 \cdot q(1-q)^2 = C \cdot q^4(1-q)^8$$

for some constant C that does not depend on q.

Then the **posterior** density of Q, given A, is

$$\pi(q|A) = \frac{\pi(q) \cdot f(A|q)}{f(A)} = C \cdot q^3(1-q)^2 \cdot q^4(1-q)^8 = Cq^7(1-q)^{10}.$$

Thus, the posterior density is **Beta** $[8, 11]$.

The **conditional** expectation of X_5, given $Q = q$, is $\mathbf{E}[X_5|Q = q] = 3q$. Hence, using (3.4), the Bayesian credibility is

$$\mathbf{E}[X|A] = \tilde{\mathbf{E}}[X|Q] = \int_{-\infty}^{\infty} \mathbf{E}[X|q] \cdot \pi(q|\mathbf{x})\,dq$$

so that the expectation is evaluated with respect to the posterior distribution of $(Q|\mathbf{X} = \mathbf{x})$.

Since the the posterior density is **Beta** $[8, 11]$, calculating the expectation of $(Q|A)$, we have

$$\mathbf{E}[X_5|A] = \tilde{\mathbf{E}}[X_5|Q] = 3\mathbf{E}[Q|A] = 3 \cdot \frac{8}{8+11} = \frac{24}{19} \approx 1.26315 \approx \mathbf{1.263}.$$

Note that the numerical values for the Bayesian credibility premium calculated in this problem and the Bühlmann's credibility premium calculated in the previous problem coincide.

4.4. Let $\pi(\theta) = \mathbf{P}[\Theta = \theta]$. Note that the table shows **joint** probabilities so that given values represent

$$\mathbf{P}[(\Theta = \theta) \cap (X = x)] = \pi(\theta) \cdot f(x|\theta).$$

Therefore, the **model** distribution can be obtained by dividing the joint probability by the marginal probability:

$$f(x|\theta) = \mathbf{P}[X = x|\Theta = \theta] = \frac{\mathbf{P}[(\Theta = \theta) \cap (X = x)]}{\mathbf{P}[\Theta = \theta]}$$

Thus, the **conditional** probabilities of $(X|\Theta = \theta)$ are

$$f(0|1) = \frac{0.06}{0.40} = 0.15, \quad f(1|1) = \frac{0.16}{0.40} = 0.40, \quad f(2|1) = \frac{0.18}{0.40} = 0.45,$$

and similarly,

$$f(0|2) = \frac{0.24}{0.60} = 0.40, \quad f(1|2) = \frac{0.24}{0.60} = 0.40, \quad f(2|2) = \frac{0.12}{0.60} = 0.20.$$

(a) Calculating the hypothetical mean as $\mu(\theta) = \mathbf{E}[X|\theta]$, we obtain

$$\mu(1) = (0)(0.15) + (1)(0.40) + (2)(0.45) = \mathbf{1.3}$$
$$\mu(2) = (0)(0.40) + (1)(0.40) + (2)(0.20) = \mathbf{0.8}.$$

The expectation of the hypothetical mean is

$$\mu = \mathbf{E}[\mu(\Theta)] = (1.3)(0.4) + (0.8)(0.6) = 0.52 + 0.48 = \mathbf{1}.$$

(b) Calculating the expected process variance, we have

$$v(1) = \mathbf{Var}(X|\theta = 1) = (0^2)(0.15) + (1^2)(0.40) + (2^2)(0.45) - (1.3)^2 = \mathbf{0.51}$$
$$v(2) = \mathbf{Var}(X|\theta = 2) = (0^2)(0.40) + (1^2)(0.40) + (2^2)(0.20) - (0.8)^2 = \mathbf{0.56}.$$

Therefore,

$$v = \mathbf{E}[\mathbf{Var}(X|\theta)] = \mathbf{E}[v(\Theta)] = (0.51)(0.4) + (0.56)(0.6) = 0.204 + 0.336 =$$
$$= \mathbf{0.54}.$$

(c) The variance of hypothetical mean is

$$a = \mathbf{Var}[\mu(\Theta)] = (1.3)^2(0.4) + (0.8)^2(0.6) - (1)^2 = 0.676 + 0.384 - 1 =$$
$$= 1.06 - 1 = \mathbf{0.06}.$$

4.5. Recall that the main elements of Bühlmann's framework were found as

$$\mu = 1, \quad v = 0.54, \quad \text{and} \quad a = 0.06.$$

(a) Using (4.4), the variance of X_1 is

$$\mathbf{Var}[X_1] = v + a - 0.54 + 0.06 = \mathbf{0.6}.$$

(b) Using (4.3), the covariance between X_1 and X_2 is

$$\mathbf{COV}[X_1, X_2] = a = \mathbf{0.06}.$$

(c) The Bühlmann's approximation of X_2, given that there were two claims during the first year, is defined as

$$\hat{X}_2 = Z \cdot X_1 + (1 - Z) \cdot \mu.$$

Calculating Z, we obtain

$$Z = \frac{1}{1 + k} = \frac{1}{1 + v/a} = \frac{a}{a + v} = \frac{0.06}{0.06 + 0.54} = \frac{0.06}{0.6} = 0.1 \Rightarrow 1 - Z = 0.9.$$

Hence,

$$\hat{X}_2 = 0.1 \cdot (2) + 0.9 \cdot (1) = 0.2 + 0.9 = \mathbf{1.1}.$$

4.6. Since the random variable Λ has gamma distribution, with parameters $\alpha = 7$ and $\theta = 5$, it follows that

$$\mathbf{E}[\Lambda] = \alpha \cdot \theta = 7 \cdot 5 = 35 \quad \text{and} \quad \mathbf{Var}[\Lambda] = \alpha \cdot \theta^2 = 7 \cdot 5^2 = 175.$$

Since the conditional random variable $(X|\Lambda)$ is Poisson-distributed,

$$\mathbf{E}[X|\Lambda = u] = \mathbf{Var}[X|\Lambda = u] = u.$$

Thus, the hypothetical mean and the process variance coincide:

$$\mu(\Lambda) = v(\Lambda) = \Lambda$$

Therefore,

$$\mu = \mathbf{E}[\Lambda] = 35, \quad v = \mathbf{E}[\Lambda] = 35 \quad \text{and} \quad a = \mathbf{Var}[\Lambda] = 175.$$

Calculating Bühlmann's k, we have

$$k = \frac{v}{a} = \frac{35}{175} = 0.2.$$

The sample mean of three observations is

$$\bar{X} = (3 + 5 + 1) \div 3 = 3.$$

Since $n = 3$, the Bühlmann's Z is

$$Z = \frac{3}{3 + 0.2} = \frac{3}{3.2} = 0.9375 \Rightarrow 1 - Z = 0.0625.$$

Therefore,

$$\hat{X}_4 = Z \cdot \bar{X} + (1 - Z) \cdot \mu = 0.9375 \cdot (3) + 0.0625 \cdot (35) = \mathbf{5}.$$

4.7. Since the random variable Λ has prior gamma distribution, with parameters $\alpha = 7$ and $\theta = 5$, its **pdf** is of the form

$$\pi(\lambda) = \frac{\lambda^6}{5^7 \Gamma(7)} e^{-\lambda/5}.$$

Since the conditional random variable is Poisson-distributed with parameter λ, its **pdf** is of the form

$$f(x|\lambda) = \frac{1}{x!} \lambda^x e^{-\lambda}.$$

Let A be the event such that

$$A = (X_1 = 3) \bigcap (X_2 = 5) \bigcap (X_3 = 1).$$

Then,

$$f(A|\lambda) = C \cdot \lambda^{X_1} e^{-\lambda} \cdot \lambda^{X_2} e^{-\lambda} \cdot \lambda^{X_3} e^{-\lambda} = C \cdot \lambda^{X_1 + X_2 + X_3} e^{-3\lambda} = C \cdot \lambda^9 e^{-3\lambda}.$$

The posterior distribution of λ is

$$\pi(\lambda|A) = \frac{\pi(\lambda)f(A|\lambda)}{f(A)} = C \cdot e^{-\lambda/\theta} \lambda^{\alpha-1} \cdot \lambda^{X_1 + X_2 + X_3} e^{-3\lambda} =$$
$$= C \cdot \lambda^{X_1 + X_2 + X_3 + \alpha - 1} e^{-\lambda(3 + 1/\theta)} = C \cdot \lambda^{15} e^{-\lambda(3 + 1/5)} = C \cdot \lambda^{15} e^{-\lambda(3.2)}.$$

This is a gamma distribution, with parameters

$$\alpha' = X_1 + X_2 + X_3 + \alpha = 16$$
$$\theta' = 1/(3 + 1/\theta) = \frac{\theta}{1 + 3\theta} = 1/3.2 = 0.3125.$$

Therefore, the posterior expectation of X_4 is equal to

$$\mathbf{E}[X_4|A] = \tilde{\mathbf{E}}[X_4|\lambda] = \int_0^\infty \mathbf{E}[X_4|\lambda] \pi(\lambda|A)\, d\lambda = \int_0^\infty \lambda \pi(\lambda|A)\, d\lambda =$$
$$= \alpha' \cdot \theta' = (X_1 + X_2 + X_3 + \alpha) \cdot \frac{\theta}{1 + 3\theta} = 16 \cdot 0.3125 = \mathbf{5}.$$

Note that the numerical values for the Bayesian credibility premium calculated in this problem and the Bühlmann's credibility premium calculated in the previous problem coincide.

4.8. Calculating Bühlmann's Z for three claims, we have the following:

$$Z = \frac{3}{3 + k}, \quad k = \frac{v}{a} = \frac{350}{70} = 5 \Rightarrow$$
$$Z = \frac{3}{3 + 5} = 0.375 \quad \text{and} \quad 1 - Z = 0.625$$

The sample mean is

$$\bar{X} = \frac{1}{3} \sum_{i=1}^{3} X_i = \frac{1}{3}(630 + 720 + 450) = \frac{1}{3} \cdot 1800 = 600.$$

Therefore,

$$\hat{Y} = Z \cdot \bar{X} + (1 - Z) \cdot \mu = 0.375 \cdot 600 + 0.625 \cdot 720 = 225 + 450 = \mathbf{675}.$$

4.9. Note that individual observations

$$\{X_1, X_2, \ldots, X_9, \ldots | \Theta\}$$

follow the Bernoulli distribution with the random success rate Θ. Hence,

$$\mu(\Theta) = \mathbf{E}[X_i | \Theta] = \Theta \quad \text{and} \quad v(\Theta) = \mathbf{Var}[X_i | \Theta] = \Theta(1 - \Theta).$$

We are given that

$$\mu = \mathbf{E}[\mu(\Theta)] = \mathbf{E}[\Theta] = 0.2 \quad \text{and} \quad a = \mathbf{Var}[\mu(\Theta)] = \mathbf{Var}[\Theta] = 0.02.$$

Calculating $\mathbf{E}[\Theta^2]$, we have

$$a = \mathbf{Var}[\Theta] = \mathbf{E}[\Theta^2] - (\mathbf{E}[\Theta])^2 = \mathbf{E}[\Theta^2] - \mu^2 \Rightarrow$$
$$\mathbf{E}[\Theta^2] = a + \mu^2 = 0.02 + (0.2)^2 = 0.06.$$

Therefore,

$$v = \mathbf{E}[\Theta(1 - \Theta)] = \mathbf{E}[\Theta] - \mathbf{E}[\Theta^2] = 0.2 - 0.06 = 0.14.$$

Calculating Bühlmann's k, we obtain

$$k = \frac{v}{a} = \frac{0.14}{0.02} = 7.$$

Hence,

$$Z = \frac{n}{n+k} = \frac{9}{9+7} = \frac{9}{16}, \text{ and } 1 - Z = \frac{7}{16}.$$

Calculating the Bühlmann's estimate for a single year, $Y = X_i$, with $i > 9$, we have

$$\hat{Y} = \frac{9}{16} \cdot \bar{X} + \frac{7}{16} \cdot \mu = \frac{9}{16} \cdot \frac{3}{9} + \frac{7}{16} \cdot 0.2 = \frac{3 + 1.4}{16} = \mathbf{0.275}.$$

Thus, the estimated number of claims for the next five years is

$$5 \times 0.275 = \mathbf{1.375}.$$

4.10. Since the random variable Q has a prior beta distribution, with parameters $a = 3$ and $b = 2$, its **pdf** is of the form

$$\pi(q) = 12 \cdot q^2 \cdot (1 - q) \ \text{ for } \ 0 < q < 1.$$

Note that, given $Q = q$, the ratio $T = X/Q$ has beta distribution

$$\frac{X}{Q} \sim \textbf{Beta}\,[3, \, 1].$$

Indeed,

$$F_T(x) = \mathbf{P}\left(\frac{1}{q} \cdot X < x\right) = \mathbf{P}\,(X < qx) = F_X(qx) \Rightarrow$$

$$f_T(x) = qf_X(qx) = q \cdot \frac{3(qx)^2}{q^3} = 3x^2,$$

which is a beta distribution, with parameters $a = 3$ and $b = 1$.

Recall that for a beta distribution, with parameters a and b,

$$\mathbf{E}[X] = \frac{a}{a+b}, \ \mathbf{E}[X^2] = \frac{a(a+1)}{(a+b)(a+b+1)}, \ \mathbf{Var}[X] = \frac{ab}{(a+b)^2(a+b+1)}.$$

Therefore,

$$\mu(q) = \mathbf{E}\,[X|Q = q] = \mathbf{E}\,[Tq|Q = q] = q \cdot \mathbf{E}\,[T|Q = q] = \frac{3}{4} \cdot q$$

$$v(q) = \mathbf{Var}[X|Q = q] = \mathbf{Var}[Tq|Q = q] = q^2 \cdot \mathbf{Var}\,(T|Q = q) = \frac{3}{16 \cdot 5} \cdot q^2 = \frac{3}{80} \cdot q^2.$$

Hence, the expected hypothetical mean and process variance are

$$\mu = \frac{3}{4} \cdot \mathbf{E}[Q] = \frac{3}{4} \cdot \frac{3}{5} = \frac{9}{20}$$

$$v = \frac{3}{80} \cdot \mathbf{E}[Q^2] = \frac{3}{80} \cdot \frac{12}{30} = \frac{3}{80} \cdot \frac{2}{5} = \frac{3}{200}.$$

Calculating the **variance of hypothetical mean**, we have

$$a = \mathbf{Var}\left[\frac{3}{4} \cdot Q\right] = \frac{9}{16} \cdot \mathbf{Var}\,(Q) = \frac{9}{16} \cdot \frac{6}{25 \cdot 6} = \frac{9}{16} \cdot \frac{1}{25} = \frac{9}{400}.$$

Calculating Bühlmann's k, we obtain

$$k = \frac{v}{a} = \frac{3}{200} \div \frac{9}{400} = \frac{2}{3}.$$

Hence,

$$Z = \frac{n}{n+k} = \frac{1}{1 + 2/3} = \frac{3}{5} = 0.6 \ \text{ and } \ 1 - Z = 0.4.$$

Finally, calculating the Bühlmann's estimate for a single year, we have

$$\hat{Y} = 0.6 \cdot 0.8 + 0.4 \cdot \frac{9}{20} = 0.48 + 0.18 = \textbf{0.66}.$$

4.11. Note that for a Poisson-distributed random variable X

$$\mathbf{HM} = \mu\left(\Lambda\right) = \mathbf{E}\left[X \,|\Lambda\right] = \Lambda$$
$$\mathbf{PV} = v\left(\Lambda\right) = \mathbf{Var}\left[X \,|\Lambda\right] = \Lambda.$$

a) To find the empirical Bayes estimate for Bühlmann's approximation, let us evaluate the sample sums.

Calculating the sample mean, we have

$$\bar{X} = \frac{1}{10{,}000} \sum_{i=1}^{10{,}000} X_i = \frac{1}{10{,}000}\left(0 + 2000 + 3000 + 1800 + 2400 + 1500\right) = \mathbf{1.07}.$$

Therefore, $\hat{\mu} = \hat{v} = 1.07$.

Calculating the average of X^2, we have

$$B = \left(\bar{X^2}\right) = \frac{1}{10{,}000} \sum_{i=1}^{10{,}000} X_i^2 = \frac{1}{10{,}000}\left(2000 + 6000 + 5400 + 9600 + 7500\right) =$$

$$= \frac{30{,}500}{10{,}000} = 3.05.$$

Using (4.15), the sample variance is

$$S^2 = \frac{n}{n-1}\left[B - \left(\bar{X}\right)^2\right] = \frac{1}{10{,}000 - 1}\left[30{,}500 - 10{,}000 \cdot (1.07)^2\right] =$$

$$= \frac{19{,}051}{9999} \approx \mathbf{1.9053}.$$

Using (4.16), the **variance of hypothetical mean** is

$$\hat{a} = S^2 - \hat{v} = 1.9053 - 1.07 = 0.8353.$$

Bühlmann's k is estimated as

$$\hat{k} = \frac{\hat{v}}{\hat{a}} = \frac{1.07}{0.8353} \approx \mathbf{1.281}.$$

Calculating the estimated Bühlmann's credibility factor Z, we obtain

$$\hat{Z} = \frac{1}{1 + \hat{k}} = \frac{1}{1 + 1.281} \approx \mathbf{0.4384} \quad \text{and} \quad 1 - \hat{Z} \approx \mathbf{0.5616}.$$

Finally, using (4.17), the empirical Bayes estimate for the insured with record $X = x$, is

$$\hat{\mathbf{E}}\left[Y \,|x = 2\right] = \hat{Z} \cdot x + \left(1 - \hat{Z}\right) \cdot \bar{X} = 0.4384 \cdot 2 + 0.5616 \cdot 1.07 =$$

$$= 0.8768 + 0.6009 \approx \mathbf{1.4777}.$$

b) As shown by H. Robbins[5] the **pure** empirical Bayes estimate for the expected value of Λ, given $X = x$, is

$$\hat{\mathbf{E}}[\Lambda|X = x] = (x + 1) \cdot \frac{n(x+1)}{n(x)},$$

where $n(x)$ is the observed count of $X = x$.

Therefore,

$$\hat{Y} = \hat{\mathbf{E}}[Y|X = 2] = 3 \cdot \frac{n(3)}{n(2)} = 3 \cdot \frac{600}{1500} = \mathbf{1.2}.$$

4.12. Note that an individual record, $X_i = \sum_{j=1}^{5} X_{i,j}$, represents the total number of claims for a five-year period. All predictions are related to the similar sum of counts, $Y = \sum_{j=1}^{5} Y_j$.

The predicted expected number for **year 6 only** will be then obtained after division of the predicted value for Y by 5.

(a) By the definition of the **pure** empirical Bayes estimate for the expected value of Y, given $X = x$,

$$\hat{\mathbf{E}}[Y|X = x] = (x + 1) \cdot \frac{n(x+1)}{n(x)},$$

where $n(x)$ is the observed count of $X = x$.

Therefore,

$$\hat{\mathbf{E}}[Y|X = 2] = (2 + 1) \cdot \frac{n(2+1)}{n(2)} = 3 \cdot \frac{n(3)}{n(2)} = 3 \cdot \frac{80}{120} = \mathbf{2}.$$

Since this is associated with the expectation for the **next five** years, for year 6, the predicted number of claims is

$$\hat{\mathbf{E}}[Y_6|X = 2] = \frac{2}{5} = \mathbf{0.4}.$$

(b) Calculating the sample mean of the number of claims, we have

$$\bar{X} = \frac{1}{800} \sum_{i=1}^{800} X_i = \frac{1}{800}[0 \cdot 300 + 1 \cdot 180 + 2 \cdot 120 + 3 \cdot 80 + 4 \cdot 70 + 5 \cdot 50] =$$

$$= \frac{1}{800} \cdot 1190 = \mathbf{1.4875}.$$

Therefore, $\bar{X} = \hat{\mu} = \hat{v} = 1.4875$.

Calculating the average of X^2, we have

$$B = (\bar{X^2}) = \frac{1}{800} \sum_{i=1}^{800} (X_i)^2 =$$

$$= \frac{1}{800} \left(0^2 \cdot 300 + 1^2 \cdot 180 + 2^2 \cdot 120 + 3^2 \cdot 80 + 4^2 \cdot 70 + 5^2 \cdot 50\right) =$$

$$= \frac{1}{800}(180 + 480 + 720 + 1120 + 1250) = \frac{1}{800} \cdot 3750 = 4.6875.$$

Using (4.15), the sample variance is

$$S^2 = \frac{n}{n-1} \left[B - \left(\bar{X} \right)^2 \right] = \frac{1}{800-1} \left[3750 - 800 \cdot (1.4875)^2 \right] =$$

$$= \frac{1979.875}{799} \approx \mathbf{2.478}.$$

Using (4.16), the variance of hypothetical mean is

$$\hat{a} = S^2 - \hat{v} = 2.478 - 1.4875 = \mathbf{0.9904}.$$

Bühlmann's k is estimated as

$$\hat{k} = \frac{\hat{v}}{\hat{a}} = \frac{1.4875}{0.9904} = \mathbf{1.5019}.$$

Calculating the estimated Bühlmann's credibility factor Z, we obtain

$$\hat{Z} = \frac{1}{1+\hat{k}} = \mathbf{0.3997} \quad \text{and} \quad 1 - \hat{Z} = \mathbf{0.6003}.$$

Using (4.17), the empirical Bayes estimate for the insured for the **next five** years with record $X = x$, is

$$\hat{\mathbf{E}} \left[Y \,|\, X = 2 \right] = \hat{Z} \cdot x + \left(1 - \hat{Z} \right) \cdot \bar{X} = 0.3997 \cdot 2 + 0.6003 \cdot 1.4875 =$$

$$= 0.7994 + 0.8929 \approx \mathbf{1.6923}.$$

Since this estimate covers the number of claims for the **next five** years, the prediction for year 6 is

$$\frac{1.6923}{5} = \mathbf{0.3385}.$$

4.13. Note that, given $\Theta = \theta$, the ratio $U = X/\Theta$ is **independent** of Θ and follows the beta distribution

$$\frac{X}{\Theta} \sim \mathbf{Beta}[4, 1].$$

Indeed,

$$F_U(x) = \mathbf{P} \left(\frac{1}{\theta} \cdot X < x \right) = \mathbf{P} \left(X < \theta x \right) = F_X(\theta x) \Rightarrow$$

$$f_U(x) = \theta f_X(\theta x) = \theta \cdot 4 \cdot \frac{(\theta x)^3}{\theta^4} = 4x^3,$$

which is a beta distribution, with parameters $a = 4$ and $b = 1$.

Recall that for a beta distribution, with parameters a and b,

$$\mathbf{E}[X] = \frac{a}{a+b}, \quad \mathbf{E}[X^2] = \frac{a(a+1)}{(a+b)(a+b+1)}, \quad \mathbf{Var}[X] = \frac{ab}{(a+b)^2(a+b+1)}.$$

Calculating the first two moments of U, we have

$$\mathbf{E}[U] = \frac{4}{5} \quad \text{and} \quad \mathbf{E}[U^2] = \frac{4 \cdot 5}{5 \cdot 6} = \frac{4}{6} = \frac{2}{3}, \quad \text{hence} \quad \mathbf{Var}[U] = \frac{4}{25 \cdot 6} = \frac{2}{75}.$$

Therefore, the hypothetical mean is

$$\mathbf{HM} = \mu(\theta) = \mathbf{E}[X|\Theta = \theta] = \mathbf{E}\left[\theta U|\Theta = \theta\right] = \theta \cdot \mathbf{E}\left[U|\Theta = \theta\right] = \frac{4}{5} \cdot \theta$$

and the process variance is

$$\mathbf{PV} = v(\theta) = \mathbf{Var}[X|\Theta = \theta] = \mathbf{Var}[\theta U|\Theta = \theta] = \theta^2 \cdot \mathbf{Var}\left(U|\Theta = \theta\right) = \frac{2}{75} \cdot \theta^2.$$

Estimating the **marginal** expected value of X^2, we have

$$B = \frac{1}{100} \sum_{i=1}^{100} (X_i)^2 = \frac{1}{100} \cdot 1576 = 15.76.$$

By the double expectation rule,

$$\mathbf{E}[X^2] = \mathbf{E}[\mathbf{E}[X^2|\Theta]] = \frac{2}{3} \cdot \mathbf{E}[\Theta^2].$$

Hence, the estimated expected value of Θ^2 is

$$\hat{\mathbf{E}}[\Theta^2] = \frac{3}{2} \cdot B = \frac{3}{2} \cdot 15.76 = 23.64.$$

Calculating the **EPV**, we obtain

$$\hat{v} = \hat{\mathbf{E}}[v(\theta)] = \frac{2}{75} \cdot 23.64 = \mathbf{0.6304}.$$

The estimated value of the expected hypothetical means (or **pure premium**) is

$$\hat{\mu} = \bar{X} = \frac{1}{100} \cdot 280 = 2.8.$$

Using (4.19), we calculate the unbiased estimate of the marginal variance:

$$S^2 = \frac{n}{n-1}\left[B - (\bar{X})^2\right] = \frac{100}{99} \cdot [15.76 - (2.8)^2] = \mathbf{8}$$

Using the identity $S^2 = \hat{v} + \hat{a}$ and $v = 0.6304$, the estimated **VHM** is

$$\hat{a} = S^2 - \hat{v} = 8 - 0.6304 = 7.3696.$$

Bühlmann's k is estimated as

$$\hat{k} = \frac{\hat{v}}{\hat{a}} = \frac{0.6304}{7.3696} = \mathbf{0.0855}.$$

Calculating the estimated Bühlmann's credibility factor Z, we obtain

$$\hat{Z} = \frac{m}{m+\hat{k}} = \frac{4}{4.0855} \approx 0.9791.$$

Finally, the loss for the selected policyholder is

$$\hat{Y}_5 = \hat{Z} \cdot \bar{Y} + (1-Z) \cdot \hat{\mu} = 0.9791 \cdot 5 + 0.0209 \cdot (2.8) = 4.8953 + 0.0586 \approx \mathbf{4.954}.$$

4.14. Since X, given $Q = q$, has binomial distribution, the hypothetical mean and the process variance are

$$\mathbf{HM} = \mu(q) = 4q \text{ and } \mathbf{PV} = v(q) = 4q(1-q) = 4q - 4q^2.$$

Note that

$$\mathbf{E}[X^2 | Q = q] = v(q) + \mu(q)^2 = 4q - 4q^2 + (4q)^2 = 4q + 12q^2 = \mu(q) + 12q^2.$$

Calculating the sample mean $\bar{X}$ and the sample second moment B, we have

$$\bar{X} = \frac{36}{100} = 0.36, \; B = (\bar{X^2}) = \frac{60}{100} = 0.6.$$

Therefore,

$$\hat{\mathbf{E}}[Q^2] = \frac{1}{12} \cdot [B - \bar{X}] = \frac{0.6 - 0.36}{12} = \frac{0.24}{12} = \mathbf{0.02}.$$

Calculating the **EPV**, we have

$$v = \mathbf{E}[v(q)] = \mathbf{E}[4q - 4q^2] = \mathbf{E}[X] - 4 \cdot \mathbf{E}[Q^2].$$

Calculating the **estimate** of the EPV, we obtain

$$\hat{v} = \hat{\mathbf{E}}[X] - 4 \cdot \hat{\mathbf{E}}[Q^2] = 0.36 - 4 \cdot 0.02 = \mathbf{0.28}.$$

The empirical variance of X is

$$S^2 = \frac{100}{99} \cdot [B - (\bar{X})^2] = \mathbf{0.4752}.$$

Therefore, variance of hypothetical mean is estimated as

$$\hat{a} = S^2 - \hat{v} = 0.4752 - 0.28 = \mathbf{0.1952}.$$

Bühlmann's k is estimated as

$$\hat{k} = \frac{\hat{v}}{\hat{a}} = \frac{0.28}{0.1952} = \mathbf{1.4348}.$$

Calculating the estimated Bühlmann's credibility factor Z, we obtain

$$\hat{Z} = \frac{m}{m+\hat{k}} = \frac{1}{1 + 1.4348} = \mathbf{0.4107}, \; 1 - \hat{Z} = \mathbf{0.5893}.$$

Finally, since $Y_1 = 2$ is the sample mean of a single observation, we have

$$\hat{Y}_2 = \hat{Z} \cdot \bar{Y} + (1-Z) \cdot \hat{\mu} = (0.4107) \cdot (2) + (0.5893)(0.36) = 0.8214 + 0.2121 = \mathbf{1.034}.$$

4.15. Since the random variable Λ has gamma distribution,

$$\mathbf{E}\left[\Lambda\right] = \alpha \cdot \beta \text{ and } \mathbf{Var}\left[\Lambda\right] = \alpha \cdot \beta^2.$$

Thus, we have two equations:

$$\alpha \cdot \beta = 1.2 \times 10^{-2} \text{ and } \alpha \cdot \beta^2 = 2.4 \times 10^{-5}$$

Solving this system for α and β,

$$1.2 \times 10^{-2} \cdot \beta = 2.4 \times 10^{-5} \Leftrightarrow \beta = 2 \cdot 10^{-3} = 0.002 \Rightarrow \frac{1}{\beta} = 500 \Rightarrow \alpha = 6.$$

Thus,

$$\Lambda \sim \mathbf{Gamma}\left[6, 0.002\right] \text{ and } \Lambda^{-1} \sim \mathbf{Inverse\ Gamma}\left[6, 500\right].$$

Note that the model distribution is $\mathbf{Gamma}\left[2, \lambda^{-1}\right]$.

Calculating the hypothetical mean and the process variance, we have

$$\mathbf{HM} = \mu\left(\Lambda\right) = \mathbf{E}\left[X\left|\Lambda\right.\right] = 2 \cdot \Lambda^{-1}$$
$$\mathbf{PV} = v\left(\Lambda\right) = \mathbf{Var}\left[X\left|\Lambda\right.\right] = 2 \cdot \Lambda^{-2}.$$

Recall that for the inverse gamma distribution, with parameters α and θ, the expected value and the variance are calculated as

$$\mathbf{E}\left[X\right] = \frac{\theta}{\alpha - 1}, \quad \mathbf{Var}(X) = \frac{\theta^2}{(\alpha - 1)^2(\alpha - 2)}.$$

Calculating the **expected hypothetical mean**, we have

$$\mu = \mathbf{E}\left[\frac{2}{\Lambda}\right] = 2\mathbf{E}\left[\frac{1}{\Lambda}\right] = \frac{2 \cdot 500}{6 - 1} = \frac{100}{5} = \mathbf{200}.$$

Calculating the **expected process variance**, we have

$$v = \mathbf{E}\left[2 \cdot \Lambda^{-2}\right] = 2\mathbf{E}\left[\Lambda^{-2}\right] = 2 \cdot \frac{500^2}{(6 - 1)(6 - 2)} = \frac{5 \cdot 10^5}{20} = 25 \cdot 10^3.$$

Calculating the **variance of the hypothetical mean**, we have

$$a = \mathbf{Var}\left[\frac{2}{\Lambda}\right] = 4 \cdot \mathbf{Var}\left[\frac{1}{\Lambda}\right] = 4 \cdot \frac{500^2}{5^2 \cdot 4} = 10^4.$$

Bühlmann's k is estimated as

$$k = \frac{v}{a} = \frac{25 \cdot 10^3}{10^4} = \mathbf{2.5}.$$

Calculating the estimated Bühlmann's credibility factor Z, we obtain

$$Z = \frac{m}{m + k} = \frac{15}{15 + 2.5} = \frac{15}{17.5} = \mathbf{0.8571}, \ 1 - Z = \mathbf{0.1429}.$$

Calculating the sample mean,

$$\bar{X} = \frac{7500}{15} = 500,$$

the Bühlmann's approximation for the next year claim severity is

$$\hat{Y} = Z \cdot \bar{X} + (1 - Z) \cdot \mu = 0.8571 \cdot 500 + 0.1429 \cdot 200 = 428.55 + 28.5714 = \mathbf{457.12}.$$

4.16. Recall that the Bühlmann's predicted value is calculated as

$$\hat{Y} = Z \cdot \bar{X} + (1 - Z) \cdot \mu.$$

Calculating the sample mean of the seven observed severity values, we have

$$\frac{1}{7} \sum_{i=1}^{7} X_i = \frac{1}{7} \left(\sum_{i=1}^{6} X_i + X_7 \right) = \frac{1}{7} \left(540 + X_7 \right).$$

Recall that Bühlmann's Z is defined as $Z = m/(m + k)$, where m indicates the sample size chosen.

Hence,

$$Z_6 = \frac{6}{6 + k}, \ 1 - Z_6 = \frac{k}{6 + k} \text{ for } m = 6$$
$$Z_7 = \frac{7}{7 + k}, \ 1 - Z_7 = \frac{k}{7 + k} \text{ for } m = 7.$$

Calculating the Bühlmann's approximation for each number of exposures, we have

$$540 + 108 \cdot k = 96(6 + k)$$
$$540 + X_7 + 108 \cdot k = 110.4(7 + k).$$

Solving this system for k and X_7, we obtain

$$540 + 108 \cdot k = 96 + 96 \cdot k \ \Leftrightarrow \ 12k = 36 \ \Leftrightarrow \ k = 3$$
$$X_7 = 110.4 \cdot 10 - 540 + 108 \cdot 7 = \mathbf{240}.$$

Part II

Statistics Review and Elements of Statistical Inference

Chapter 5

Statistics Review

When a sample is drawn from the population that is described in terms of a partially specified distribution, there are several main types of statistical inferences. Usually, there is a parameter of interest, θ, and conclusions about θ are desired. In this chapter we consider three types of statistical inferences:

1. **Point estimation.** In this case, we are looking for a certain **statistic** or an estimate of a parameter, that is, a function of observations.

2. **Hypothesis testing.** Instead of a point estimate, the so-called **null** hypothesis about θ is tested. When a parameter is real-valued, the alternative is also specified, so we need to decide if the null hypothesis or its alternative is more plausible.

3. **Confidence intervals.** For a real-valued parameter θ or for a real-valued function of θ, we construct the interval with endpoints determined by a sample that contains the unknown true value with a given probability, called **confidence level**.

In addition, we describe regression models.

After studying this chapter, readers will become familiar with basic statistical techniques and develop skills required to make inferences from data.

Exercises will further deepen and develop readers' knowledge of material presented.

5.1 Point Estimation

In this chapter we will outline several common statistical models and briefly describe basic statistical procedures. The setup in most cases is such that a sample is a collection of n independent observations of a random variable, X, where n is a sample size. The observations

$$\mathbf{X} = \{X_1, X_2, \ldots, X_n\}$$

follow a certain partially known distribution with the cumulative distribution function (CDF) depending on an unknown parameter θ:

$$F(x) = \mathbf{P}\left[X \leq x\right] = F_\theta\left(x\right) = F\left(x; \theta\right),$$

where θ is a real-valued or vector-valued parameter.

Following are typical examples of point estimates.

5.1.1 Normal Model

Parameter $\boldsymbol{\theta} = (\mu, \sigma^2)$ is a pair, where $\mu = \mathbf{E}[X]$ is the expectation of X, and $\sigma^2 = \mathbf{Var}[X]$ is the variance of X. The **CDF** can be also expressed as

$$F\left(x; \mu, \sigma^2\right) = \Phi\left(\frac{x-\mu}{\sigma}\right),$$

where $\Phi(z)$ is the **CDF** of the standard normal random variable, Z. A common notation for this model is $\mathbf{N}(\mu, \sigma^2)$.

Point estimates of μ and σ^2 (known as the **sample mean** and **sample variance**) are defined as follows:

$$\bar{X} = \frac{1}{n}\sum_{i=1}^{n} X_i \quad\text{and}\quad s^2 = \frac{1}{n-1}\sum_{i=1}^{n}\left(X_i - \bar{X}\right)^2$$

The sample variance can also be evaluated as

$$s^2 = \frac{1}{n-1}\left[\sum_{i=1}^{n}\left(X_i\right)^2 - n\left(\bar{X}\right)^2\right].$$

The **sampling** distribution of $\bar{X}$ is also normal, that is $\mathbf{N}\left[\mu, \frac{\sigma^2}{n}\right]$, which will be used for more advanced inferences about this parameter. Note that the statistic

$$\chi^2 = \frac{(n-1)s^2}{\sigma^2}$$

follows the chi-squared distribution, with $(n-1)$ degrees of freedom.

Since $\chi^2(n)$ is a member of a gamma family, this statistic can also be considered as having gamma distribution, with parameters $\alpha = 0.5(n-1)$ and $\theta = 2$: **Gamma** $[0.5(n-1), 2]$.

5.1.2 Lognormal Model

In this case the observed values in the array $\mathbf{X}$ are viewed as a sample from the lognormal distribution, so $\mathbf{Y}\ \{Y_i = \ln X_i : 1 \le i \le n\}$ would follow the normal distribution, $\mathbf{N}(\mu, \sigma^2)$. Therefore, parameters of the lognormal distribution, such as mean and variance, are estimated according to the identities

$$\mathbf{E}[X] = e^{\mu + 0.5\sigma^2} \quad\text{and}\quad \mathbf{Var}[X] = e^{2\mu + \sigma^2}\left(e^{\sigma^2} - 1\right).$$

After estimates for μ and σ^2 are obtained, one can use them to estimate the mean and variance for a lognormally-distributed variable X.

5.1.3 Binary Data

Often the observations presented as an array, $\mathbf{X}$, are assumed to follow the Bernoulli distribution:

$$\mathbf{P}[X = 1] = p, \quad\text{and}\quad \mathbf{P}[X = 0] = 1 - p,$$

where the parameter is $\theta = p$ and $0 < p < 1$. Having n records, the natural estimate for p is the **sample proportion**

$$\hat{p} = \frac{1}{n} \sum_{i=1}^{n} X_i = \frac{Y}{n},$$

where $Y = \sum_{i=1}^{n} X_i$ is the number of **successes** among n independent Bernoulli trials.

It is known from probability theory that Y has binomial distribution, with parameters n and p, $\mathbf{Bin}\,[n, p]$, which is the explanatory tool for this model.

5.2   Point Estimator's Performance

Suppose that a sample, $\mathbf{X} = \{X_i : \ 1 \leq i \leq n\}$, of size n is drawn. Their common distribution is described by a parameter, θ, which may be one-dimensional or vector-valued. Let $T = T(\mathbf{X})$ be a function of observed records viewed as an estimate for θ.

5.2.1   Bias of the Estimator

Bias of the estimator T is the excess of the expected value of the estimator over its true value:

$$\mathbf{Bias}_{\theta}\,[T] = \mathbf{Bias}\,[T; \theta] = \mathbf{E}\,[T] - \theta$$

An estimator is called **unbiased** if $\mathbf{Bias}_{\theta}\,[T] = 0$.

An estimator is called **asymptotically unbiased** if

$$\lim_{n \to \infty} \mathbf{Bias}_{\theta}\,[T] = 0.$$

5.2.2   Mean Square Error

Mean square error is the average square difference between the estimator and the true value of the parameter

$$\mathbf{MSE}_{\theta}\,[T] = \mathbf{E}_{\theta}\,[(T - \theta)^2].$$

The lower the MSE, the better the estimator.

The estimator is called a **uniformly minimum variance unbiased estimator** if it's unbiased and if there is no other unbiased estimator with a smaller variance for any true value of θ.

There is an important connection between the MSE, bias, and variance:

$$\mathbf{MSE}_{\theta}\,[T] = \mathbf{Var}\,[T; \theta] + (\mathbf{Bias}\,[T; \theta])^2$$

An alternative name for **MSE** is **quadratic risk**.

Although there are many alternative measures of efficiency, the **MSE** is considered the main characteristic for optimal estimation. If T and $\tilde{T}$ are two estimates, and $\mathbf{MSE}\,[T] < \mathbf{MSE}\,[\tilde{T}]$, then T is considered more efficient than $\tilde{T}$.

5.2.3   Examples of Unbiased Estimates

In this section we provide examples of unbiased estimates for selected distributions.

5.2.3.1   Normal Data

When a sample, $\mathbf{X}$, of size n is drawn from a normal population, $\mathbf{N}\left[\mu, \sigma^2\right]$, the estimates of μ and σ^2 are known as sample mean, $\bar{X}$, and variance, S^2. They are defined as

$$\bar{X} = \frac{1}{n} \sum_{i=1}^{n} X_i \quad \text{and} \quad S^2 = \frac{1}{n-1} \sum_{i=1}^{n} (X_i - \bar{X})^2$$

and are known to be unbiased estimates of μ and σ^2:

$$\mathbf{E}\left[\bar{X}\right] = \mu \quad \text{and} \quad \mathbf{E}\left[S^2\right] = \sigma^2.$$

Their distributions are also known:

$$\bar{X} \sim \mathbf{N}\left[\mu, \frac{\sigma^2}{n}\right] \quad \text{and} \quad \frac{(n-1)S^2}{\sigma^2} \sim \chi^2\left[n-1\right]$$

Calculating **MSE** for the estimator $\bar{X}$, we have

$$\mathbf{MSE}\left[\bar{X}\right] = \mathbf{Var}\left[\bar{X}\right] = \frac{\sigma^2}{n}.$$

To evaluate **MSE** for S^2 note that a random variable distributed as a χ^2 with $(n-1)$ degrees of freedom can also be viewed as Gamma-distributed with parameters $\alpha = (n-1)/2$ and $\theta = 2$: $\mathbf{Gamma}\left[((n-1)/2, 2)\right]$. Thus, the distribution of $(n-1)S^2/\sigma^2$ is Gamma

$$\frac{(n-1)S^2}{\sigma^2} \sim \mathbf{Gamma}\left[\frac{n-1}{2}, 2\right]$$

and the distribution of S^2 is Gamma

$$S^2 \sim \mathbf{Gamma}\left[\frac{n-1}{2}, \frac{2\sigma^2}{n-1}\right].$$

Therefore,

$$\mathbf{MSE}\left[S^2\right] = \mathbf{Var}\left[S^2\right] = \alpha \cdot \theta^2 = \left(\frac{n-1}{2}\right) \cdot \left(\frac{2\sigma^2}{n-1}\right)^2 = \frac{2\sigma^4}{n-1}.$$

5.2.3.2   Bernoulli Distribution

When a sample, $\mathbf{X}$, of size n is formed by binary records with a common success rate, $\theta = p$, their sum has binomial distribution:

$$Y = \sum_{i=1}^{n} X_i \sim \mathbf{Bin}\left[n, p\right]$$

The unbiased estimate of θ is known as sample proportion, $\hat{p} = Y/n$, with mean and variance as follows:

$$\mathbf{E}\left[\hat{p}\right] = p \quad \text{and} \quad \mathbf{Var}\left[\hat{p}\right] = \frac{p(1-p)}{n}$$

Therefore, **MSE** for this unbiased estimate also coincides with its variance:

$$\textbf{MSE}\left[\hat{p}\right] = \textbf{Var}\left[\ddot{p}\right] = \frac{p(1-p)}{n}$$

5.3 Hypothesis Testing

Assuming that the observed records follow a certain partially known distribution, the hypothesis-testing procedures can be outlined as follows:

The **null hypothesis**,

$$H_0 : \theta = \theta_0,$$

completely specifies the underlying distribution.

The **alternative** (or alternative hypothesis) ideally would look like

$$H_1 : \theta = \theta_1 \neq \theta_0,$$

but this is a purely theoretical setup. In reality, one deals with a real-valued parameter, say τ, which may be either a univariate θ itself, or a certain transform, or a component when θ is a vector. The alternative for a real-valued parameter may be one-sided or two-sided.

If a hypothesis is defined as $\theta = \theta^*$, we will call it **simple**. Otherwise, we call it **composite**.

5.3.1 Significance Level

In the ideal situation, when the simple, or completely specified, null hypothesis, $H_0 : \theta = \theta_0$, is being tested against (or **versus**) a simple alternative, $H_1 : \theta = \theta_1$, there are two potentially available **decisions**: We either **reject** the null hypothesis in favor of the alternative, or we **fail to reject** it.

There are two sources of uncertainty in any hypothesis testing situation: Either the H_0 hypothesis is true or the H_1 hypothesis is true.

The consequences of decision can be outlined by the following table:

	True	
Decision	H_0	H_1
Reject H_0	Type I error	OK
Do not reject H_0	OK	Type II error

The probabilities of type I and type II errors can be considered as the measures of statistical decision-making risk.

The probability to reject the null hypothesis, while it is true, or probability of type I error, is known as the **significance level**. It is denoted as α. Thus,

$$\alpha = \mathbf{P}\left[\text{Reject } H_0 \,|\, H_0 \text{ is true}\right]. \tag{5.1}$$

The probability to not reject the null hypothesis, while the alternative hypothesis is true, or probability of type II error, is denoted as β. Thus,

$$\beta = \mathbf{P}\left[\text{Do not reject } H_0 \,|\, H_1 \text{ is true}\right].$$

It is possible to evaluate β only if the alternative is simple, that is, specifying completely the value of the parameter of interest. As we move on to more realistic situations, evaluating β becomes progressively more difficult.

The following examples explore introduced notions.

5.3.2 Normal Theory: Known Variance

In case of a known variance, the parameter $\boldsymbol{\theta} = (\mu, \sigma^2)$ is replaced by μ. As noticed in section 5.1.1, the sampling distribution of $\bar{X}$ is normal, with parameters:

$$\mathbf{E}\left[\bar{X}\right] = \mu \quad \text{and} \quad \mathbf{Var}\left[\bar{X}\right] = \frac{\sigma^2}{n},$$

which implies that if the parameter μ were known, then the **pivotal** statistic,

$$Z = \sqrt{n} \cdot \frac{\bar{X} - \mu}{\sigma} = \frac{\bar{X} - \mu}{\sigma/\sqrt{n}} \tag{5.2}$$

has the standard normal distribution.

The null hypothesis specifies the value of μ as $\mu = \mu_0$. There are several commonly used types of alternatives:

1. **Right-sided** alternative states: $(H_1 : \mu > \mu_0)$

2. **Left-sided** alternative states: $(H_1 : \mu < \mu_0)$

3. **Two-sided** or **double-sided** alternatives, which do not specify the direction for the parameter and states: $(H_1 : \mu \neq \mu_0)$

Right- and left-sided alternatives can be viewed as one-sided.

The following operating rules describe testing procedures, known as a **Z-test**, for each alternative.

For the right-sided alternative, the deviation of the Z-statistic to the right becomes a significant reason for rejecting the null hypothesis. Using the significance level introduced in (5.1), we reject the null hypothesis in favor of the right-sided alternative if $Z > z_\alpha$, where $z_\alpha = \Phi^{-1}(1 - \alpha)$ is the right-sided α-quantile, defined as

$$\mathbf{P}\left[Z > z_\alpha\right] = \alpha.$$

The value z_α is referred to as the **right-sided critical** value.

For the left-sided alternative, the deviation of the Z-statistic to the left becomes a significant reason for rejecting the null hypothesis. Using the significance level introduced in (5.1), we reject the null hypothesis in favor of the left-sided alternative if $Z < z_{1-\alpha}$, where $z_{1-\alpha} = \Phi^{-1}(\alpha)$ is the left-sided α-quantile, defined as

$$\mathbf{P}\left[Z < z_{1-\alpha}\right] = \alpha.$$

The value $z_{1-\alpha}$ is referred to as the **left-sided critical** value.

Note that, due to symmetry of the normal distribution, $z_{1-\alpha} = -z_\alpha$.

Finally, for the two-sided alternative, two critical values are needed. The significance level has to be split evenly between the two tails of the normal distribution, so the critical values are defined as

$$\mathbf{LCV} = -z_{\alpha/2} \text{ and } \mathbf{RCV} = z_{\alpha/2}.$$

The null hypothesis is rejected in favor of the double-sided alternative if

$$\text{either } Z > z_{\alpha/2} \text{ or } Z < -z_{\alpha/2}.$$

5.3.3 Normal Theory: Unknown Variance

When the underlying normal distribution has unknown variance, the procedure based on the pivotal Z-statistic defined in (5.2) becomes useless. It is tempting to replace the standard deviation of the sample mean, $\sigma/\sqrt{n}$, by its sample version, which results in the pivotal statistic,

$$T = \sqrt{n} \cdot \frac{\bar{X} - \mu}{s} = \frac{\bar{X} - \mu}{s/\sqrt{n}}, \tag{5.3}$$

where $s = \sqrt{s^2}$ is the sample standard deviation based on the **same** sample as the statistic $\bar{X}$.

The T-statistic has the so-called Student's t-distribution with $(n-1)$ degrees of freedom.

Similar to the normal distribution, the t-distribution is also symmetric. Similar operating rules describe testing procedures, known as a **T-test**, for each alternative.

Critical values of t-distribution are tabulated for commonly used percentiles. As the sample size, n, increases, the critical t-values approach the corresponding critical values for Z, which means that

$$t[n-1;\alpha] \longrightarrow z_\alpha, \text{ as } n \longrightarrow \infty.$$

The hypothesis-testing procedures are essentially modifications of what was outlined previously, by using the adjustments suggested by (5.3), with critical Z-values being replaced by critical T-values.

5.3.4 Hypothesis Testing for Variance

Assuming that the sample $\mathbf{X}$ is drawn from the normal population, $\mathbf{N}[\mu, \sigma^2]$, hypothesis testing for the population variance can be outlined similarly, with caution for the pivotal statistic. In this case, the key tool is the sample variance, s^2. The pivotal statistic is

$$\chi^2 = \frac{(n-1)s^2}{\sigma^2}, \tag{5.4}$$

which follows the chi-squared distribution with $(n-1)$ degrees of freedom. Critical values are tabulated.

The following operating rules describe testing procedures for each alternative:

1. Right-sided alternative operates with $(H_0 : \sigma^2 = \sigma_0^2)$ being tested against the alternative $(H_1 : \sigma^2 > \sigma_0^2)$. For the specified significance level, α, set the right-sided critical value, $\mathbf{RCV} = \chi^2\,[n-1; \alpha]$, such that the test statistic defined in (5.4) exceeds this value with probability equal α. Then the rejection of the null hypothesis in favor of the right-sided alternative occurs when the test statistic exceeds the right-sided critical value.

2. In the case of left-sided alternative, when $(H_0 : \sigma^2 = \sigma_0^2)$ is being tested against the alternative, $(H_1 : \sigma^2 < \sigma_0^2)$, set the left-sided critical value, $\mathbf{LCV} = \chi^2\,[n-1; 1-\alpha]$, so the test statistic will fall below this value, with probability equal to the significance level. The null hypothesis will then be rejected in favor of the left-sided alternative if the test statistic is below the left-sided critical value.

3. In the case of double-sided alternative, $(H_1 : \sigma^2 \neq \sigma_0^2)$, two critical values are required,

$$\mathbf{LCV} = \chi^2\,[n-1; 1-\alpha/2] \quad \text{and} \quad \mathbf{RCV} = \chi^2\,[n-1; \alpha/2]\,.$$

The null hypothesis will be rejected in favor of the double-sided alternative (at the significance level α) if either the test statistic (5.4) exceeds the right-sided critical value or it falls below the left-sided critical value.

5.3.5 Z-Test for Population Proportion

Assume that the sample $\mathbf{X}$ of **large** size n is a collection of zero-one variables, with the common unknown rate $p = \mathbf{P}\,[X = 1]$.

The sample proportion, $\hat{p} = Y/n$, is based on the sum $Y = \sum_{i=1}^{n} X_i$, which is the number of successes. Being a sum of n Bernoulli random variables, Y follows the binomial distribution $\mathbf{Bin}\,[n, p]$. Since the sample size is large, by the central limit theorem the **approximate** distribution is normal, with the mean and variance of Y determined as

$$\mu = np \quad \text{and} \quad \sigma^2 = np\,(1-p)\,.$$

Using rules for expectation and variance, we conclude that

$$\mathbf{E}\,[\hat{p}] = p \quad \text{and} \quad \mathbf{Var}\,[\hat{p}] = \frac{p\,(1-p)}{n}\,.$$

Hence, the test statistic, defined as,

$$Z = \frac{Y - np}{\sqrt{np\,(1-p)}} = \frac{\hat{p} - p}{\mathbf{SD}\,[\hat{p}]}, \quad \mathbf{SD}\,[\hat{p}] = \sqrt{\frac{p\,(1-p)}{n}} \tag{5.5}$$

is approximately standard normal, $\mathbf{N}\,[0, 1]\,.$

The same operating rules for normal sample are applicable in this situation:

1. If the null hypothesis, $(H_0 : p = p_0)$, is being tested against the right-sided alternative, set $\mathbf{RCV} = z_\alpha$ and reject the null hypothesis in favor of the right-sided alternative, $(H_1 : p > p_0)$, if the test statistic defined by (5.5) exceeds the right-sided critical value.

2. If the null hypothesis is being tested against the left-sided alternative, ($H_1 : p < p_0$), set **LCV** $= -z_\alpha$ and then the null hypothesis will be rejected in favor of the left-sided alternative if the test statistic from (5.5) falls below this value.

3. Finally, for the two-sided alternative, ($H_1 : p \neq p_0$), set two critical values,

$$\textbf{LCV} = -z_{\alpha/2} \ \text{ and } \ \textbf{RCV} = z_{\alpha/2},$$

so that the null hypothesis is rejected in favor of the two-sided alternative when either $Z > \textbf{RCV}$ or $Z < \textbf{LCV}$.

5.3.6 Kolmogorov–Smirnov Goodness-of-Fit Test

The following procedure, referred to as the Kolmogorov–Smirnov goodness-of-fit or K–S GOF test, differs from the ones outlined. In particular, the null hypothesis assumes that the observations $\mathbf{X} = \{X_1, X_2, \dots, X_n\}$ represent a large sample from a continuous distribution, with the cumulative distribution function (**CDF**),

$$F(x) = \mathbf{P}\left[X \leq x\right].$$

The null hypothesis is that the sample is drawn from the known reference distribution (in the one-sample case) or that the samples are drawn from the same distribution (in the two-sample case). The alternative is relatively vague, and this is common for the so-called **non-parametric** problems. The common non-parametric tool is known as **order statistics**. Continuity of the underlying distribution allows one to define ordered values based on the sample so that

$$X(1) < X(2) < \cdots < X(k) < \dots < X(n)$$

are all distinct with probability one.

Let F^* be the **fitted** distribution function,

$$F^*(x) = \frac{F(x) - F(d)}{1 - F(d)}, \tag{5.6}$$

if observed data are left-truncated at d, and

$$F^*(x) = \frac{F(x)}{F(u)},$$

if observed data are right-truncated at u. Note that $F^*(x) = F(x)$ for untruncated data.

Let $\hat{F}$ be the **empirical CDF** defined as

$$\hat{F}(x) = \frac{k}{n} \ \text{ for } \ X(k) \leq x < X(k+1), \tag{5.7}$$

where $1 \leq k \leq n - 1$. The edges are handled so that $\hat{F}(x) = 0$ for $x < X(1)$ and $\hat{F}(x) = 1$ for $x \geq X(n)$.

The following procedure is known as **Smirnov transformation**. For each X_i, consider $Y_i = F^*(X_i)$. Then the Y_i values form a sample from a uniform distribution, **UNIF** $(0,1)$. The underlying **CDF** is then $F_Y(y) = y$.

The Kolmogorov–Smirnov statistic quantifies a distance between the empirical distribution function of the sample and the cumulative distribution function of the reference distribution, or between the empirical distribution functions of two samples. It is defined as

$$D = D_n = \sqrt{n} \max_{0 \leq t \leq 1} \left| \hat{F}(x) - F^*(x) \right|$$

and can be evaluated using the two auxiliary statistics

$$D^+ = \sqrt{n} \max_{1 \leq k \leq n} \left[Y(k) - \frac{k}{n} \right] \quad \text{and} \quad D^- = \sqrt{n} \max_{1 \leq k \leq n} \left[Y(k) - \frac{k-1}{n} \right]$$

so that $D = \max [D^+, D^-]$.

Critical values of the statistic $D = D_n$, are tabulated (see appendix A).

The deviation of D to the right indicates that the null hypothesis has to be rejected at the specified significance level. If D_α is such a value that $\mathbf{P}[D > D_\alpha] = \alpha$, then the null hypothesis about the true distribution is rejected at the significance level α when D exceeds the critical value. Otherwise, we have no sufficient evidence to reject the null hypothesis.

Note that the K–S test uses a single point to calculate its statistic, the point of maximal difference between the empirical and the fitted **CDF**. The following test integrates the difference over the entire range of data[1].

5.3.7 Anderson–Darling Goodness-of-Fit Test

The Anderson–Darling goodness-of-fit test is also used to provide a decision about whether to accept or reject a null hypothesis that the data is drawn from the referenced distribution.

Let F, F^* and $\hat{F}$ be the reference, fitted and empirical **CDF**, respectively, where F^* and $\hat{F}$ are given by (5.6) and (5.7). Let S be the corresponding survival function. In addition, let t be the lower truncation point and u be the upper censoring point of observations. The Anderson–Darling statistic A^2 is defined as

$$A^2 = n \int_t^u \frac{(\hat{F}(x) - F^*(x))^2}{F^*(x)(1 - F^*(x))} f^*(x) \, dx.$$

In this formula n includes censored observations.

For individual data A^2 is defined as a sum,

$$A^2 = -nF^*(u) + n \sum_{j=0}^{k} \left(\hat{S}(y_j) \right)^2 (\ln S^*(y_j) - \ln S^*(y_{j+1})) +$$

$$+ n \sum_{j=1}^{k} \left(\hat{F}(y_j) \right)^2 (\ln F^*(y_{j+1}) - \ln F^*(y_j)), \tag{5.8}$$

where k is the number of unique non-censored data points:

$$t = y_0' < y_1 < \cdots < t_t < y_{k+1} = u.$$

Note that the statistic is always nonnegative. As with the K–S test, if the test statistic does not exceed the critical value, we do not reject the null hypothesis.

Critical values for the A–D statistic A^2 for specific null distribution models are tabulated (see appendix B). The A–D test is widely used in industry.

5.3.8 Chi-Squared Goodness-of-Fit Test

This testing procedure is to some extent more universal than the K–S test. It is applicable to both discrete and continuous distributions.

5.3.8.1 Chi-Squared GOF Test: Discrete Observations

Assume a random variable X takes only one of the values $\{x_j : 1 \leq j \leq m\}$. Then the null hypothesis specifies the **theoretical** probabilities or proportions, so the parameter in this case can be viewed as a vector,

$$\mathbf{p} = (p_1, p_2, \ldots, p_m), \ 0 < p_j < 1, \ \forall j = 1, 2, \ldots, m, \ \sum_{j=1}^{m} p_j = 1.$$

The alternative claims that the true distribution of X is characterized by a different (unspecified) vector

$$\mathbf{q} = (q_1, q_2, \ldots, q_m), \ q_j > 0, \ \forall j = 1, 2, \ldots, m, \ \sum_{j=1}^{m} q_j = 1.$$

As in the situation with the K–S test, the alternative becomes composite, and the approximate distribution of the test statistic under the null hypothesis is utilized for this procedure.

Assuming that a large sample of size n is collected, let us introduce the **observed frequency**, f_j, as the count of X values equal x_j, for $j = 1, 2, \ldots, m$. The expected count, E_j, for the event $[X = x_j]$ to occur is $E_j = np_j$.

It follows the properties of binomial distribution, once we treat the event $[X = x_j]$ as a success, and the complementary event as a failure.

In addition to the assumption about the large sample size, it is usually assumed that all expected counts satisfy the condition $E_j \geq 5$. Otherwise, the hidden normal approximation to the binomial will not be legitimate.

Once the preparations are made, the hypothesis-testing procedure is based on the statistic,

$$\chi^2 = \sum_{j=1}^{m} \frac{(f_j - E_j)^2}{E_j} = \sum_{j=1}^{m} \frac{f_j^2}{E_j} - m. \tag{5.9}$$

Under the null hypothesis this goodness-of-fit statistic will approximately follow the χ^2-distribution with $(m - 1)$ degrees of freedom. Large deviations of this statistic will favor the rejection, so the procedure works as follows:

Given the significance level α, choose the critical value, $\mathbf{CV} = \chi^2\,[m-1,\alpha]$, such that the probability to exceed it is α:

$$\mathbf{P}[\chi^2 > \mathbf{CV}] = \alpha$$

Then evaluate the test statistic in (5.9). If the test statistic exceeds the critical value, then the null hypothesis is rejected in favor of the alternative at the specified significance level. Otherwise, the null hypothesis is not rejected.

5.3.8.2 Chi-Squared GOF Test: Continuous Observations

If the observations are continuously distributed, the preliminary step should be implemented to make a reasonable number of groups or a partition of the real line. Assume that $(m+1)$ subintervals are set up so that

$$-\infty < x_1 < x_2 < \ldots < x_m < \infty,$$

and for each j, such that $2 \leq j \leq m+1$, the observed frequencies are defined so that f_j is the count of how many X-values are inside the interval $x_{j-1} < X \leq x_j$. Denote f_1 as the count of X-values below x_1.

Now introduce the theoretical proportions

$$\begin{aligned}
p_1 &= \mathbf{P}\,[X \leq x_1] = F\,(x_1) \\
p_j &= \mathbf{P}\,[x_j < X \leq x_{j+1}] = F\,(x_{j+1}) - F\,(x_j), \quad \text{for } 1 \leq j \leq m-1 \\
p_{m+1} &= \mathbf{P}\,[X > x_m] = 1 - F\,(x_m).
\end{aligned}$$

Set $E_j = np_j$ for $1 \leq j \leq m+1$ and assume that those expected counts are all at the level of 5 or higher. Then one can apply the procedure outlined for discrete data. The only difference is that now we are facing $(m+1)$ distinct groups instead of m. All steps in this procedure can be repeated, similar to the test statistic defined by (5.9).

5.4   Confidence Intervals

Point estimation of an unknown parameter is an example of a statistical decision. However, numerous applications require a certain interval of parameter values that has a relatively large probability to cover the unknown true value. This probability is called a **confidence level**. Typically, the confidence level is set as 90%, 95%, or 99%. The pivotal statistic plays an important role in deriving the confidence intervals. We are going to illustrate confidence intervals for several situations.

5.4.1   Normal Data with Specified Variance

Assume that the sample of size n is drawn from the normal population, $\mathbf{N}\,[\mu, \sigma^2]$, with the population variance specified. Then,

$$\mathbf{X} = \{X_i : \ 1 \leq i \leq n\}$$

is the sample and $\bar{X} = \frac{1}{n}\sum_{i=1}^{n} X_i$ is the sample mean. According to (5.2), the pivotal statistic,

$$Z = \frac{\bar{X} - \mu}{\sigma/\sqrt{n}},$$

has the standard normal distribution. If C is a given confidence level, then the symmetric bounds for Z are such that

$$\mathbf{P}\left[Z > z^+\right] = \mathbf{P}\left[Z < z^-\right] = \frac{\alpha}{2},$$

where $\alpha = 1 - C$. Therefore,

$$\mathbf{P}\left[z^- < Z < z^+\right] = 1 - \alpha/2 - \alpha/2 = C,$$

where $z^- = \Phi^{-1}(\alpha/2)$ and $z^+ = \Phi^{-1}(1 - \alpha/2)$. Alternatively, due to symmetry of the standard normal distribution,

$$z^+ = \Phi^{-1}\left(\frac{1+C}{2}\right) \quad \text{and} \quad z^- = -z^+ = \Phi^{-1}\left(\frac{1-C}{2}\right).$$

Converting the Z-scores into the scale for $\bar{X}$ using (5.2), we obtain the confidence limits in the format:

$$\mathbf{LCL} = \bar{X} - z^+ \cdot \frac{\sigma}{\sqrt{n}} \quad \text{and} \quad \mathbf{UCL} = \bar{X} + z^+ \cdot \frac{\sigma}{\sqrt{n}},$$

where **LCL** and **UCL** denote the **lower** and **upper** confidence limits. The confidence is of the form

$$(\mathbf{UCL}, \mathbf{LCL}) = \bar{X} \pm z^+ \cdot \frac{\sigma}{\sqrt{n}}.$$

The width of the interval is the difference $\mathbf{UCL} - \mathbf{LCL}$, which equals the double margin of error, where the margin of error is

$$\mathbf{ME} = z^+ \left(\frac{\sigma}{\sqrt{n}}\right). \tag{5.10}$$

The **random** interval with the end points $(\mathbf{LCL}, \mathbf{UCL})$, with the probability equal the confidence level, C, contains the true value of the population mean, μ.

5.4.1.1 Designing a Study

When one needs to design a study to ensure that the confidence interval has the margin of error no bigger than a specified value, say B, the procedure outlined for the confidence interval can be utilized.

Assume that the confidence level, C, is specified and the confidence interval is expected to have the margin of error **ME**, no bigger than the given value of B. Let us calculate the smallest sample size needed.

Once the confidence level is given, the critical value, z^+, can be found. For the commonly used values, the following table may help.

$C =$ Confidence level	0.80	0.90	0.95	0.98	0.99
$q = 1 - \alpha/2 = (1+C)/2$	0.90	0.95	0.975	0.99	0.995
$z^+ = \Phi^{-1}(q)$	1.282	1.645	1.960	2.326	2.576

Since the desired margin of error should not exceed B, the following inequality holds:

$$\mathbf{ME} = z^+ \left(\frac{\sigma}{\sqrt{n}} \right) \leq B$$

Solving for n, we obtain

$$n \geq \left(\frac{z^+ \sigma}{B} \right)^2 .$$

Thus, the smallest sample size is $n = (z^+ \sigma / B)^2$ rounded to the next integer.

5.4.2 Normal Data with Unknown Variance

Assume that the sample of size n is drawn from the normal population, $\mathbf{N}\left[\mu, \sigma^2\right]$, with the population variance **unknown**. Thus,

$$\mathbf{X} = \{X_i : \ 1 \leq i \leq n\}$$

is the sample and $\bar{X} = \frac{1}{n} \sum_{i=1}^{n} X_i$ is the sample mean.

Since the population variance is unknown, the statistic that needs to be utilized is the sample variance:

$$s^2 = \frac{1}{n-1} \sum_{i=1}^{n} \left(X_i - \bar{X} \right)^2$$

Instead of the population standard deviation for $\bar{X}$, we will use its sample-based version, known as the **standard error**:

$$\mathbf{SE} = \frac{s}{\sqrt{n}}$$

The pivotal statistic is now switched from (5.2) to (5.3), and the sampling distribution of this t-statistic is the t-distribution with $(n-1)$ degrees of freedom.

Similar to the previously described procedure, after this modification we obtain the upper and lower confidence limits in the form

$$(\mathbf{UCL}, \mathbf{LCL}) = \bar{X} \pm t^+ \, \mathbf{SE},$$

where $t^+ = t\left[(n-1), \alpha/2\right]$ is the critical value from the table of selected critical values for the t-distribution. Since the t-distribution is also symmetric, the width of the confidence interval is twice the margin of error:

$$\mathbf{UCL} - \mathbf{LCL} = 2 \cdot t^+ \cdot \mathbf{SE}$$

Note that the distribution of the pivotal statistic depends on the sample size, thus making it difficult to design the study similar to the one with the known sample variance.

5.4.2.1 Confidence Intervals for the Population Variance

Again, assume that the sample of size n is drawn from the normal population, $\mathbf{N}\left[\mu, \sigma^2\right]$, with the population variance **unknown**. The targeted parameter is now the population variance, σ^2. According to (5.4), the pivotal statistic,

$$\chi^2 = \frac{(n-1)\, s^2}{\sigma^2},$$

has χ^2-distribution with $(n-1)$ degrees of freedom. Let C be the desired confidence level. Similar to the two-sided alternative, define two critical values:

$$\mathbf{LCV} = \chi^2 \left[(n-1), 1 - \frac{\alpha}{2} \right] \text{ and } \mathbf{RCV} = \chi^2 \left[(n-1), \frac{\alpha}{2} \right]$$

The pivotal statistic will satisfy conditions:

$$\mathbf{P}\left[\chi^2 > \mathbf{RCV}\right] = \mathbf{P}\left[\chi^2 < \mathbf{LCV}\right] = \frac{\alpha}{2}.$$

Thus,

$$\mathbf{P}\left(\mathbf{LCV} < \chi^2 < \mathbf{RCV}\right) = C, \ \alpha = 1 - C.$$

Solving this inequality for the unknown value of σ^2, obtain the upper and lower confidence limits, $\mathbf{LCL}_{\sigma^2}$ and $\mathbf{UCL}_{\sigma^2}$, for σ^2:

$$\chi^2 > \mathbf{LCV} \Leftrightarrow \frac{(n-1)\,s^2}{\sigma^2} > \mathbf{LCV} \Leftrightarrow \sigma^2 < \frac{(n-1)\,s^2}{\mathbf{LCV}} \Rightarrow \mathbf{UCL} = \frac{(n-1)\,s^2}{\mathbf{LCV}}$$

$$\chi^2 < \mathbf{RCV} \Leftrightarrow \frac{(n-1)\,s^2}{\sigma^2} < \mathbf{RCV} \Leftrightarrow \sigma^2 > \frac{(n-1)\,s^2}{\mathbf{RCV}} \Rightarrow \mathbf{LCL} = \frac{(n-1)\,s^2}{\mathbf{RCV}}$$

Unlike the confidence intervals for the population mean, the χ^2-distribution is not symmetric, so the left critical value is still positive (and not opposite to the right critical value).

5.4.3 Confidence Intervals for the Population Proportion

Similar to the hypothesis-testing part for the population proportion, consider a large sample of binary variables,

$$\mathbf{X} = \{X_i : \ 1 \leq i \leq n\},$$

and introduce $Y = \sum_{i=1}^{n} X_i$, as a count of successes after n trials.

According to (5.5), the distribution of Y is nearly normal and so is the distribution of the sample proportion $\hat{p}$ with the mean p and standard deviation $\sqrt{p\,(1-p)\,/n}$.

Unlike the hypothesis testing, here there is no information about the true proportion p. However, since the sample size n is large, we can introduce the standard error of the sample proportion:

$$\mathbf{SE} = \sqrt{\frac{\hat{p}\,(1-\hat{p})}{n}}$$

Then the confidence interval for the population proportion is

$$(\mathbf{UCL}, \mathbf{LCL}) = \hat{p} \pm z^+ \cdot \mathbf{SE},$$

where $z^+ = \Phi^{-1}\left(1 - \alpha/2\right)$ is the critical value for the standard normal distribution. The amount $z^+ \cdot \mathbf{SE}$ also represents the margin of error for the interval estimate of the population proportion.

5.4.3.1   Designing a Study

Similar to the confidence intervals for the population mean, consider the design of a study aimed at constructing a confidence interval with the margin of error bounded by the given value B. Let C be the specified confidence level and z^+ be the corresponding critical value such that

$$\mathbf{P}\left[Z > z^+\right] = \mathbf{P}\left[Z < -z^+\right] = \frac{\alpha}{2}, \text{ and } \alpha = 1 - C.$$

The margin of error for the confidence interval is determined as

$$\mathbf{ME} = z^+ \cdot \mathbf{SE} = z^+ \cdot \frac{\sqrt{\hat{p}\left(1 - \hat{p}\right)}}{\sqrt{n}},$$

where $\hat{p}$ is also unknown.

The theoretical suggestion is to consider the **worst-case** scenario that corresponds to the largest possible value of the numerator in the expression for the margin of error. It is easy to see that, given the confidence level (and related critical value z^+), the maximal margin of error corresponds to $\hat{p} = 0.5$. Therefore, the objective is to make sure that, even in this case, the margin of error will not exceed B. Setting up the inequality

$$z^+ \cdot \frac{\sqrt{0.5\left(1 - 0.5\right)}}{\sqrt{n}} \le B$$

and solving for n, we obtain

$$n \ge \left(\frac{z^+}{2B}\right)^2,$$

which leads to the **smallest** number of records to be collected as $n = \left(z^+/2B\right)^2$, rounded up to the next integer value.

5.5   Linear Regression and Least Squares Method

Let the acronym **LS** indicate the method of the **least squares**.

5.5.1   Random Variables with Known Variance-Covariance Matrix

Consider random variables $Y, \{X_1, X_2, \ldots, X_m\}$ having finite second moments. Let $X_0 = 1$ be the identity random variable.

The inner product is defined as

$$A_j = Y \times X_j = \mathbf{E}\left[YX_j\right] \text{ for } 1 \le j \le m$$
$$C_{jk} = X_j \times X_k = \mathbf{E}\left[X_jX_k\right] \text{ for } 0 \le j, k \le m.$$

In particular,

$$C_{0k} = \mathbf{E}\left[X_k\right] \text{ and } A_0 = \mathbf{E}\left[Y\right].$$

The goal is to build an orthogonal projection of a variable Y onto a subspace spanned over the variables $\{X_j : 0 \le j \le m\}$. Such projection denoted as $\hat{Y}$ will be presented as

$$\hat{Y} = b_0 + \sum_{j=1}^{m} b_j X_j. \tag{5.11}$$

The implementation of **LS** is based on the system of so-called **normal equations**,

$$\hat{Y} \cdot X_j = Y \cdot X_j, \quad \text{for} \ \ 0 \le j \le m. \tag{5.12}$$

The system will **always** have a unique solution. Assuming that the matrix,

$$\mathbf{C} = [C_{jk} : \ 0 \le j, k \le m]$$

has the full rank of $(m+1)$, the coefficients in (5.11) for vector $b = (b_0, b_1, \ldots, b_m)$ of dimension $(m+1)$ can be expressed in the matrix form as $b = C^{-1}A$.

Since $\hat{Y}$ and $Y - \hat{Y}$ are orthogonal, by the Pythagorean theorem

$$\mathbf{Var}\left[Y\right] = \mathbf{Var}\left[\hat{Y}\right] + \mathbf{Var}\left[Y - \hat{Y}\right].$$

The solution for b can be also rewritten in terms of the **centered** variables,

$$Y - \mathbf{E}\left[Y\right] = \sum_{j=1}^{m} b_j \left(X_j - \mathbf{E}\left[X_j\right]\right),$$

which separates $X_0 = 1$ from other variables.

The tool known as orthogonal projection in (5.11) is usually viewed as the minimization of the expression

$$\mathbf{E}\left[\left(Y - \hat{Y}\right)^2\right] = \mathbf{E}\left(\left[Y - \left(b_0 + \sum_{j=1}^{m} b_j X_j\right)\right]\right)^2$$

in $(b_0, b_1, \ldots, b_m)$, which explains the name of **least squares**.

5.5.2 Least Squares Method in Statistics

Suppose that a random variable Y is observed so that $\mathbf{Y} = \{Y_i : \ 1 \le i \le n\}$ is an n-dimensional vector of observations.

In addition, given are n values of the m-dimensional vector X that can be viewed as either a vector of **control** variables or as a set of observations related to this vector. Let

$$\mathbf{X_i} = \{X_{ij} = X_i\left(j\right) \ 1 \le j \le m\}; \ 1 \le i \le n$$

so that $X_i\left(j\right) = X_{ij}$ is the jth component of a vector X_i for $j = 1, 2, \ldots, m$ and for $i = 1, 2, \ldots, n$. It is convenient to introduce the $n \times (m+1)$ matrix, with columns

$$\mathbf{X} = [X_0 = \mathbf{1}, X_1, X_2, \ldots, X_m],$$

where each column is an $n \times 1$ vector and $X_0 = \mathbf{1}$ has all n components equal 1:

$$X = \begin{bmatrix} 1 & X_{11} & X_{12} & \dots & X_{1m} \\ 1 & X_{21} & X_{22} & \dots & X_{2m} \\ & & \dots & & \\ 1 & X_{n1} & X_{n2} & \dots & X_{nm} \end{bmatrix}$$

This matrix is called the **design matrix**.

There are other assumptions that essentially lead to the same **linear regression model**, or **regression** of Y on $\{X_0, X_1, \dots, X_m\}$, that fit the values of Y and define the linear function

$$\hat{\mathbf{Y}} = \mathbf{X} \cdot \mathbf{b}, \tag{5.13}$$

where $\mathbf{b} = (b_0, b_1, \dots, b_m)'$ is a column vector with $(m+1)$ components, called the **vector of parameters**, and $\hat{\mathbf{Y}} = \left(\hat{Y}_1, \hat{Y}_2, \dots, \hat{Y}_n\right)'$ is a column vector with (n) components, called the **vector of responses**:

$$\begin{bmatrix} \hat{Y}_1 \\ \hat{Y}_2 \\ \vdots \\ \hat{Y}_n \end{bmatrix} = \begin{bmatrix} 1 & X_{11} & X_{12} & \dots & X_{1m} \\ 1 & X_{21} & X_{22} & \dots & X_{2m} \\ & & \dots & & \\ 1 & X_{n1} & X_{n2} & \dots & X_{nm} \end{bmatrix} \cdot \begin{bmatrix} b_0 \\ b_1 \\ \vdots \\ b_m \end{bmatrix}$$

Hence, the ith component of vector $\hat{Y}$ equals

$$\hat{Y}_i = b_0 + \sum_{j=1}^{m} b_j \cdot X_{ij}, \ i = 1, 2, \dots, n. \tag{5.14}$$

Here and later, for any matrix, $\mathbf{A}$, its transposed is denoted as $\mathbf{A}'$. Hence, $\mathbf{b}'$ is a row with $(m+1)$ components, while $\mathbf{X}'$ is a matrix with $(m+1)$ rows and n columns:

$$X' = \begin{bmatrix} 1 & 1 & \dots & 1 \\ X_{11} & X_{21} & \dots & X_{n1} \\ X_{12} & X_{22} & \dots & X_{n2} \\ & & \dots & \\ X_{1m} & X_{2m} & \dots & X_{nm} \end{bmatrix}$$

Consider a set of errors:

$$\epsilon = \mathbf{Y} - \hat{\mathbf{Y}} = \mathbf{Y} - \mathbf{X} \cdot \mathbf{b}$$

We would like to minimize the sum of squared errors:

$$f(\mathbf{b}) = \sum_{i=1}^{n} \left[Y_i - \hat{Y}_i\right]^2 = \sum_{i=1}^{n} \epsilon_i^2 = [\epsilon_1, \epsilon_2, \dots, \epsilon_n] \cdot \begin{bmatrix} \epsilon_1 \\ \epsilon_2 \\ \vdots \\ \epsilon_n \end{bmatrix} = \epsilon' \cdot \epsilon = (\mathbf{Y} - \mathbf{X} \cdot \mathbf{b})' \cdot (\mathbf{Y} - \mathbf{X} \cdot \mathbf{b})$$

The minimum is taken over all possible $(m+1)$-dimensional vectors $\mathbf{b}$, and the minimizing solution is the estimated vector β.

Consider the function

$$f(\mathbf{b}) = \sum_{i=1}^{n} \left[Y_i - \hat{Y}_i\right]^2 = \sum_{i=1}^{n} \left[Y_i - \left(b_0 + \sum_{j=1}^{m} b_j \cdot X_{ij}\right)\right]^2 = \sum_{i=1}^{n} \left[Y_i - b_0 - \sum_{j=1}^{m} b_j \cdot X_{ij}\right]^2.$$

Taking the derivatives with respect to $b_0, b_1, \ldots, b_m$, we obtain

$$\frac{\partial f}{\partial b_0} = -2 \sum_{i=1}^{n} \left(Y_i - b_0 - \sum_{j=1}^{m} b_j \cdot X_{ij}\right) \cdot 1$$

$$\frac{\partial f}{\partial b_1} = -2 \sum_{i=1}^{n} \left(Y_i - b_0 - \sum_{j=1}^{m} b_j \cdot X_{ij}\right) X_{i1}$$

$$\frac{\partial f}{\partial b_2} = -2 \sum_{i=1}^{n} \left(Y_i - b_0 - \sum_{j=1}^{m} b_j \cdot X_{ij}\right) X_{i2}$$

$$\vdots$$

$$\frac{\partial f}{\partial b_j} = -2 \sum_{i=1}^{n} \left(Y_i - b_0 - \sum_{j=1}^{m} b_j \cdot X_{ij}\right) X_{ij}$$

$$\vdots$$

$$\frac{\partial f}{\partial b_m} = -2 \sum_{i=1}^{n} \left(Y_i - b_0 - \sum_{j=1}^{m} b_j \cdot X_{ij}\right) X_{im}.$$

This $m + 1$ column vector can be written as

$$\frac{df}{db} = -2\mathbf{X}'(\mathbf{Y} - \mathbf{X}\cdot\mathbf{b}) = -2 \begin{bmatrix} 1 & 1 & \cdots & 1 \\ X_{11} & X_{21} & \cdots & X_{n1} \\ X_{12} & X_{22} & \cdots & X_{n2} \\ & & \cdots & \\ X_{1m} & X_{2m} & \cdots & X_{nm} \end{bmatrix} \cdot \begin{bmatrix} Y_1 - b_0 - \sum_{j=1}^{m} b_j \cdot X_{1j} \\ Y_2 - b_0 - \sum_{j=1}^{m} b_j \cdot X_{2j} \\ \vdots \\ Y_n - b_0 - \sum_{j=1}^{m} b_j \cdot X_{nj} \end{bmatrix}.$$

Equating this to zero, we obtain

$$\frac{df}{db} = 0 \Leftrightarrow \mathbf{X}'(\mathbf{Y} - \mathbf{X} \cdot \mathbf{b}) = 0 \Leftrightarrow \mathbf{X}'\mathbf{Y} = \mathbf{X}'\mathbf{X} \cdot \mathbf{b}.$$

The $(m + 1) \times (m + 1)$ matrix, $\mathbf{C} = \mathbf{X}'\mathbf{X}$, typically has the inverse, and the **LS** estimate, **b**, can be written in the matrix form as

$$\mathbf{b} = \mathbf{C}^{-1} \cdot (\mathbf{X}'\mathbf{Y}) = (\mathbf{X}'\mathbf{X})^{-1} \cdot (\mathbf{X}'\mathbf{Y}).$$

The vector of fitted values then can be expressed as

$$\hat{\mathbf{Y}} = \mathbf{X} \cdot \mathbf{b} = \mathbf{X} (\mathbf{X}\mathbf{X}')^{-1} \cdot (\mathbf{X}'\mathbf{Y}).$$

Even if the matrix $\mathbf{C}$ is singular, that is, the rank of $\mathbf{C}$ is smaller than $m + 1$, the formulae presented here can be extended using the generalized inverse matrices, while the matrix

$$\mathbf{Q} = \mathbf{X} \cdot (\mathbf{X}\mathbf{X}')^{-1} \cdot \mathbf{X}'$$

will be replaced by the matrix of the orthogonal projection of a vector Y onto the subspace in n-dimensional space spanned over the $(m + 1)$ vectors, $\{X_0, X_1, \ldots, X_m\}$.

To conclude, regardless of what setup leads to the system (5.12) or to the fitted model (5.11), the minimization of the **squared length** of $\left(Y - \hat{Y}\right)$ remains the unifying part of **LS** method. The model can be presented as either

$$\hat{Y} = b_0 + \sum_{j=1}^{m} b_j X_j \tag{5.15}$$

or its **centered** form

$$\hat{Y} - \mathbf{E}[Y] = \sum_{j=1}^{m} b_j \left(X_j - \mathbf{E}[X_j]\right). \tag{5.16}$$

When instead of expectations and variances one has to use observations, the expectations in (5.16) are replaced by sample means, and the same applies to all other evaluations related to expectations.

5.5.3   Simple Linear Regression

When $m = 1$, this is the simple linear regression model. If this is the case, the fitted value from (5.14) is simply a linear function of the predicting variable, $X = X_1$, so the equation (5.14) can be simplified to

$$\hat{Y}_i = b_0 + b_1 \cdot X_i, \quad \text{for} \ \ i = 1, 2, \ldots, n.$$

The coefficient b_1 in this model is called a **slope**, and the coefficient b_0 is called the **intercept**.

Assumptions for applicability of the multivariate linear regression model can vary. The most general setup is based on the assumption that observations $\{Y_i : 1 \leq i \leq n\}$ are independent and normally-distributed, with the expected values

$$\mathbf{E}[Y_i] = \beta_0 + \sum_{j=1}^{m} \beta_j \cdot X_{ij}, \quad \text{for} \ \ 1 \leq i \leq n,$$

and the variance (usually unknown) is equal σ^2, so

$$\mathbf{Var}[Y_i] = \sigma^2, \quad \text{for} \ \ 1 \leq i \leq n.$$

The coefficients presented as vector $\mathbf{b}$ in equations (5.13) and (5.14) can be viewed as the estimate of the **theoretical** vector, $\beta = (\beta_0, \beta_1, \ldots, \beta_m)$.

5.5.4   Alternative Approach to Linear Regression

Another possible setup that essentially leads to the same least squares is based on assumptions that vectors $\{X_0 = \mathbf{1}, X_1, \ldots, X_m\}$ are not random. In this case, vectors are called co-variates, and the estimation procedure utilizes the same minimization principle, similar to the one considered in section 5.5.2.

Conclusion

In this chapter we reviewed common notions and techniques used in statistics. Detailed explanations may be found in G. Casella and R. Berger[3] although any textbook focused on statistical inferences covering point estimation, confidence intervals, and hypothesis testing would also be appropriate.

Readers will recognize several traditional topics, such as Z-test, T-test or χ^2-test, as they solve exercises that follow.

Exercises

5.1. Mean Square Error of an Estimator

$\hat{\theta}$ is an estimator for θ. $\mathbf{E}[\hat{\theta}] = 5$ and $\mathbf{E}[\hat{\theta}^2] = 32$. Suppose $\theta = 7$.

Calculate the mean square error of $\hat{\theta}$.

5.2. Mean Square Error of an Estimator

Two different estimators, $\hat{\alpha}$ and $\hat{\beta}$, are available for estimating the parameter, γ, of a given loss distribution. To test their performance, you have conducted 85 simulated trials of each estimator, using $\gamma = 3$, with the following results:

$$\sum_{i=1}^{85} \hat{\alpha}_i = 179, \quad \sum_{i=1}^{85} \hat{\alpha}_i^2 = 390, \quad \sum_{i=1}^{85} \hat{\beta}_i = 154, \quad \sum_{i=1}^{85} \hat{\beta}_i^2 = 286$$

Calculate $\mathbf{MSE}_{\hat{\beta}}(\gamma)/\mathbf{MSE}_{\hat{\alpha}}(\gamma)$.

5.3. Mean Square Error of an Estimator

A population contains the values 2, 5, 8, 9, and 12. A sample of 4 without replacement is drawn from this population. Let Y be the median of this sample.

Calculate the mean square error of Y as an estimator of the population mean.

5.4. Kolmogorov–Smirnov Goodness-of-Fit Test

You are given the following data sample:

$$0.3 \quad 0.6 \quad 0.8 \quad 0.8$$

You wish to test the goodness-of-fit of the distribution with a probability density function given by

$$f(x) = \frac{1}{4}(3 + 2x), \quad 0 \le x \le 1.$$

Calculate the Kolmogorov–Smirnov goodness-of-fit statistic and provide a conclusion about the acceptance-rejection level of the null hypothesis.

5.5. Anderson–Darling Goodness-of-Fit Test

An insurer offers a coverage with a policy limit of 1500. The following four claims are observed on this coverage:

$$600 \quad 749 \quad 804 \quad 1250$$

It is also known that there are two additional claims for an amount over 1500 that are censored at 1500.

An actuary models ground-up losses using an exponential distribution with parameter $\theta = 1000$. This model is tested against the experience using the Anderson–Darling A^2 statistic.

Calculate A^2 and provide a conclusion about the acceptance-rejection level of the null hypothesis.

5.6. Chi-Squared Goodness-of-Fit Test

You are given the following information:

(i) A random sample of 120 observed accident losses have been recorded.

(ii) The losses are grouped as follows:

Interval ($000)	Number of Losses
$(2, 2.5)$	50
$[2.5, 4)$	45
$[4, \infty)$	25

You are testing the null hypothesis, H_0, that the random variable X underlying the observed losses has the density function

$$f(x) = \frac{24}{x^4}, \quad x > 2.$$

Using the chi-square goodness-of-fit test, determine which of the following statements is true:

(A) H_0 will be rejected at the 0.01 significance level.

(B) H_0 will be rejected at the 0.025 significance level but not at the 0.01 level.

(C) H_0 will be rejected at the 0.05 significance level but not at the 0.025 level.

(D) H_0 will be rejected at the 0.10 significance level but not at the 0.05 level.

(E) H_0 will be accepted at the 0.10 significance level.

5.7. Known Population Variance

Suppose that an individual car insurance policy premium is described as a normally-distributed variable, with unknown mean μ and population standard deviation $\sigma = 50$.

A sample of $n = 25$ car insurance premium policies produced the following summaries of sample mean and standard deviation:

$$\bar{X} = 522 \quad \text{and} \quad s = 62.50$$

Determine if there is sufficient evidence that the population mean **exceeds** 500 at the significance level of

(a) $\alpha = 5\%$ and

(b) $\alpha = 1\%$.

5.8. Known Population Variance

Suppose that an individual car insurance policy premium is described as a normally-distributed variable, with unknown mean μ and population standard deviation $\sigma = 50$.

A sample of $n = 25$ car insurance premium policies produced the following summaries of sample mean and standard deviation:

$$\bar{X} = 522 \quad \text{and} \quad s = 62.50$$

Determine if there is sufficient evidence that the population mean **differs** from 500 at the significance level of

(a) $\alpha = 5\%$ and

(b) $\alpha = 1\%$.

5.9. Unknown Population Variance

Suppose that an individual car insurance policy premium is described as a normally-distributed variable, with unknown mean μ and unknown population standard deviation.

A sample of $n = 25$ car insurance premium policies produced the following summaries of sample mean and standard deviation:

$$\bar{X} = 522 \quad \text{and} \quad s = 62.50$$

The null hypothesis, $H_0 : \mu = 500$, is being tested against the right-sided alternative, $H_1 : \mu > 500$.

Determine if there is sufficient evidence that the population mean $\mu > 500$ at the significance level of

(a) $\alpha = 5\%$ and

(b) $\alpha = 1\%$.

5.10. Unknown Population Variance

Suppose that an individual car insurance policy premium is described as a normally-distributed variable, with unknown mean μ and unknown population standard deviation.

A sample of $n = 25$ car insurance premium policies produced the following summaries of sample mean and standard deviation:

$$\bar{X} = 522 \quad \text{and} \quad s = 62.50$$

The null hypothesis, $H_0 : \mu = 500$, is being tested against the right-sided alternative, $H_1 : \mu > 500$.

Determine if there is sufficient evidence that the population mean $\mu \neq 500$ at the significance level of

(a) $\alpha = 5\%$ and

(b) $\alpha = 1\%$.

5.11. Confidence Interval: Known Population Variance

Suppose that an individual car insurance policy premium is described as a normally-distributed variable, with unknown mean μ and population standard deviation $\sigma = 50$.

A sample of $n = 25$ car insurance premium policies produced the following summaries of sample mean and standard deviation:

$$\bar{X} = 522 \quad \text{and} \quad s = 62.50$$

Estimate the unknown population mean μ at the confidence level of

(a) $C = 0.95$ and

(b) $C = 0.99$.

5.12. Confidence Interval: Unknown Population Variance

Suppose that an individual car insurance policy premium is described as a normally-distributed variable, with unknown mean μ and unknown population standard deviation.

A sample of $n = 25$ car insurance premium policies produced the following summaries of sample mean and standard deviation:

$$\bar{X} = 522 \quad \text{and} \quad s = 62.50$$

Estimate the unknown population mean μ at the confidence level of

(a) $C = 0.95$ and

(b) $C = 0.99$.

Solutions

5.1. By definition, the mean square error of an estimator is

$$\mathbf{MSE}_{\hat{\theta}}(\theta) = \mathbf{Var}(\hat{\theta}) + \mathbf{Bias}^2_{\hat{\theta}}(\theta).$$

Calculating the variance and the bias, we have

$$\mathbf{Var}(\hat{\theta}) = \mathbf{E}[\hat{\theta}^2] - \mathbf{E}[\hat{\theta}]^2 = 32 - 25 = 7$$
$$\mathbf{Bias}_{\hat{\theta}}(\theta) = \mathbf{E}[\hat{\theta}|\theta] - \theta = 5 - 7 = -2.$$

Therefore,

$$\mathbf{MSE}_{\hat{\theta}}(\theta) = 7 + 4 = \mathbf{11}.$$

5.2. By definition, the mean square error of an estimator is

$$\mathbf{MSE}_{\hat{\theta}}(\theta) = \mathbf{Bias}^2_{\hat{\theta}}(\theta) + \mathbf{Var}(\hat{\theta}).$$

The variance and the bias are calculated as follows:

$$\mathbf{Var}(\hat{\theta}) = \mathbf{E}[\hat{\theta}^2] - \mathbf{E}[\hat{\theta}]^2, \quad \mathbf{Bias}_{\hat{\theta}}(\theta) = \mathbf{E}[\hat{\theta}|\theta] - \theta$$

Calculating the variance and the expected value of each estimator, we have

$$\mathbf{E}[\hat{\alpha}] = \frac{1}{85} \sum_{i=1}^{85} \hat{\alpha}_i = \frac{1}{85} \cdot 179$$

$$\mathbf{E}[\hat{\alpha}^2] = \frac{1}{85} \sum_{i=1}^{85} \hat{\alpha}_i^2 = \frac{1}{85} \cdot 390$$

$$\mathbf{Var}(\hat{\alpha}) = \frac{1}{85^2} \left(390 \cdot 85 - 179^2\right) = \frac{1}{85^2} \cdot 1109$$

$$\mathbf{Var}(\hat{\beta}) = \frac{1}{85^2} \left(286 \cdot 85 - 154^2\right) = \frac{1}{85^2} \cdot 594.$$

Thus, the bias of each estimator is

$$\mathbf{Bias}_{\hat{\alpha}}(\gamma) = \frac{1}{85} \left(179 - 85 \cdot 3\right) = -\frac{1}{85} \cdot 76$$

$$\mathbf{Bias}_{\hat{\beta}}(\gamma) = \frac{1}{85} \left(154 - 85 \cdot 3\right) = -\frac{1}{85} \cdot 101.$$

Finally, the mean square errors are

$$\mathbf{MSE}_{\hat{\alpha}}(\gamma) = \frac{1}{85^2} \left(1109 + 76^2\right) = \frac{1}{85^2} \cdot 6885$$

$$\mathbf{MSE}_{\hat{\beta}}(\gamma) = \frac{1}{85^2} \left(594 + 101^2\right) = \frac{1}{85^2} \cdot 10{,}795.$$

Therefore,

$$\frac{\mathbf{MSE}_{\hat{\beta}}(\gamma)}{\mathbf{MSE}_{\hat{\alpha}}(\gamma)} = \frac{10{,}795}{6885} = \mathbf{1.5679}.$$

5.3. 1) To find a sample median, sort the data and take the middle number if the sample size is odd and mean of the two middle numbers if the sample size is even. For a sample of 2, 5, 8, 9, and 12, the sample median is $Y = 8$.

2) The number of possible combinations of k elements out of a set of n elements is

$$\binom{n}{k} = \frac{n!}{k!(n-k)!}.$$

Thus, the number of different 4 values out of the set of 5 is $\binom{5}{4} = 5$:

$$2, 5, 8, 9 \Rightarrow Y = \frac{5+8}{2} = 6.5$$

$$2, 5, 8, 12 \Rightarrow Y = \frac{5+8}{2} = 6.5$$

$$5, 8, 9, 12 \Rightarrow Y = \frac{9+8}{2} = 8.5$$

$$2, 5, 9, 12 \Rightarrow Y = \frac{5+9}{2} = 7$$

$$2, 8, 9, 12 \Rightarrow Y = \frac{9+8}{2} = 8.5$$

Thus,

$$Y = \begin{cases} 6.5, & p = \frac{2}{5} = 0.4 \\ 7, & p = \frac{1}{5} = 0.2 \\ 8.5, & p = \frac{2}{5} = 0.4. \end{cases}$$

$$\mathbf{E}[Y] = 6.5 \cdot 0.4 + 7 \cdot 0.2 + 8.5 \cdot 0.4 = 7.4$$
$$\mathbf{Var}(Y) = \mathbf{E}[(Y - \mathbf{E}[Y])^2] = (5.5 - 7.4)^2 \cdot 0.4 + (7 - 7.4)^2 \cdot 0.2 +$$
$$+ (8.5 - 7.4)^2 \cdot 0.4 = 0.324 + 0.032 + 0.484 = 0.84.$$

The population mean is

$$\mathbf{E}[X] = (2 + 5 + 8 + 9 + 12)\frac{1}{5} = \frac{36}{5} = 7.2.$$

Therefore, the bias and the mean square error of Y as an *estimator* of the population mean are

$$\mathbf{Bias}_Y(\mathbf{E}[X]) = \mathbf{E}[Y] - \mathbf{E}[X] = 7.4 - 7.2 = 0.2$$
$$\mathbf{MSE}_Y(\mathbf{E}[X]) = \mathbf{Var}(Y) + (\mathbf{Bias}_Y(\mathbf{E}[X]))^2 = 0.84 + 0.2^2 = \mathbf{0.88}.$$

5.4. The cumulative probability function is given by

$$F(x) = \int_0^x f(t)\, dt = \int_0^x \frac{1}{4}(3 + 2t)\, dt = \frac{3}{4}x + \frac{1}{4}x^2 = \frac{1}{4}x(3 + x).$$

For a sample $x_1 \leq x_2 \leq \cdots \leq x_n$, the Kolmogorov–Smirnov statistic D is defined as $D = \max_j D_j$, where

$$D_j = \max\left(\left| F^*(x_j) - \frac{j}{n} \right|, \left| F^*(x_j) - \frac{j-1}{n} \right| \right), \quad \text{if } x_j \neq x_{j+1}$$

$$D_j = \max\left(\left| F^*(x_j) - \frac{j-1}{n} \right|, \left| F^*(x_j) - \frac{j+1}{n} \right| \right), \quad \text{if } x_j = x_{j+1}.$$

The number of data points is $n = 4$. Calculating the elements of the K–S statistic, we have

j	x_j	$F^*(x_j)$	$\frac{j}{n}$	$\frac{j-1}{n}$	$\frac{j+1}{n}$	$\left\| F^*(x_j) - \frac{j}{n} \right\|$	$\left\| F^*(x_j) - \frac{j-1}{n} \right\|$	$\left\| F^*(x_j) - \frac{j+1}{n} \right\|$	D_j
1	0.3	0.2475	0.25	0.00	0.50	0.0025	0.2475	0.2525	0.2475
2	0.6	0.5400	0.50	0.25	0.75	0.0400	0.2900	0.2100	0.2900
3	0.8	0.7600	0.75	0.50	1.00	0.0100	0.2600	0.2400	0.2600

Hence, $D = \sqrt{4} \max_j D_j = 2 \cdot 0.29 = 0.58$.

Based on the Kolmogorov–Smirnov table (appendix A), the null hypothesis about the true distribution is not rejected at significance levels 0.1 and lower.

5.5. For individual data A^2 is defined in (5.8) as follows:

$$A^2 = -nF^*(u) + n \sum_{j=0}^{k} \left(\hat{S}(y_j) \right)^2 \left(\ln S^*(y_j) - \ln S^*(y_{j+1}) \right) +$$

$$+ n \sum_{j=1}^{k} \left(\hat{F}(y_j) \right)^2 \left(\ln F^*(y_{j+1}) - \ln F^*(y_j) \right),$$

where k is the number of unique non-censored data points

$$t = y_0 < y_1 < \cdots < t_t < y_{k+1} = u.$$

Since our data is not truncated, $F^* = F$.

The number of data points is $n = 6$ and $k = 4$. Evaluating the elements of the A–D statistic at each data point, we have the following:

j	y_j	$F(y_j)$	$S(y_j)$	$\hat{F}(y_j)$	$\hat{S}(y_j)$	$\ln(F(y_j))$	$\ln(S(y_j))$
0	0	0	1	0	1		0
1	600	0.4512	0.5488	0.1667	0.8333	-0.7959	-0.6000
2	749	0.5272	0.4728	0.3333	0.6667	-0.6402	-0.7490
3	804	0.5525	0.4475	0.5000	0.5000	-0.5934	-0.8040
4	1250	0.7135	0.2865	0.6667	0.3333	-0.3376	-1.2500
5 = 6	1500	0.7769	0.2231	1.0000	0.0000	-0.2525	-1.5000

The corresponding logarithmic differences and total components of each sum are as follows:

j	y_j	$\ln S(y_j)-$ $-\ln S(y_{j+1})$	$\ln F(y_{j+1})-$ $-\ln F(y_j)$	$\left(\hat{S}(y_j)\right)^2 \times$ $\times (\ln S(y_j) - \ln S(y_{j+1}))$	$\left(\hat{F}(y_j)\right)^2 \times$ $\times (\ln F(y_{j+1}) - \ln F(y_j))$
0	0	0.6000		0.6000	
1	600	0.1490	0.1556	0.0449	0.0317
2	749	0.0550	0.0469	0.0123	0.0130
3	804	0.4460	0.2558	0.0893	0.0781
4	1250	0.2500	0.0851	0.0205	0.0433
Total				0.7670	0.1661

Thus,

$$A^2 = -6 \cdot 0.78 + 6 \cdot 0.7670 + 6 \cdot 0.1661 = 0.9375.$$

Using the table for critical values for the A–D statistic for specific null distribution models (appendix B), we note that for exponential distribution,

$$0.9160 < 0.9375 < 1.062,$$

which corresponds to significance level of 0.1 for 1.062 and 0.15 for 0.9160. Therefore, H_0 is not rejected at significance levels 0.1 and below, but rejected at significance levels 0.15 and above.

5.6. Suppose the data is divided into k groups, n being the total number of observations. Let p_j be the probability that X is in the jth group under the hypothesis, O_j be the number of observations in group j, and $E_j = np_j$ be the expected number of observations in group j. Then the chi-square statistic is

$$Q = \sum_{j=1}^{k} \frac{(O_j - E_j)^2}{E_j} = \sum_{j=1}^{k} \frac{O_j^2}{E_j} - n.$$

Note that if a distribution with parameters is given, or is fitted by a formal approach like maximum likelihood but using a different set of data, then there are $k - 1$ degrees of freedom. On the other hand, if the r parameters are fitted from the data, then there are $k - 1 - r$ degrees of freedom.

Note that $k = 3$, $n = 120$. Since a distribution with parameters is given, the number of degrees of freedom is $k - 1 = 2$.

To calculate p_j in the expression for E_j, let us determine the cumulative distribution function of the random variable X:

$$F(x) = \int_2^x f(t)\, dt = \int_2^x \frac{24}{t^4}\, dt = -\frac{8}{t^3}\bigg|_2^x = 1 - \frac{8}{x^3}$$

Hence, the survival function is

$$S(x) = 1 - F(x) = \frac{8}{x^3}.$$

Thus,

$$p_1 = S(2) - S(2.5) = 1 - 0.512 = 0.488 \Rightarrow E_1 = 120 \cdot 0.488 = 58.56$$
$$p_2 = S(2.5) - S(4) = 0.512 - 0.125 = 0.387 \Rightarrow E_2 = 120 \cdot 0.387 = 46.44$$
$$p_3 = S(4) - S(\infty) = 0.125 \Rightarrow E_3 = 120 \cdot 0.125 = 15.$$

We are given that

$$O_1 = 50, \ O_2 = 45, \ \text{and} \ O_3 = 25.$$

Therefore, using the alternative expression for Q, we obtain

$$Q = \frac{50^2}{58.56} + \frac{45^2}{46.44} + \frac{25^2}{15} - 120 = 127.9626 - 120 = 7.9626.$$

Using the chi-square table for 2 degrees of freedom, our statistic Q falls between the value $\chi_0^2 = 7.378$, corresponding to the significance level $\alpha = 0.025$ and the value $\chi_0^2 = 9.21$, corresponding to the significance level $\alpha = 0.01$. Therefore, the null hypothesis H_0 will be rejected at the 0.025 significance level but not at the 0.01 level. The answer is B.

Note: The distribution given in this problem is the single-parameter Pareto with $\alpha = 3$ and $\theta = 2$:

$$f(x) = \frac{\alpha \theta^\alpha}{x^{\alpha+1}}, \ x > \theta$$

5.7. Let us test the null hypothesis H_0 about the population mean, $H_0 : \mu = \mu_0 = 500$, against the alternative, $H_1 : \mu > 500$.

Since the population standard deviation is specified, its sample analogue is ignored.

The standard deviation for $\bar{X}$ is

$$\mathbf{SD} = \mathbf{SD}\,[\bar{X}] = \frac{\sigma}{\sqrt{n}} = \frac{50}{\sqrt{25}} = 10$$

and the **pivotal statistic** is

$$Z = \frac{\bar{X} - \mu_0}{\mathbf{SD}} = \frac{522 - 500}{10} = \mathbf{2.2}.$$

The alternative is right-sided, so the critical values for $\alpha = 0.05$ or $\alpha = 0.01$, are, respectively,

$$z_{0.05} = 1.645 \ \text{and} \ z_{0.01} = 2.326.$$

They can be found from the t-distribution table using the infinite number of degrees of freedom.

The rejection rule states to reject the null hypothesis in favor of the alternative if the test statistic Z exceeds the critical value. When $\alpha = 0.05$, since $Z = 2.2 > 1.645$, we have sufficient evidence to reject the null hypothesis.

When the significance level is set as $\alpha = 0.01$, since the right-sided critical value is 2.326 and $Z < 2.326$, there is no significant evidence against the null hypothesis, which means that it is not rejected.

5.8. Let us test the null hypothesis H_0 about the population mean, $H_0 : \mu = \mu_0 = 500$, against the **two-sided** alternative, $H_1 : \mu \neq 500$.

The **pivotal statistic** is the same as in the previous exercise because the population standard deviation was given:

$$Z = \frac{\bar{X} - \mu_0}{\text{SD}} = \frac{522 - 500}{10} = \mathbf{2.2}$$

The rejection rule in this case will change.

Since we are facing a two-sided alternative, the test statistic Z should be compared with **two** critical values, because its deviations to the left or to the right of zero are equally important.

Thus, we first need to split the significance level into halves and then set critical values as $\pm z_{\alpha/2}$.

The same table of t-distribution provides critical values.

When $\alpha = 0.05$, the critical values are

$$\pm z_{\alpha/2} = \pm z_{0.025} = \pm 1.960.$$

When $\alpha = 0.01$, the critical values are

$$\pm z_{\alpha/2} = \pm z_{0.005} = \pm 2.576.$$

The rejection rule states that $H_0 : \mu = 500$ will be rejected in favor of the two-sided alternative at the significance level if

$$\text{either } Z > z_{\alpha/2} \text{ or } Z < -z_{\alpha/2}.$$

At the level of $\alpha = 0.05$, the pivotal statistic Z is **outside** of the interval between -1.960 and 1.960. Hence, the null hypothesis is rejected.

At the level of $\alpha = 0.01$, the pivotal statistic Z is $-2/576 < Z < 2.576$. Therefore, the null hypothesis is not rejected.

5.9. First note that the **pivotal** statistic in this case has to be modified compared to previous situations. Instead of standard deviation for $\bar{X}$, we have to use its sample analogue, named **standard error** and defined as

$$\text{SE} = \frac{s}{\sqrt{n}} = \frac{62.50}{\sqrt{25}} = \mathbf{12.5}.$$

Instead of Z, the pivotal statistic is

$$T = \frac{\bar{X} - \mu_0}{\text{SE}} = \frac{22}{12.5} = \mathbf{1.76}.$$

Since inferences are based on a sample of size $n = 25$, the distribution of this statistic is $t[24]$, or Student's t with $n - 1 = 24$ degrees of freedom.

(a) At the 5% significance level, testing H_0 against right-sided alternative, we use

$$t[24, 0.05] = 1.711.$$

Since the test statistic is $T = 1.76 > 1.711$, we have enough evidence to reject it.

(b) At the 1% significance level, for the same case, the critical value is

$$t[24, 0.01] = 2.492.$$

Since $T = 1.76 < 2.492$, we do not have sufficient evidence against the null hypothesis and hence do not reject it.

5.10. The pivotal statistic is

$$T = \frac{\bar{X} - \mu_0}{\text{SE}} = \frac{22}{12.5} = \mathbf{1.76}.$$

Since inferences are based on a sample of size $n = 25$, the distribution of this statistic is $t[24]$, or Student's t with $n - 1 = 24$ degrees of freedom. The two-sided alternative, $H_1 : \mu \neq 500$, requires **two** critical values, $\pm t[24, \alpha/2]$.

(a) At the 5% significance level, testing H_0 against right-sided alternative we use

$$\pm t[24, 0.025] = \pm 2.064.$$

The test statistic value $T = 1.76$ is within the interval $(-2.064, 2.064)$, Hence, the null hypothesis is not rejected at the level of $\alpha = 0.05$.

(b) At the 1% significance level, for the same case, the critical value is

$$\pm t[24, 0.005] = \pm 2.797.$$

The test statistic value $T = 1.76$ is within the interval $(-2.797, 2.797)$, Hence, the null hypothesis is not rejected at the level of $\alpha = 0.01$.

5.11. Since the population standard deviation is given, the standard deviation for $\bar{X}$ is

$$\text{SD}[\bar{X}] = \frac{\sigma}{\sqrt{n}} = \mathbf{10}.$$

Therefore, the pivotal statistic

$$Z = \frac{\bar{X} - \mu}{\text{SD}}$$

belongs to the interval bounded by two critical values, $(-z_{\alpha/2}, z_{\alpha_2})$, with probability $C = 1 - \alpha$, or, equivalently, $\alpha = 1 - C$.

(a) For $C = 0.95$, the critical values are ± 1.960. Therefore, the 95% confidence interval is

$$(\mathbf{UCL, LCL}) = \bar{X} \pm (1.960)(\mathbf{SD}) = 522 \pm (1.96) \cdot (10) = 522 \pm 19.6, \text{ or }$$
$$\mathbf{UCL} = 541.6 \text{ and } \mathbf{LCL} = 502.4.$$

Equivalently, with 95% confidence, the unknown true population mean is in the interval (502.4, 541.6).

(b) For $C = 0.99$, the critical values are ± 2.576. Therefore, the 99% confidence interval is

$$(\mathbf{UCL, LCL}) = 522 \pm (2.576) \cdot (10) = 522 \pm 25.76, \text{ or }$$
$$\mathbf{UCL} = 544.76 \text{ and } \mathbf{LCL} = 499.24.$$

Equivalently, with 99% confidence, the unknown true population mean is in the interval (499.24, 544.76).

Note that the interval will change when one data set is replaced by another one due to both endpoints being sample-based.

5.12. The pivotal statistic is now based on the standard error,

$$\mathbf{SE} = \frac{s}{\sqrt{n}} = \frac{62.5}{\sqrt{25}} = \mathbf{12.5},$$

and it is defined as

$$T = \frac{\bar{X} - \mu}{\mathbf{SE}}.$$

Since the population standard deviation is unknown, we use critical values for Student's $t[24]$-distribution.

(a) For $C = 0.95$, the complementary probability is $\alpha = 0.05$, its half becomes $\alpha/2 = 0.025$, and the critical value is $t[24, 0.025] = 2.064$. Therefore, the 95% confidence interval is

$$(\mathbf{UCL, LCL}) = \bar{X} \pm (2.064) \cdot (\mathbf{SE}) = 522 \pm (2.064) \cdot 12.5 = 522 \pm 25.8,$$
$$\text{or } \mathbf{UCL} = 547.8 \text{ and } \mathbf{LCL} = 496.2.$$

(b) For $C = 0.99$, the complementary probability is $\alpha = 0.01$, its half becomes $\alpha/2 = 0.005$, and the critical value is $t[24, 0.005] = 2.797$. Therefore, the 99% confidence interval is

$$(\mathbf{UCL, LCL}) = \bar{X} \pm (2.797) \cdot (\mathbf{SE}) = 522 \pm (2.797) \cdot 12.5 = 522 \pm 34.9625,$$
$$\text{or } \mathbf{UCL} = 556.9625 \text{ and } \mathbf{LCL} = 487.0375.$$

Chapter 6

Parametric Statistical Inference

One of the most important tasks for an actuary faced with a set of data is to understand an underlying distribution of probability that guides its behavior. The process of using data analysis to build an underlying probability model is called **statistical inference**.

There are two approaches to statistical inference. The first approach is called a **parametric** approach. An actuary assumes that the data can be modeled using one of the parametric distributions and estimates the corresponding small number of parameters. Examples of nonparametric distributions are any well-known continuous or discrete distributions such as normal, Pareto, or Poisson.

The second approach is called a **nonparametric, data-dependent, or data-driven** approach, and it uses the entire data set to deduce the distribution. Examples of nonparametric distributions are the empirical distribution based on a sample of size n, a kernel-smoothed distribution, or an orthonormal series distribution. Note that the specification of this distribution requires at least as many "parameters" as the number of data points in the sample used to create it.

In this chapter we will focus on the first, parametric, approach to model behavior of data. We will discuss common methods of data assessment that should aid an analyst in making an informed modeling decision, as well as advantages and disadvantages of each method. Particular attention will be paid to the **maximum likelihood estimator** method of data modeling.

After completing this chapter, readers will be prepared to perform an optimal parametric estimation of the given data set.

Exercises will further deepen and develop readers' knowledge of material presented in this chapter.

6.1   Method of Moments

Let $X_1, X_2, \ldots, X_n$ be n independent identically distributed (iid) observations of a random variable having a parametric distribution with K parameters $\alpha^T = (\alpha_1, \alpha_2, \ldots, \alpha_K)$. Let

$$\mu_k'(\alpha) = \mathbf{E}[X^k | \alpha], \ k = 1, 2, \ldots$$

be the kth raw moment of a random variable X. Note that $\mu_1' = \mu_1$.

The **method of moments** consists of matching the first K **estimated or empirical** raw moments to the **theoretical** raw moments of the assumed parametric distribution. In particular, the following system of K equations with K unknowns should be solved:

$$\hat{\mu}_k' = \mu_k'(\alpha), \ k = 1, 2, \ldots, K, \tag{6.1}$$

where, by (1.5), an empirical or the sample k^{th} raw moment is defined as

$$\hat{\mu}_k' = \frac{1}{n} \sum_{i=1}^{n} X_i^k.$$

Note that depending on the coefficients of the unknowns in the system (6.1), it may have infinitely many solutions, a single unique solution, or no solution.

The method of moments was formally introduced by a Russian mathematician Pafnuty Chebyshev in 1887 in the proof of the central limit theorem. However, the idea of matching empirical moments of a distribution to the population moments dates back to Karl Pearson, an British mathematician and biostatistician.

Let us demonstrate the method of moments for various distributions. These distributions will have one or two parameters. Distributions with higher number of parameters will require moments that either fail to exist or are expressed in a more complicated form, which will require computerized calculations. In the following discussion

$$\hat{\mu}_1 = \frac{1}{n} \sum_{i=1}^{n} X_i = \bar{X}, \ \hat{\mu}_2' = \frac{1}{n} \sum_{i=1}^{n} X_i^2.$$

6.1.1 Method of Moments for Exponential Distribution

By (1.33), a random variable X has an exponential distribution with a scale parameter $\theta > 0$ if its **pdf** is of the form

$$f(x) = f(x \mid \theta) = \frac{1}{\theta} e^{-x/\theta}.$$

Then the expected value of an exponentially-distributed random variable with parameter θ is

$$\mathbf{E}[X] = \theta.$$

Thus, we need to match the first theoretical and sample moments to obtain

$$\hat{\theta} = \hat{\mu}_1. \tag{6.2}$$

6.1.2 Method of Moments for Gamma Distribution

By (1.38), a random variable X has a gamma distribution with a shape parameter α and a scale parameter θ if its **pdf** is of the form

$$f(x) = f(x \mid \alpha, \theta) = \frac{1}{\theta^\alpha \Gamma(a)} x^{\alpha-1} e^{-x/\theta} \ \text{ for } \ 0 < x < \infty.$$

By (1.39), first two central moments of a general gamma-distributed random variable X are

$$\mathbf{E}[X] = \alpha\theta \ \text{ and } \ \mathbf{Var}[X] = \alpha\theta^2.$$

Calculating the second raw moment, we have

$$\mathbf{E}\left[X^2\right] = \mathbf{Var}\left[X\right] + \mathbf{E}\left[X\right]^2 = \theta^2\alpha(\alpha+1).$$

Thus, we need to solve the following system of equations:

$$\begin{cases} \hat{\mu}_1 = \theta\alpha \\ \hat{\mu}_2' = \theta^2\alpha(\alpha+1) \end{cases} \Leftrightarrow \begin{cases} \hat{\mu}_1^2 = \theta^2\alpha^2 \\ \hat{\mu}_2' = \theta^2\alpha(\alpha+1) \end{cases}$$

Dividing the first equation by the second, we have

$$\frac{\alpha}{\alpha+1} = \frac{\hat{\mu}_1^2}{\hat{\mu}_2'} \Leftrightarrow \alpha\hat{\mu}_2' = \alpha\hat{\mu}_1^2 + \hat{\mu}_1^2 \Leftrightarrow \alpha = \frac{\hat{\mu}_1^2}{\hat{\mu}_2' - \hat{\mu}_1^2}.$$

From the first equation,

$$\theta = \frac{\hat{\mu}_2' - \hat{\mu}_1^2}{\hat{\mu}_1}.$$

Thus, using the method of moments, the parameters of the gamma distribution are estimated as

$$\hat{\alpha} = \frac{\hat{\mu}_1^2}{\hat{\mu}_2' - \hat{\mu}_1^2}, \ \hat{\theta} = \frac{\hat{\mu}_2' - \hat{\mu}_1^2}{\hat{\mu}_1}. \tag{6.3}$$

6.1.3   Method of Moments for Pareto Distribution

By (1.53), a random variable X has a Pareto distribution with parameters α and θ if its **pdf** is of the form

$$f_X(x) = \frac{\alpha\theta^\alpha}{(x+\theta)^{\alpha+1}}.$$

By (1.54), first two raw moments of a Pareto-distributed random variable X are

$$\mathbf{E}[X] = \frac{\theta}{\alpha-1} \ \text{ and } \mathbf{E}[X^2] = \frac{2\theta^2}{(\alpha-1)(\alpha-2)}.$$

Thus, we need to solve the following system of equations:

$$\begin{cases} \hat{\mu}_1 = \frac{\theta}{\alpha-1} \\ \hat{\mu}_2' = \frac{2\theta^2}{(\alpha-1)(\alpha-2)} \end{cases} \Leftrightarrow \begin{cases} \hat{\mu}_1^2 = \frac{\theta^2}{(\alpha-1)^2} \\ \hat{\mu}_2' = \frac{2\theta^2}{(\alpha-1)(\alpha-2)} \end{cases}$$

Dividing the first equation by the second, we have

$$\frac{\alpha-2}{2(\alpha-1)} = \frac{\hat{\mu}_1^2}{\hat{\mu}_2'} \Leftrightarrow 2\alpha\hat{\mu}_1^2 - 2\hat{\mu}_1^2 = \alpha\hat{\mu}_2' - 2\hat{\mu}_2' \Leftrightarrow \alpha = \frac{2(\hat{\mu}_1^2 - \hat{\mu}_2')}{2\hat{\mu}_1^2 - \hat{\mu}_2'}.$$

From the first equation,

$$\theta = \frac{\hat{\mu}_1 \cdot \hat{\mu}_2'}{\hat{\mu}_2' - 2\hat{\mu}_1^2}.$$

Thus, using the method of moments, the parameters of the Pareto distribution are estimated as

$$\hat{\alpha} = \frac{2(\hat{\mu}_2' - \hat{\mu}_1^2)}{\hat{\mu}_2' - 2\hat{\mu}_1^2}, \ \hat{\theta} = \frac{\hat{\mu}_1 \cdot \hat{\mu}_2'}{\hat{\mu}_2' - 2\hat{\mu}_1^2}. \tag{6.4}$$

6.1.4 Method of Moments for Normal Distribution

If X is a normally-distributed random variable with parameters μ and σ^2, its expected value is equal to μ and its variance is equal to σ^2. Thus,

$$\mathbf{E}[X] = \mu \quad \text{and} \quad \mathbf{E}[X^2] = \sigma^2 + \mu^2.$$

Thus, we need to solve the following system of equations:

$$\begin{cases} \hat{\mu}_1 = \mu \\ \hat{\mu}_2' = \sigma^2 + \mu^2 \end{cases} \Leftrightarrow \begin{cases} \hat{\mu}_1^2 = \mu^2 \\ \hat{\mu}_2' = \sigma^2 + \mu^2 \end{cases}$$

Subtracting the first equation by the second, we have

$$\sigma^2 = \hat{\mu}_2' - \hat{\mu}_1^2.$$

Thus, using the method of moments, the parameters of the normal distribution are estimated as

$$\hat{\mu} = \hat{\mu}_1, \ \hat{\sigma}^2 = \hat{\mu}_2' - \hat{\mu}_1^2. \tag{6.5}$$

6.1.5 Method of Moments for Lognormal Distribution

By definition, a random variable Y is lognormal, with parameters μ and σ, if it can be represented as $Y = e^X$, where X is a normally-distributed random variable with parameters μ and σ^2. By (1.52), the first two moments of a lognormally-distributed random variable are

$$\mathbf{E}[Y] = \exp\left[\mu + \frac{1}{2}\sigma^2\right]$$
$$\mathbf{E}[Y^2] = \exp\left[2\mu + 2\sigma^2\right].$$

Thus, we need to solve the following system of equations:

$$\begin{cases} \hat{\mu}_1 = \exp\left[\mu + \frac{1}{2}\sigma^2\right] \\ \hat{\mu}_2' = \exp\left[2\mu + 2\sigma^2\right] \end{cases} \Leftrightarrow \begin{cases} \mu + \frac{1}{2}\sigma^2 = \ln\hat{\mu}_1 \\ 2\mu + 2\sigma^2 = \ln\hat{\mu}_2' \end{cases} \Leftrightarrow \begin{cases} 2\mu + \sigma^2 = 2\ln\hat{\mu}_1 \\ 2\mu + 2\sigma^2 = \ln\hat{\mu}_2' \end{cases}$$

Subtracting the first equation by the second, we have

$$\sigma^2 = \ln\hat{\mu}_2' - 2\ln\hat{\mu}_1.$$

From the first equation,

$$\mu = \ln\hat{\mu}_1 - \frac{1}{2}\ln\hat{\mu}_2' + \ln\hat{\mu}_1 = 2\ln\hat{\mu}_1 - \frac{1}{2}\ln\hat{\mu}_2'.$$

Thus, using the method of moments, the parameters of the lognormal distribution are estimated as

$$\hat{\mu} = 2\ln\hat{\mu}_1 - \frac{1}{2}\ln\hat{\mu}_2', \ \hat{\sigma}^2 = \ln\hat{\mu}_2' - 2\ln\hat{\mu}_1. \tag{6.6}$$

6.1.6 Method of Moments for Uniform Distribution

By (1.21), a random variable X has a uniform distribution with parameter θ if its **pdf** is of the form

$$f_X(x) = \frac{1}{\theta}.$$

The expected value of a uniformly-distributed random variable is $\mathbf{E}[X] = \theta/2$. Therefore, the parameter estimate using the method of moments is

$$\hat{\theta} = 2\hat{\mu}_1. \tag{6.7}$$

6.1.7 Method of Moments for Beta Distribution

By (1.29), a random variable X has a gamma distribution with a shape parameter α and a scale parameter θ if its **pdf** is of the form

$$f(x) = f(x\,|a,b) = \frac{\Gamma(a+b)}{\Gamma(a)\Gamma(b)}\, x^{a-1}(1-x)^{b-1} \quad \text{and} \quad f(x) = 0 \ \text{ otherwise.}$$

By (1.30) and (1.31), first two central moments of a beta-distributed random variable X are

$$\mathbf{E}[X] = \frac{a}{a+b} \quad \text{and} \quad \mathbf{E}[X^2] = \frac{a(a+1)}{(a+b)(a+b+1)}.$$

Thus, we need to solve the following system of equations:

$$\begin{cases} \frac{a}{a+b} = \hat{\mu}_1 \\ \frac{a(a+1)}{(a+b)(a+b+1)} = \hat{\mu}_2' \end{cases} \Leftrightarrow \begin{cases} \frac{a}{a+b} = \hat{\mu}_1 \\ \frac{a+1}{a+b+1} = \frac{\hat{\mu}_2'}{\hat{\mu}_1} \end{cases}$$

From the first equation, $a + b = a/\hat{\mu}_1$. Using it in the second equation, we obtain

$$\frac{(a+1)\hat{\mu}_1}{a+\hat{\mu}_1} = \frac{\hat{\mu}_2'}{\hat{\mu}_1} \Leftrightarrow \hat{\mu}_1^2(a+1) = \hat{\mu}_2' \cdot a + \hat{\mu}_1\hat{\mu}_2' \Leftrightarrow$$

$$a = \frac{\hat{\mu}_1\hat{\mu}_2' - \hat{\mu}_1^2}{\hat{\mu}_1^2 - \hat{\mu}_2'} = \frac{\hat{\mu}_1\left(\hat{\mu}_2' - \hat{\mu}_1\right)}{\hat{\mu}_1^2 - \hat{\mu}_2'}.$$

Calculating b, we have

$$b = a\left(\frac{1}{\hat{\mu}_1} - 1\right) = a \cdot \frac{1-\hat{\mu}_1}{\hat{\mu}_1} = \frac{\left(\hat{\mu}_2' - \hat{\mu}_1\right)\left(1-\hat{\mu}_1\right)}{\hat{\mu}_1^2 - \hat{\mu}_2'}.$$

Thus, using the method of moments, the parameters of the beta distribution are estimated as

$$\hat{a} = \frac{\hat{\mu}_1\left(\hat{\mu}_2' - \hat{\mu}_1\right)}{\hat{\mu}_1^2 - \hat{\mu}_2'}, \ \hat{b} = \frac{\left(\hat{\mu}_2' - \hat{\mu}_1\right)\left(1-\hat{\mu}_1\right)}{\hat{\mu}_1^2 - \hat{\mu}_2'}. \tag{6.8}$$

6.1.8 Advantages and Disadvantages of the Method of Moments

Although the method of moments is easy to use and yields statistically *consistent* estimators, these estimators are often *biased*. As a result, particularly for small samples, the estimates given by the method of moments may fall outside of the parameter domain, rendering them unfit.

The method of moments may be more appropriate for large samples and for data with small skewness, indicating relative symmetry of the underlying distribution. However, for a data population with a heavy tail, such as Pareto, lognormal, or Weibull distribution, the method of moments may provide controversial results.

While focusing on calculation of the sample moments, the parameter estimates produced by the method of moments may not yield *sufficient* statistics, meaning they may not take into account *all* relevant information in the sample.

An assumption of the data set being drawn from a single distribution of the same random variable proves to be a disadvantage when an analyst considers a set of observations with characteristics of different nature, such as various deductibles or policy limits.

Due to the method of moments' simplistic setup, it is often used in situations where other methods yield only numerical solutions. Such estimates may serve as the first approximations to the solutions for the equations produced by other methods and then can be utilized in the successive improved approximations such as the Newton–Raphson method.

6.2 Method of Percentile Matching

Let $X_1, X_2, \ldots, X_n$ be n independent identically distributed (iid) observations of a random variable, having a parametric distribution with K parameters $\alpha^T = (\alpha_1, \alpha_2, \ldots, \alpha_K)$. Let

$$\pi_p = F^{-1}(p|\alpha)$$

be a $100p^{th}$ percentile of a random variable X. Here, F^{-1} is an *inverse* function of the cumulative distribution function F.

The **method of percentile matching** consists of matching the K **empirical estimates** of the percentiles to the corresponding number of **theoretical** percentiles of the assumed parametric distribution for K arbitrarily chosen values of probability p. In particular, the following system of K equations with K unknowns should be solved:

$$\pi_p^{(k)} = \hat{\pi}_p^{(k)}, \ k = 1, 2, \ldots, K \tag{6.9}$$

Since percentiles for a discrete random variables are not well defined, **smoothed empirical estimates** of the percentiles are used. They are defined as follows:

Let n be the sample size, $X_{(k)}$ be the kth order statistic of the sample. Then the smoothed empirical estimate of the $100p^{th}$ percentile is

$$\hat{\pi}_p = x_{(n+1)p} \tag{6.10}$$

if $(n+1)p$ is an integer, and

$$\hat{\pi}_p = ((n+1)p - a) \, x_{(a+1)} + (a + 1 - (n+1)p) \, x_{(a)}, \ a = \lfloor (n+1)p \rfloor \tag{6.11}$$

if $(n+1)p$ is not an integer.

Note that depending on the coefficients of the unknowns in the system (6.9), it may have infinitely many solutions, a single unique solution, or no solution.

The method of percentile matching was introduced as an alternative method to the method of moments for distributions whose moments do not exist. An example of such distribution is the Cauchy distribution, considered in statistics a "pathological" distribution since both its expected value and its variance are undefined. The Cauchy distribution does not have finite moments of order greater than or equal to one. Only fractional absolute moments exist. On the other hand, percentiles always exist.

6.2.1 Percentile Matching for Exponential Distribution

By (1.33), a random variable X has an exponential distribution with a scale parameter $\theta > 0$ if its **pdf** is of the form

$$f(x) = f(x \mid \theta) = \frac{1}{\theta} e^{-x/\theta}.$$

Then the **CDF** of an exponentially-distributed random variable with parameter θ is

$$F(x) = 1 - e^{-x/\theta}.$$

Calculating its inverse, we obtain

$$p = 1 - e^{-x/\theta} \Leftrightarrow e^{-x/\theta} = 1 - p \Leftrightarrow -\frac{x}{\theta} = \ln(1-p) \Leftrightarrow x = -\theta \ln(1-p).$$

Thus,

$$F^{-1}(p) = -\theta \ln(1-p).$$

Therefore, we need to match a theoretical percentile and a smoothed empirical estimate of a percentile for some value of probability p to obtain

$$-\theta \ln(1-p) = \hat{\pi}_p \Leftrightarrow \hat{\theta} = -\frac{\hat{\pi}_p}{\ln(1-p)}. \tag{6.12}$$

6.2.2 Percentile Matching for Inverse Exponential Distribution

A random variable X has an inverse exponential distribution with a scale parameter $\theta > 0$ if its **CDF** is of the form

$$F(x) = e^{-\theta/x}.$$

Calculating its inverse, we obtain

$$p = e^{-\theta/x} \Leftrightarrow -\frac{\theta}{x} = \ln p \Leftrightarrow x = -\frac{\theta}{\ln p}.$$

Thus,

$$F^{-1}(p) = -\frac{\theta}{\ln p}.$$

Therefore, we need to match a theoretical percentile and a smoothed empirical estimate of a percentile for some value of probability p to obtain

$$-\frac{\theta}{\ln p} = \hat{\pi}_p \Leftrightarrow \hat{\theta} = -\hat{\pi}_p \ln p. \tag{6.13}$$

Alternatively, if $X_1, X_2, \ldots, X_n$ are n independent identically distributed (iid) observations of a random variable, having an inverse exponential distribution with parameter θ, observations

$$\frac{1}{X_1}, \frac{1}{X_2}, \ldots, \frac{1}{X_n}$$

are independent identically distributed (iid) observations of a random variable, having an exponential distribution with parameter $\tilde{\theta} = 1/\theta$.

Lemma 6.2.1 *If Y has a certain distribution and π_p is its $100p^{th}$ percentile, then $1/Y$ has an inverse distribution with its $100p^{th}$ percentile π_p^I of the form*

$$\pi_p^I = \frac{1}{\pi_{1-p}}. \tag{6.14}$$

Proof. By definition of a percentile,

$$1 - p = \mathbf{P}\left(Y < \pi_{1-p}\right).$$

On the other hand,

$$p = \mathbf{P}\left(\frac{1}{Y} < \pi_p^I\right) = \mathbf{P}\left(Y > \frac{1}{\pi_p^I}\right) \Leftrightarrow \mathbf{P}\left(Y < \frac{1}{\pi_p^I}\right) = 1 - p.$$

The last equation is the definition of π_{1-p}. Hence,

$$\pi_p^I = \frac{1}{\pi_{1-p}}.$$

Let π_p^{IE} and π_p^E be the $100p^{th}$ percentiles of the inverse exponential and exponential distributions. Using (6.14),

$$\pi_p^{IE} = \frac{1}{\pi_{1-p}^E}.$$

Using (6.12), the estimation of the parameter is $\tilde{\theta}$ is

$$\tilde{\theta} = \frac{1}{\hat{\theta}} = -\frac{\hat{\pi}_p^E}{\ln(1-p)} = -\frac{\hat{\pi}_{1-p}^E}{\ln p} = -\frac{1}{\pi_p^{IE} \ln p}.$$

Therefore, the estimation of the parameter is θ is

$$\hat{\theta} = -\pi_p^{IE} \ln p.$$

which is the same as (6.13).

6.2.3 Percentile Matching for Weibull Distribution

A random variable X has a Weibull distribution with parameters θ and τ if its **CDF** is of the form

$$F_X(x) = 1 - \exp\left(-\left(\frac{x}{\theta}\right)^\tau\right).$$

Calculating its inverse, we obtain

$$p = 1 - \exp\left(-\left(\frac{x}{\theta}\right)^\tau\right) \Leftrightarrow \exp\left(-\left(\frac{x}{\theta}\right)^\tau\right) = 1 - p \Leftrightarrow -\left(\frac{x}{\theta}\right)^\tau = \ln(1-p) \Leftrightarrow$$
$$\frac{x}{\theta} = (-\ln(1-p))^{1/\tau} \Leftrightarrow x = \theta\left(-\ln(1-p)\right)^{1/\tau}.$$

Thus,

$$F^{-1}(p) = \theta\left(-\ln(1-p)\right)^{1/\tau}.$$

Since the distribution has two parameters, we arbitrarily choose two probabilities, p and q. Calculating corresponding smoothed empirical estimates of the percentiles $\hat{\pi}_p$ and $\hat{\pi}_q$, we obtain the following system of equations:

$$\begin{cases} \theta\left(-\ln(1-p)\right)^{1/\tau} = \hat{\pi}_p \\ \theta\left(-\ln(1-q)\right)^{1/\tau} = \hat{\pi}_q \end{cases}$$

Dividing the first equation by the second, we have

$$\left(\frac{\ln(1-p)}{\ln(1-q)}\right)^{1/\tau} = \frac{\hat{\pi}_p}{\hat{\pi}_q} \Leftrightarrow \frac{1}{\tau} \cdot \ln\left(\frac{\ln(1-p)}{\ln(1-q)}\right) = \ln\left(\frac{\hat{\pi}_p}{\hat{\pi}_q}\right) \Leftrightarrow \tau = \frac{\ln\left(\frac{\ln(1-p)}{\ln(1-q)}\right)}{\ln\left(\frac{\hat{\pi}_p}{\hat{\pi}_q}\right)}.$$

From the first equation,

$$\theta = \frac{\hat{\pi}_p}{(-\ln(1-p))^{1/\tau}} = \frac{\hat{\pi}_p}{(-\ln(1-p))^{\ln\left(\frac{\hat{\pi}_p}{\hat{\pi}_q}\right)/\ln\left(\frac{\ln(1-p)}{\ln(1-q)}\right)}}.$$

Thus, using the method of percentile matching, the parameters of the Weibull distribution are estimated as

$$\hat{\tau} = \frac{\ln\left(\frac{\ln(1-p)}{\ln(1-q)}\right)}{\ln\left(\frac{\hat{\pi}_p}{\hat{\pi}_q}\right)}, \quad \hat{\theta} = \frac{\hat{\pi}_p}{(-\ln(1-p))^{\ln\left(\frac{\hat{\pi}_p}{\hat{\pi}_q}\right)/\ln\left(\frac{\ln(1-p)}{\ln(1-q)}\right)}}. \tag{6.15}$$

6.2.4 Percentile Matching for Pareto Distribution

By (1.53), a random variable X has a Pareto distribution with parameters α and θ if its **CDF** is of the form

$$F_X(x) = 1 - \left(\frac{\theta}{x+\theta}\right)^\alpha.$$

Calculating its inverse, we obtain

$$p = 1 - \left(\frac{\theta}{x+\theta}\right)^\alpha \Leftrightarrow \left(\frac{\theta}{x+\theta}\right)^\alpha = 1 - p \Leftrightarrow \frac{x+\theta}{\theta} = (1-p)^{-\frac{1}{\alpha}} \Leftrightarrow x = \theta\left((1-p)^{-\frac{1}{\alpha}} - 1\right).$$

Thus,

$$F^{-1}(p) = \theta\left((1-p)^{-\frac{1}{\alpha}} - 1\right)..$$

Since the distribution has two parameters, we arbitrarily choose two probabilities, p and q. Calculating corresponding smoothed empirical estimates of the percentiles $\hat{\pi}_p$ and $\hat{\pi}_q$, we obtain the following system of equations:

$$\begin{cases} \theta\left((1-p)^{-\frac{1}{\alpha}} - 1\right) = \hat{\pi}_p \\ \theta\left((1-q)^{-\frac{1}{\alpha}} - 1\right) = \hat{\pi}_q \end{cases}$$

Dividing the first equation by the second, we have an equation for α:

$$\frac{(1-p)^{-\frac{1}{\alpha}} - 1}{(1-q)^{-\frac{1}{\alpha}} - 1} = \frac{\hat{\pi}_p}{\hat{\pi}_q} \tag{6.16}$$

Alternatively, calculating α from each equation, we have

$$(1-p)^{-\frac{1}{\alpha}} = \frac{\hat{\pi}_p}{\theta} + 1 \Leftrightarrow -\frac{1}{\alpha}\ln(1-p) = \ln\left(\frac{\hat{\pi}_p}{\theta} + 1\right) \Leftrightarrow \alpha = -\frac{\ln(1-p)}{\ln\left(\frac{\hat{\pi}_p}{\theta} + 1\right)}.$$

Thus,

$$\frac{\ln(1-p)}{\ln\left(\frac{\hat{\pi}_p}{\theta} + 1\right)} = \frac{\ln(1-q)}{\ln\left(\frac{\hat{\pi}_q}{\theta} + 1\right)}. \tag{6.17}$$

Either one of the equations (6.16) or (6.17) requires numerical methods. Fixing one of the parameters, however, allows estimation of the other.

If α is fixed, the parameter θ is estimated as follows:

$$\hat{\theta} = \frac{\hat{\pi}_p}{(1-p)^{-\frac{1}{\alpha}} - 1}$$

If θ is fixed, the parameter α is estimated as follows:

$$\hat{\alpha} = -\frac{\ln(1-p)}{\ln\left(\frac{\hat{\pi}_p}{\theta} + 1\right)}$$

6.2.5 Percentile Matching for Normal Distribution

Let z_p be the $100p^{th}$ percentile corresponding to the standard normal distribution with parameters 0 and 1. Then

$$\pi_p = \mu + z_p\sigma$$

is the $100p^{th}$ percentile corresponding to the normal distribution with parameters μ and σ^2.

Since the distribution has two parameters, we arbitrarily choose two probabilities, p and q. Calculating corresponding smoothed empirical estimates of the percentiles $\hat{\pi}_p$ and $\hat{\pi}_q$, we obtain the following system of equations:

$$\begin{cases} \mu + z_p\sigma = \hat{\pi}_p \\ \mu + z_q\sigma = \hat{\pi}_q \end{cases}$$

Subtracting the second equation from the first, we have

$$\sigma = \frac{\hat{\pi}_p - \hat{\pi}_q}{z_p - z_q}.$$

Using the first equation to calculate parameter μ, we obtain

$$\mu = \hat{\pi}_p - z_p\sigma = \hat{\pi}_p - z_p \cdot \frac{\hat{\pi}_p - \hat{\pi}_q}{z_p - z_q} = \frac{z_p\hat{\pi}_q - z_q\hat{\pi}_p}{z_p - z_q}.$$

Thus, using the method of percentile matching, the parameters of the normal distribution are estimated as

$$\hat{\sigma} = \frac{\hat{\pi}_p - \hat{\pi}_q}{z_p - z_q}, \quad \hat{\mu} = \frac{z_p\hat{\pi}_q - z_q\hat{\pi}_p}{z_p - z_q}. \tag{6.18}$$

6.2.6 Percentile Matching for Lognormal Distribution

Let z_p be the $100p^{th}$ percentile corresponding to the standard normal distribution with parameters 0 and 1. Then

$$\pi_p = e^{\mu + z_p\sigma} \Leftrightarrow \ln\hat{\pi}_p = \mu + z_p\sigma$$

is the $100p^{th}$ percentile corresponding to the lognormal distribution with parameters μ and σ.

Since the distribution has two parameters, we arbitrarily choose two probabilities, p and q. Calculating corresponding smoothed empirical estimates of the percentiles $\hat{\pi}_p$ and $\hat{\pi}_q$, we obtain the following system of equations:

$$\begin{cases} \mu + z_p\sigma = \ln\hat{\pi}_p \\ \mu + z_q\sigma = \ln\hat{\pi}_q \end{cases}$$

Subtracting the second equation from the first, we have

$$\sigma = \frac{\ln\hat{\pi}_p - \ln\hat{\pi}_q}{z_p - z_q}.$$

Using the first equation to calculate parameter μ, we obtain

$$\mu = \ln\hat{\pi}_p - z_p\sigma = \ln\hat{\pi}_p - z_p \cdot \frac{\ln\hat{\pi}_p - \ln\hat{\pi}_q}{z_p - z_q} = \frac{z_p\ln\hat{\pi}_q - z_q\ln\hat{\pi}_p}{z_p - z_q}.$$

Thus, using the method of percentile matching, the parameters of the lognormal distribution are estimated as

$$\hat{\sigma} = \frac{\ln\hat{\pi}_p - \ln\hat{\pi}_q}{z_p - z_q}, \quad \hat{\mu} = \frac{z_p\ln\hat{\pi}_q - z_q\ln\hat{\pi}_p}{z_p - z_q}. \tag{6.19}$$

6.2.7 Percentile Matching for Loglogistic (Fisk) Distribution

For a loglogistic (Fisk) distribution, the **CDF** is

$$F(x) = \frac{(x/\theta)^\gamma}{1 + (x/\theta)^\gamma}.$$

Calculating its inverse, we obtain

$$p = \frac{(x/\theta)^{\gamma}}{1 + (x/\theta)^{\gamma}} \Leftrightarrow \frac{1 + (x/\theta)^{\gamma}}{(x/\theta)^{\gamma}} = \frac{1}{p} \Leftrightarrow \left(\frac{\theta}{x}\right)^{\gamma} + 1 = \frac{1}{p} \Leftrightarrow \frac{\theta}{x} = \left(\frac{1}{p} - 1\right)^{1/\gamma} \Leftrightarrow$$

$$x = \theta \left(\frac{1}{p} - 1\right)^{-1/\gamma} \Rightarrow F^{-1}(p) = \theta \left(\frac{1}{p} - 1\right)^{-1/\gamma}.$$

Since the distribution has two parameters, we arbitrarily choose two probabilities, p and q. Calculating corresponding smoothed empirical estimates of the percentiles $\hat{\pi}_p$ and $\hat{\pi}_q$, we obtain the following system of equations:

$$\begin{cases} \hat{\pi}_p = \theta \left(\frac{1}{p} - 1\right)^{-1/\gamma} \\ \hat{\pi}_q = \theta \left(\frac{1}{q} - 1\right)^{-1/\gamma} \end{cases}$$

Dividing these equations and solving for γ, we have

$$\left(\frac{1/p - 1}{1/q - 1}\right)^{-1/\gamma} = \frac{\hat{\pi}_p}{\hat{\pi}_q} \Leftrightarrow -\frac{1}{\gamma} \ln \left(\frac{(1-p)q}{(1-q)p}\right) = \ln \frac{\hat{\pi}_p}{\hat{\pi}_q} \Leftrightarrow \gamma = -\frac{\ln \left(\frac{(1-p)q}{(1-q)p}\right)}{\ln \frac{\hat{\pi}_p}{\hat{\pi}_q}}.$$

Solving for θ, we have

$$\theta = \frac{\hat{\pi}_p}{\left(\frac{1}{p} - 1\right)^{-1/\gamma}} = \frac{\hat{\pi}_p}{\left(\frac{1}{p} - 1\right)^{\ln \frac{\hat{\pi}_p}{\hat{\pi}_q} / \ln\left(\frac{(1-p)q}{(1-q)p}\right)}}.$$

Thus, using the method of percentile matching, the parameters of the loglogistic distribution are estimated as

$$\hat{\gamma} = -\frac{\ln \left(\frac{(1-p)q}{(1-q)p}\right)}{\ln \frac{\hat{\pi}_p}{\hat{\pi}_q}}, \quad \hat{\theta} = \frac{\hat{\pi}_p}{\left(\frac{1}{p} - 1\right)^{\ln \frac{\hat{\pi}_p}{\hat{\pi}_q} / \ln\left(\frac{(1-p)q}{(1-q)p}\right)}}. \tag{6.20}$$

6.2.8 Advantages and Disadvantages of Percentile Matching

One of the advantages of the method of percentile matching is that percentiles always exist. On the other hand, it's not always easy to obtain a theoretical expression for an inverse function and thus a percentile, of a distribution. Furthermore, even if an analytical expression for a percentile is obtained, it is not always possible to calculate the exact expressions of parameters, as we saw in section 6.2.4.

As with the method of moments, the method of percentile matching may be more appropriate for large samples modeling symmetric distributions.

While focusing on calculation of the sample percentiles, the parameter estimates produced by the method of percentile matching may not yield *sufficient* statistics, meaning that they may not take into account *all* relevant information in the sample.

An assumption of the data set being drawn from a single distribution of the same random variable proves to be a disadvantage when an analyst considers a set of observations with characteristics of different nature, such as various deductibles or policy limits.

6.3   Maximum Likelihood Estimation

Let $B_1, B_2, \ldots, B_n$ be n events resulting from observing random variables X_i. Each event may consist of a single point, several points, or an interval. Observations across the events and within the events are independent[2]. Suppose that the random variables in the random variable vector $\mathbf{X} = \{X_1, X_2, \ldots, X_n\}$ depend on the common set of K parameters $\theta^T = (\theta_1, \theta_2, \ldots, \theta_K)$ but are not necessarily identically distributed.

The **likelihood function** based on observations of n independent random variables is defined as

$$L(\theta) = L(\theta; \mathbf{X}) = \prod_{i=1}^{n} \mathbf{P}\left(X_i \in B_i | \theta\right).$$

Note that we may have different random variables with different distributions, each having its own number of observations, which may or may not belong to the same event B_j.

To consider two simplified cases, for a single observation x_i of each random variable in $\mathbf{X}$,

$$L(\theta) = \prod_{i=1}^{n} f_{X_i}(x_i, \theta),$$

so that it is a joint probability function associated with the sample viewed as a function of θ only. Here, $f_{X_i}(x, \theta)$ is the **pdf** or the **pmf** of a random variable X_i.

For n observations of one random variable, X,

$$L(\theta) = \prod_{i=1}^{n} f_X(x_i, \theta) = \prod_{i=1}^{n} f(x_i, \theta). \tag{6.21}$$

Unless otherwise specified, we will assume that (6.21) holds.

The **maximum likelihood estimator** or the **ML** estimate of θ is the vector of parameters that maximizes the likelihood function.

For purposes of the calculations, it is convenient to analyze the **log-likelihood function** defined as

$$l(\theta) = \ln L(\theta) = \sum_{i=1}^{n} \ln f(x_i, \theta) = \sum_{i=1}^{n} l(x_i, \theta), \tag{6.22}$$

where

$$l(x, \theta) = \ln f(x, \theta).$$

When the common probability function, $f(x; \theta)$, is differentiable and its derivatives of first and second orders have finite expectations, a family, $\{f(x; \theta)\}$, of probability functions is called **regular**.

6.3.1   Likelihood for Censored and Truncated Data

Note that data is considered **censored** when a range of values rather than an exact value is provided. An example of such data is a *policy limit* on an insurance policy. Data can be censored from above or below.

On the other hand, data is considered **truncated** when no information is provided for certain ranges (observations below a certain number are not available). An example of such data is a *deductible* on an insurance policy. Data can be left- or right-truncated.

The structure of the likelihood function changes depending on whether data is censored or truncated.

For censored data, if the data is censored from above at value u, the likelihood function can be written as

$$L(\theta) = \left[\prod_{i=1}^{n} f(x_i, \theta)\right] (S(u))^m, \qquad (6.23)$$

where n is the number of uncensored observations and m is the number of censored observations.

In case of data being censored from below at value d, the likelihood function can be written as

$$L(\theta) = F(d)^m \cdot \prod_{i=1}^{n} f(x_i, \theta).$$

For a left-truncated data at d, the likelihood function takes the form of

$$L(\theta) = \prod_{i=1}^{n} \tilde{f}(x_i, \theta), \text{ where } \tilde{f}(x_i, \theta) = \frac{f(x_i, \theta)}{S(d)}. \qquad (6.24)$$

For a right-truncated data at u, the likelihood function takes the form of

$$L(\theta) = \prod_{i=1}^{n} \tilde{f}(x_i, \theta), \text{ where } \tilde{f}(x_i, \theta) = \frac{f(x_i, \theta)}{F(u)}.$$

6.3.2   The Score Function

It follows from (6.22) that the derivative of log-likelihood function is

$$l'(\theta) = \sum_{i=1}^{n} l'(x_i, \theta) = \sum_{i=1}^{n} Y(x_i, \theta), \qquad (6.25)$$

where Y is the **score function** defined as

$$Y(x, \theta) = \frac{\partial l(x, \theta)}{\partial \theta}. \qquad (6.26)$$

Note that

$$Y(x, \theta) = \frac{\partial}{\partial \theta} l(x, \theta) = \frac{\partial}{\partial \theta} \ln(f(x; \theta)) = \frac{1}{f(x; \theta)} \cdot \frac{\partial f(x; \theta)}{\partial \theta} \qquad (6.27)$$

and

$$Y(x_i, \theta) = \frac{f'(x_i; \theta)}{f(x_i; \theta)}.$$

6.3.3 Moments of the Score Function

If $\{f(x; \theta)\}$ is a regular family, then for each θ,

$$\mathbf{E}\left[Y|\theta\right] = 0.$$

Indeed. Since $f(x; \theta)$ is a density function,

$$\int_{-\infty}^{\infty} f(x; \theta)\, dx = 1.$$

By definition of the expected value,

$$\mathbf{E}\left[Y|\theta\right] = \int_{-\infty}^{\infty} \frac{1}{f(x; \theta)} \cdot \frac{\partial f(x; \theta)}{\partial \theta} \cdot f(x; \theta)\, dx =$$

$$= \int_{-\infty}^{\infty} \frac{\partial f(x; \theta)}{\partial \theta}\, dx = \frac{\partial}{\partial \theta} \int_{-\infty}^{\infty} f(x; \theta)\, dx = 0.$$

The second moment of Y is

$$\mathbf{E}\left[Y^2|\theta\right] = \mathbf{E}\left[\left(\frac{\partial l(x; \theta)}{\partial \theta}\right)^2 \Big| \theta\right] = \mathbf{E}\left[\left(\frac{f'(x; \theta)}{f(x; \theta)}\right)^2 \Big| \theta\right] =$$

$$= \int_{-\infty}^{\infty} \frac{1}{f^2(x; \theta)} \cdot \left(\frac{\partial f(x; \theta)}{\partial \theta}\right)^2 \cdot f(x; \theta)\, dx = \int_{-\infty}^{\infty} \frac{1}{f(x; \theta)} \cdot \left(\frac{\partial f(x; \theta)}{\partial \theta}\right)^2\, dx.$$

In mathematical statistics, the **Fisher's information** (or the **information**) is one of the measures of the amount of information that an observable random variable X carries about an unknown parameter θ of a distribution that models X. It is defined as the the variance of the score function Y. Since the expected value of Y is zero, its variance coincides with its second moment. Thus,

$$\mathbf{I}(\theta) = \mathbf{Var}\left[Y|\theta\right] = \mathbf{E}\left[Y^2|\theta\right] = \int_{-\infty}^{\infty} \frac{1}{f(x; \theta)} \cdot \left(\frac{\partial f(x; \theta)}{\partial \theta}\right)^2. \qquad (6.28)$$

Let us denote

$$\mathbf{Var}\left[Y|\theta\right] = \sigma^2.$$

When a sample $\mathbf{X}$ of size n is considered, by (6.25),

$$l'(\theta) = \sum_{i=1}^{n} Y(x_i, \theta).$$

Since variables $\{Y(x_i, \theta) : 1 \leq i \leq n\}$ are independent and identically distributed with zero mean and variance σ^2, the central limit theorem implies that

$$\frac{1}{\sqrt{n}} \cdot l'(\theta) = \frac{1}{\sqrt{n}} \cdot \sum_{i=1}^{n} Y(x_i, \theta) \sim \mathbf{N}\left[0, \sigma^2\right]. \qquad (6.29)$$

6.3.4 Definitions of Fisher's Information

There are several equivalent definitions for Fisher's information based on a sample of n independent observations of a random variable X.

One definition is based on the variance σ^2 associated with the score function. For a sample of n observations of a random variable X,

$$\mathbf{I}_l(\theta) = \mathbf{Var}\left[l'(\theta)\right] = \mathbf{Var}\left[\sum_{i=1}^{n} Y(x_i, \theta)\right] = n \cdot \sigma^2,$$

which allows us to interpret σ^2 as the amount of information carried out by a single observation.

The alternative definition is based on the **second** derivative of a log-likelihood function:

$$l''(\theta) = \left[l'(\theta)\right]' = \sum_{i=1}^{n} l''(x_i, \theta) = \sum_{i=1}^{n} Y'(x_i, \theta)$$

Considering a second derivative of l for a single observation, we have

$$\frac{\partial Y(x, \theta)}{\partial \theta} = \frac{\partial}{\partial \theta}\left(\frac{f'(x; \theta)}{f(x; \theta)}\right) = \frac{\partial^2 f(x, \theta)}{\partial \theta^2} \cdot \frac{1}{f(x; \theta)} - \frac{1}{f^2(x; \theta)}\left(\frac{\partial f(x; \theta)}{\partial \theta}\right)^2. \quad (6.30)$$

Calculating the expectation of $\partial Y(x, \theta)/\partial \theta$, note that the expectation of first term in (6.30) vanishes. Indeed. Since $f(x; \theta)$ is a density function,

$$\int_{-\infty}^{\infty} f(x; \theta)\, dx = 1.$$

By definition of the expected value,

$$\mathbf{E}\left[\frac{\partial^2 f(x, \theta)}{\partial \theta^2} \cdot \frac{1}{f(x; \theta)}\right] = \int_{-\infty}^{\infty} \frac{\partial^2 f(x, \theta)}{\partial \theta^2} \cdot \frac{1}{f(x; \theta)} \cdot f(x; \theta)\, dx =$$

$$= \int_{-\infty}^{\infty} \frac{\partial^2 f(x, \theta)}{\partial \theta^2}\, dx = \frac{\partial^2}{\partial \theta^2}\left(\int_{-\infty}^{\infty} f(x; \theta)\, dx\right) = 0.$$

Therefore, using (6.28),

$$\mathbf{E}\left[\frac{\partial Y(x, \theta)}{\partial \theta}\right] = -\mathbf{E}\left[(Y(x, \theta))^2\right] = -\mathbf{I}(\theta) = -\sigma^2$$

or

$$\mathbf{I}(\theta) = \mathbf{E}\left[(Y(x, \theta))^2\right] = -\mathbf{E}\left[\frac{\partial Y(x, \theta)}{\partial \theta}\right]. \quad (6.31)$$

For the n observations,

$$\mathbf{E}\left[l''(\theta)\right] = \mathbf{E}\left[\sum_{i=1}^{n} Y'(x_i, \theta)\right] = \sum_{i=1}^{n} \mathbf{E}\left[Y'(x_i, \theta)\right] = n\mathbf{E}\left[Y'(x, \theta)\right] = -n\mathbf{I}(\theta) = -\mathbf{I}_l(\theta)$$

or

$$\mathbf{I}_l(\theta) = -\mathbf{E}\left[l''(\theta)\right].$$

On the other hand, since $\mathbf{E}\left[Y(x, \theta)\right] = 0$,

$$\mathbf{E}\left[(l'(\theta))^2\right] = \mathbf{E}\left[\left(\sum_{i=1}^{n} Y(x_i, \theta)\right)^2\right] = \mathbf{Var}\left(\sum_{i=1}^{n} Y(x_i, \theta)\right) + \left(\mathbf{E}\left[\sum_{i=1}^{n} Y(x_i, \theta)\right]\right)^2 =$$

$$= n\mathbf{Var}\left(Y(x, \theta)\right) + (n\mathbf{E}\left[Y(x, \theta)\right])^2 = n\mathbf{Var}\left(Y(x, \theta)\right) = n\mathbf{I}(\theta).$$

Therefore,

$$\mathbf{I}_l(\theta) = \mathbf{E}\left[(l'(\theta))^2\right].$$

Combining the three definitions,

$$\mathbf{I}_l(\theta) = \mathbf{E}\left[(l'(\theta))^2\right] = -\mathbf{E}\left[l''(\theta)\right] = n \cdot \sigma^2. \tag{6.32}$$

Finally, for a parameter vector $\theta^T = (\theta_1, \theta_2, \ldots, \theta_K)$, the **Fisher's information matrix** is a matrix whose entries are defined as

$$\mathbf{I}(\theta)_{rs} = -\mathbf{E}_X\left[\frac{\partial^2 l(\theta)}{\partial \theta_s \partial \theta_r}\right] = \mathbf{E}_X\left[\frac{\partial l(\theta)}{\partial \theta_s} \cdot \frac{\partial l(\theta)}{\partial \theta_r}\right],$$

$$1 \leq r \leq K, \ 1 \leq s \leq K. \tag{6.33}$$

Note that it is usually easier to use the expression with second derivatives rather than the expression with squares or products of first derivatives. This is due to the random variable X often disappearing in the differentiation process. In this case, the expected value is the second derivative itself. In addition, it's usually easier to differentiate twice than to calculate the square or product of first derivatives.

6.3.5 Asymptotic Behavior of the Maximum Likelihood Estimation

The definition of MLE requires maximization of $L(\theta)$ or, equivalently, of $l(\theta)$, in θ. Let $\hat{\theta}$ be the value of θ that maximizes $l(\theta)$. Let us show that $\hat{\theta}$ is asymptotically normal, that is,

$$\sqrt{n} \cdot (\hat{\theta} - \theta) \xrightarrow{d} \mathbf{N}\left[0, \sigma_{\hat{\theta}}^2\right],$$

converges in distribution to normal distribution with zero mean and variance $\sigma_{\hat{\theta}}^2$, which is called the **asymptotic variance of the estimate** $\hat{\theta}$.

Since $\hat{\theta}$ maximizes $l(\theta)$, it follows that $l'(\hat{\theta}) = 0$. By the mean value theorem,

$$0 = l'(\hat{\theta}) = l'(\theta) + l''(\hat{\theta}_1)(\hat{\theta} - \theta)$$

for some $\hat{\theta}_1 \in [\hat{\theta}, \theta]$. Solving for $\hat{\theta} - \theta$, we have

$$\hat{\theta} - \theta = -\frac{l'(\theta)}{l''(\hat{\theta}_1)} = -\frac{1}{\sqrt{n}} \cdot \left(\frac{l'(\theta)/\sqrt{n}}{l''(\hat{\theta}_1)/n}\right) \Leftrightarrow \sqrt{n}(\hat{\theta} - \theta) = -\frac{l'(\theta)/\sqrt{n}}{l''(\hat{\theta}_1)/n}.$$

We have shown in (6.29) that

$$\frac{1}{\sqrt{n}} \cdot l'(\theta) \sim \mathbf{N}\left[0, \sigma^2\right].$$

Also, by the law of large numbers, using (6.31), as $n \to \infty$, we have

$$\frac{l''(\hat{\theta}_1)}{n} = \frac{1}{n} \sum_{i=1}^{n} Y'(x_i, \hat{\theta}_1) \to \mathbf{E}\left[Y'(x, \hat{\theta}_1)\right] = -\mathbf{E}[Y^2(x, \hat{\theta}_1)].$$

Since $\hat{\theta}_1 \in [\hat{\theta}, \theta]$, it follows that if $\hat{\theta} \to \theta$, then $\hat{\theta}_1 \to \theta$. Therefore, by the Portmanteau theorem,

$$\mathbf{E}[Y^2(x, \hat{\theta}_1)] \to \mathbf{E}[Y^2(x, \theta)] = -\mathbf{I}(\theta).$$

Thus,

$$\sqrt{n}(\hat{\theta} - \theta) \xrightarrow{d} \mathbf{N}\left[0, \frac{\sigma_\theta^2}{(\mathbf{I}(\theta))^2} = \frac{1}{\mathbf{I}(\theta)}\right].$$

Thus, asymptotically, as $n \to \infty$, we can conclude that

$$\mathbf{E}\left[\hat{\theta}\right] \approx \theta \quad \text{and} \quad \mathbf{Var}\left[\hat{\theta}\right] \approx \frac{1}{n\mathbf{I}(\theta)} = \frac{1}{\mathbf{I}_l(\theta)}.$$

6.3.6 Information Bounds and Cramér–Rao Inequality

Consider an arbitrary estimate, $T = T(\mathbf{X})$, based on a sample of size n drawn from the population with common probability function, $f(x; \theta)$.

Lemma 6.3.1 *If $\mathbf{E}[T] = \phi(\theta)$, then*

$$\mathbf{Var}(T) \geq \frac{[\phi'(\theta)]^2}{\mathbf{I}(\theta)}.$$

Proof. Let $Y(x, \theta)$ be a score function defined in (6.27):

$$Y(x, \theta) = \frac{\partial}{\partial \theta} \ln(f(x; \theta)) = \frac{1}{f(x; \theta)} \cdot \frac{\partial f(x; \theta)}{\partial \theta}$$

Consider the covariance of Y and T: $\mathbf{Cov}(Y, T) = \mathbf{E}[YT] - \mathbf{E}[Y]\mathbf{E}[T]$. We have shown in section 6.3.3 that $\mathbf{E}[Y|\theta] = 0$. Therefore, $\mathbf{Cov}(Y, T) = \mathbf{E}[YT]$. By definition of the expected value,

$$\mathbf{Cov}(Y, T) = \mathbf{E}[YT] = \int_{-\infty}^{\infty} T(x) \cdot \frac{1}{f(x; \theta)} \cdot \frac{\partial f(x; \theta)}{\partial \theta} \cdot f(x; \theta) \, dx =$$

$$= \int_{-\infty}^{\infty} T(x) \cdot \frac{\partial f(x; \theta)}{\partial \theta} \, dx = \frac{\partial}{\partial \theta} \int_{-\infty}^{\infty} T(x) f(x; \theta) \, dx = \frac{\partial}{\partial \theta} \mathbf{E}[T] = \phi'(\theta).$$

Recall that

$$\mathbf{Cov}(Y, T) = \rho_{Y,T} \cdot \sigma_Y \cdot \sigma_T,$$

where $\rho_{Y,T}$ is the correlation coefficient of Y and T, $|\rho_{Y,T}| \leq 1$. Therefore,

$$\sqrt{\mathbf{Var}(T) \cdot \mathbf{Var}(Y)} \geq |\mathbf{Cov}(Y, T)| = |\phi'(\theta)|,$$

But $\mathbf{Var}(Y) = \mathbf{I}(\theta)$. Hence,

$$\mathbf{Var}(T) \geq \frac{[\phi'(\theta)]^2}{\mathbf{I}(\theta)}.$$

Note that if $T = T(\mathbf{X})$ is an unbiased estimate of θ, then $\mathbf{E}[T] = \theta$ and $\phi'(\theta) = 1$ and the estimate for the variance of T becomes

$$\mathbf{Var}(T) \geq \frac{1}{\mathbf{I}(\theta)}.$$

The **asymptotic covariance matrix** of the maximum likelihood estimator is the *inverse* of the (Fisher's) information matrix.

The inverse of the Fisher's information matrix is called the **Cramér–Rao lower bound** for the variance of any unbiased estimator. Thus, the maximum likelihood estimator's variance is the lowest of any asymptotically unbiased estimator.

6.3.7 True and Observed Information

Recall that, by the definition of the information matrix (6.33), its members are negative the expected values of the second derivatives. These expected values are usually functions of the parameters. Since in practice the parameters are often unknown, the parameter estimates are used to compute the value of the information matrix.

The information matrix calculated using the parameter estimates in the expression for the members of the Fisher's information matrix is called the **true information**:

$$\mathbf{I}^T(\theta) = \mathbf{I}(\theta)|_{\theta=\hat{\theta}} = -\mathbf{E}_X \left[\frac{d^2 l}{d\theta^2} \right] \Bigg|_{\theta=\hat{\theta}}$$

The direct value of the negative second derivative calculated at $\theta = \hat{\theta}$ is called the **observed information**:

$$\mathbf{I}^O(\theta) = -\frac{d^2 l}{d\theta^2} \Bigg|_{\theta=\hat{\theta}}$$

6.4 Examples of MLE

In this section we calculate the MLE and its variance for selected distributions.

6.4.1 MLE for Bernoulli Trials

Suppose that $\mathbf{X} = \{X_j : j \geq 1\}$ are independent Bernoulli-distributed with a common success rate, q, such that $0 < q < 1$. When the targeted parameter is $\theta = q$, the MLE is easy to determine, and its performance is based on evaluation of its bias and variance.

For a single observation, X, the probability function of a Bernoulli trial is

$$f(x) = q^x \cdot (1-q)^x \quad \text{for} \quad x = 0 \quad \text{or} \quad x = 1.$$

Then the sample $\mathbf{X}$ has likelihood

$$L(q) = q^w \cdot (1-q)^{n-w},$$

where $w = \sum_{j=1}^n x_j$ is the value of a random variable, $W = \sum_{j=1}^n X_j$, which represents the total number of successes.

By definition, given a set $\mathbf{X}$ of independent identically distributed data conditioned on an unknown parameter θ, a **sufficient statistic** is a function $T(X)$ whose value contains all the information needed to compute any estimate of the parameter (e.g., a maximum likelihood estimate). Thus, W is a *sufficient* statistic for this model.

The log-likelihood function is

$$l(q) = \ln L(q) = w \cdot \ln q + (n - w) \cdot \ln(1 - q).$$

Differentiating $l(q)$ with respect to q and equating the derivative to zero, we obtain

$$\frac{w}{q} - \frac{n - w}{1 - q} = 0 \;\Rightarrow\; w \cdot (1 - q) = (n - w) \cdot q \;\Rightarrow\; w = n \cdot q \;\Rightarrow\; \hat{q} = \frac{w}{n}.$$

Thus, the MLE for a set of for Bernoulli trials is

$$\hat{q} = \frac{w}{n}. \tag{6.34}$$

Since $W \sim \mathbf{Bin}\,[n, q]$, its expectation and variance are

$$\mathbf{E}[W] = nq \quad \text{and} \quad \mathbf{Var}(W) = nq(1 - q) \tag{6.35}$$

Thus,

$$\mathbf{E}[\hat{q}] = q \quad \text{and} \quad \mathbf{Var}(\hat{q}) = \frac{q(1 - q)}{n}, \; q \in (0, 1). \tag{6.36}$$

Therefore, the estimate $\hat{q}$ is unbiased and its mean square error coincides with the variance:

$$\mathbf{E}\left[\hat{q} - q\right]^2 = \frac{q(1 - q)}{n}$$

Checking the information bounds, note that

$$\frac{dl}{dq} = \frac{W}{q} - \frac{n - W}{1 - q} = \frac{W - nq}{q(1 - q)}.$$

Using (6.32), $I(q)$ is evaluated as

$$\mathbf{I}(q) = \mathbf{E}\left[\left(\frac{dl}{dq}\right)^2\right] = \mathbf{E}\left[\left(\frac{W - nq}{q(1 - q)}\right)^2\right] = \frac{1}{q^2(1 - q)^2}\left[\mathbf{Var}(W - nq) + \mathbf{E}(W - nq)\right].$$

Since by (6.35), $\mathbf{E}[W] = nq$ and $\mathbf{Var}(W) = nq(1 - q)$

$$\mathbf{I}(q) = \frac{1}{q^2(1 - q)^2}\mathbf{Var}(W - nq) = \frac{1}{q^2(1 - q)^2}\mathbf{Var}(W) = \frac{nq(1 - q)}{q^2(1 - q)^2} = \frac{n}{q(1 - q)}.$$

By definition, the estimator is a **finite-sample efficient estimator** in the class of unbiased estimators if it reaches the lower bound in the Cramér–Rao inequality, for all $\theta \in \Theta$:

$$\mathbf{Var}(\hat{q}) \geq \mathbf{I}_\theta(q)^{-1}$$

Since by (6.36),

$$\mathbf{Var}(\hat{q}) = \frac{1}{\mathbf{I}(q)},$$

it follows that $\hat{q}$ is an *efficient* estimator.

By the **invariance principle**, for a transformed parameter, $G(q)$, the corresponding $G(\hat{q})$ is the MLE for $G(q)$. Note that its efficiency is asymptotic and observed only as the sample size (n) increases.

For example, if $G(q) = q^2$ is estimated, the transformation $(\hat{q})^2$ leads to the MLE for q^2. Its performance is asymptotic, as $n \to \infty$.

To find an unbiased estimate $T = T(W)$ of q^2, since W is sufficient, let

$$T(W) = aW^2 + bW + c.$$

We would like to find coefficients a, b and c, such that $\mathbf{E}[T(W)] = q^2$. Calculating $\mathbf{E}[T(W)]$, using (6.35), we obtain

$$\mathbf{E}[T(W)] = a\mathbf{E}[W^2] + b\mathbf{E}[W] + c = a\left(nq(1-q) + n^2q^2\right) + bnq + c =$$
$$= an(n-1)q^2 + n(a+b)q + c.$$

Equating this to q^2 and forming corresponding coefficient equalities, we have

$$an(n-1) = 1, \; n(a+b) = 0, \; c = 0 \Leftrightarrow a = \frac{1}{n(n-1)}, \;\; b = -\frac{1}{n(n-1)}, \; c = 0.$$

Thus, the unbiased estimate for q^2 is

$$T = T(W) = \frac{W^2 - W}{n(n-1)}.$$

Asymptotically, using (6.34), it is equivalent to

$$\hat{q}^2 = \frac{W^2}{n^2} = \left(\frac{W}{n}\right)^2,$$

but usually bias reduction for a finite sample size increases the variance.

6.4.2 MLE for Normal Distribution

Suppose that observations $\mathbf{X} = \{X_j : 1 \leq j \leq n\}$ are independently drawn from a normal population, $\mathbf{N}[\mu, \sigma^2]$, where the mean and the variance may be known or unknown.

The normal distribution has its probability density function given by

$$f(x) = \frac{1}{\sigma\sqrt{2\pi}}e^{-(x-\mu)^2/2\sigma^2}.$$

The likelihood function based on $\mathbf{X}$ is

$$L(\mu, \sigma^2) = \frac{1}{\sigma^n(2\pi)^{n/2}}e^{-\sum_{j=1}^{n}(X_j-\mu)^2/2\sigma^2}.$$

The log-likelihood function based on $\mathbf{X}$ is

$$l(\mu, \sigma^2) = \ln L(\mu, \sigma^2) = -\frac{n}{2}\ln(2\pi) - \frac{n}{2}\ln(\sigma^2) - \frac{1}{2\sigma^2} \cdot \sum_{j=1}^{n}(X_j - \mu)^2.$$

Differentiating in μ and $\tau = \sigma^2$ and equating the partial derivatives to zero, we obtain

$$\frac{\partial l}{\partial \mu} = \frac{1}{\tau} \cdot \sum_{j=1}^{n} (X_j - \mu) = 0,$$

$$\frac{\partial l}{\partial \tau} = -\frac{n}{2\tau} + \frac{1}{2\tau^2} \cdot \sum_{j=1}^{n} (X_j - \mu)^2 = 0.$$

Solving this system of equations, we obtain the MLE for μ and $\tau = \sigma^2$:

$$\hat{\mu} = \bar{X} = \frac{1}{n} \cdot \sum_{j=1}^{n} X_j, \quad \hat{\tau} = \frac{1}{n} \cdot \sum_{j=1}^{n} (X_j - \bar{X})^2. \tag{6.37}$$

If the value of μ were known, the estimate for τ would be modified to an unbiased estimate:

$$\tilde{\tau} = \frac{1}{n} \cdot \sum_{j=1}^{n} (X_j - \mu)^2$$

Note that estimation of two parameters is conducted almost independent from each other. Sampling distributions of $\bar{X}$ and $\hat{\tau}$ allow us to check their efficiency.

6.4.2.1 Information for Normal Distribution

Suppose that both parameters μ and $\tau = \sigma^2$ are unknown. Let us calculate the information bounds for population mean and for variance.

The first two derivatives of the log-likelihood in μ are

$$\frac{\partial l}{\partial \mu} = \frac{1}{\tau} \cdot \sum_{j=1}^{n} (X_j - \mu) = \frac{n}{\tau} \left(\bar{X} - \mu \right), \quad \frac{\partial^2 l}{\partial \mu^2} = -\frac{n}{\tau}.$$

The information in μ is

$$I_\mu(\mu, \tau) = -\mathbf{E}\left[\frac{\partial^2 l}{\partial \mu^2} \right] = \frac{n}{\sigma^2}.$$

Since

$$\mathbf{Var}(\hat{\mu}) = \frac{\sigma^2}{n}$$

it follows that

$$I_\mu(\mu, \tau) = \frac{1}{\mathbf{Var}(\hat{\mu})},$$

which implies efficiency in the Cramér–Rao spirit.

The first two derivatives of the log-likelihood in $\tau = \sigma^2$ are

$$\frac{\partial l}{\partial \tau} = -\frac{n}{2\tau} + \frac{1}{2\tau^2} \cdot \sum_{j=1}^{n} (X_j - \mu)^2$$

$$\frac{\partial^2 l}{\partial \tau^2} = \frac{n}{2\tau^2} - \frac{1}{\tau^3} \cdot \sum_{j=1}^{n} (X_j - \mu)^2.$$

The information in τ is

$$I_\tau(\mu, \tau) = -\mathbf{E}\left[\frac{\partial^2 l}{\partial \tau^2}\right] = -\mathbf{E}\left[\frac{n}{2\tau^2} - \frac{1}{\tau^3} \cdot \sum_{j=1}^{n}(X_j - \mu)^2\right] =$$

$$= -\frac{n}{2\tau^2} + \frac{1}{\tau^3}\,\mathbf{E}\left[\sum_{j=1}^{n}(X_j - \mu)^2\right] = -\frac{n}{2\tau^2} + \frac{1}{\tau^3}\sum_{j=1}^{n}\mathbf{E}_X\left[(X_j - \mu)^2\right].$$

Since $\mathbf{E}\left[(X_j - \mu)^2\right] = \tau = \sigma^2$, it follows that

$$I_\tau(\mu, \tau) = -\frac{n}{2\tau^2} + \frac{1}{\tau^3} \cdot n\tau = -\frac{n}{2\tau^2} + \frac{n}{\tau^2} = \frac{n}{2\tau^2} = \frac{n}{2\sigma^4}.$$

Since for a known μ, the variance of MLE is

$$\mathbf{Var}\left[\tilde{\tau}\right] = \frac{2\sigma^4}{n},$$

it follows that the information coincides with the information bound

$$I_\tau(\mu, \tau) = \frac{1}{\mathbf{Var}(\tilde{\tau})},$$

which implies efficiency in the Cramér–Rao spirit.

For unknown μ, this is the asymptotic variance of $\hat{\tau}$.

Recall that the traditionally used estimate for $\tau = \sigma^2$ is

$$S^2 = \frac{1}{n-1} \cdot \sum_{j=1}^{n}(X_j - \bar{X})^2.$$

The statistic,

$$W = \frac{(n-1)S^2}{\sigma^2} \sim \chi^2\left[n-1\right]$$

has χ^2-distribution with $(n-1)$ degrees of freedom.

Note that the $\chi^2[m]$-distribution is the same as Gamma distribution with the shape parameter $a = m/2$ and the scale parameter $\theta = 2$. Calculating the first two moments using (1.39), we have

$$\mathbf{E}\left[W\right] = \alpha\theta = m = n - 1 \quad \text{and} \quad \mathbf{Var}\left[W\right] = \alpha\theta^2 = m/2 \cdot 4 = 2m = 2 \cdot (n-1).$$

Therefore,

$$\mathbf{E}\left[S^2\right] = \sigma^2 \quad \text{and} \quad \mathbf{Var}\left[S^2\right] = 2 \cdot (n-1) \cdot \frac{\sigma^4}{(n-1)^2} = \frac{2\sigma^4}{n-1}.$$

Regardless of the variance estimator, $\hat{\tau}$, or $\tilde{\tau}$, its square root viewed as an estimate of σ is biased and its performance is asymptotic.

Note that the second mixed derivative of the log-likelihood function is

$$\frac{\partial^2 l}{\partial \mu \partial \tau} = \frac{\partial}{\partial \tau}\left(\frac{\partial l}{\partial \mu}\right) = \frac{\partial}{\partial \tau}\left(\frac{n}{\tau}(\bar{X} - \mu)\right) = -\frac{n}{\tau^2}(\bar{X} - \mu).$$

The corresponding entry in the information matrix is

$$\mathbf{I}(\mu, \tau)_{12} = \mathbf{I}(\theta)_{21} = -\mathbf{E}_X \left[\frac{\partial^2 l}{\partial \mu \partial \tau} \right] = \frac{n}{\tau^2} \mathbf{E}_X \left[\bar{X} - \mu \right] = 0$$

Therefore, the information and covariance matrices are

$$\mathbf{I}(\mu, \sigma^2) = \begin{pmatrix} n/\sigma^2 & 0 \\ \\ 0 & n/2\sigma^4 \end{pmatrix}, \quad \mathbf{Cov}(\mu, \sigma^2) = \mathbf{I}^{-1}(\mu, \sigma^2) = \begin{pmatrix} \sigma^2/n & 0 \\ \\ 0 & 2\sigma^4/n \end{pmatrix}.$$

6.4.3   MLE for Lognormal Distribution

Suppose that observations $\mathbf{X} = \{X_j : 1 \leq j \leq n\}$ are independently drawn from a lognormal distribution with parameters μ and σ. Then the vector of observations $\mathbf{Y} = \{Y_j = \ln X_j : 1 \leq j \leq n\}$ is normal $\mathbf{N}[\mu, \sigma^2]$ with parameters μ and σ^2. The lognormal distribution has its probability density function given by

$$f(x) = \frac{1}{x\sigma\sqrt{2\pi}} e^{-(x-\mu)^2/2\sigma^2}.$$

The likelihood function based on $\mathbf{X}$ is

$$L(\mu, \sigma) = \frac{1}{\sigma^n (2\pi)^{n/2} \prod_{i=1}^n X_i} e^{-\sum_{j=1}^n (\ln X_j - \mu)^2/2\sigma^2}.$$

The log-likelihood function based on $\mathbf{X}$ is

$$l(\mu, \sigma) = \ln L(\mu, \sigma) = -\frac{n}{2} \ln(2\pi) - n \ln(\sigma) - \sum_{i=1}^n \ln X_i - \frac{1}{2\sigma^2} \sum_{j=1}^n (\ln X_j - \mu)^2.$$

Differentiating in μ and σ and equating the partial derivatives to zero, we obtain

$$\frac{\partial l}{\partial \mu} = \frac{1}{\sigma^2} \sum_{j=1}^n (\ln X_j - \mu) = 0,$$

$$\frac{\partial l}{\partial \sigma} = \frac{1}{\sigma^3} \sum_{i=1}^n (\ln X_i - \mu)^2 - \frac{n}{\sigma} = 0.$$

Solving this system of equations, we obtain the MLE for μ and σ for lognormal distribution:

$$\hat{\mu} = \bar{Y} = \frac{1}{n} \sum_{j=1}^n \ln X_j,$$

$$\hat{\sigma} = \sqrt{\frac{1}{n} \sum_{j=1}^n (\ln X_j - \bar{Y})^2} = \sqrt{\frac{1}{n} \sum_{i=1}^n (\ln X_i)^2 - \hat{\mu}^2} \tag{6.38}$$

6.4.3.1 Information for Lognormal Distribution

Suppose that both parameters, μ and σ are unknown. Let us calculate the information bounds for these parameters.

The first two derivatives of the log-likelihood in μ are

$$\frac{\partial l}{\partial \mu} = \frac{1}{\sigma^2} \cdot \sum_{j=1}^{n} (\ln X_j - \mu) = \frac{n}{\sigma^2} (\bar{Y} - \mu), \quad \frac{\partial^2 l}{\partial \mu^2} = -\frac{n}{\sigma^2}.$$

The information in μ is

$$I_\mu(\mu, \sigma) = -\mathbf{E}\left[\frac{\partial^2 l}{\partial \mu^2}\right] = \frac{n}{\sigma^2}.$$

Since

$$\mathbf{Var}(\hat{\mu}) = \frac{\sigma^2}{n}$$

it follows that

$$I_{(1,1)}(\mu, \tau) = \frac{1}{\mathbf{Var}(\hat{\mu})},$$

which implies efficiency in the Cramér–Rao spirit.

The first two derivatives of the log-likelihood in σ are

$$\frac{\partial l}{\partial \sigma} = -\frac{n}{\sigma} + \frac{1}{\sigma^3} \cdot \sum_{j=1}^{n} (\ln X_j - \mu)^2$$

$$\frac{\partial^2 l}{\partial \sigma^2} = \frac{n}{\sigma^2} - \frac{3}{\sigma^4} \cdot \sum_{j=1}^{n} (\ln X_j - \mu)^2.$$

The information in σ is

$$I_{(2,2)}(\mu, \sigma) = -\mathbf{E}\left[\frac{\partial^2 l}{\partial \sigma^2}\right] = -\mathbf{E}\left[\frac{n}{\sigma^2} - \frac{3}{\sigma^4} \cdot \sum_{j=1}^{n} (\ln X_j - \mu)^2\right] =$$

$$= \frac{3}{\sigma^4} \cdot \sum_{j=1}^{n} \mathbf{E}\left[(\ln X_j - \mu)^2\right] - \frac{n}{\sigma^2}.$$

Since $\mathbf{E}\left[(\ln X_j - \mu)^2\right] = \sigma^2$, it follows that

$$I_{(2,2)}(\mu, \sigma) = \frac{3n\sigma^2}{\sigma^4} - \frac{n}{\sigma^2} = \frac{2n}{\sigma^2}.$$

Since for a known μ, the variance of MLE is

$$\mathbf{Var}\left[\tilde{\sigma}\right] = \frac{\sigma^2}{2n},$$

it follows that the information coincides with the information bound

$$I_{(2,2)}(\mu, \sigma) = \frac{1}{\mathbf{Var}(\tilde{\sigma})},$$

which implies efficiency in the Cramér–Rao spirit.

For unknown μ, this is the asymptotic variance of $\hat{\sigma}$.

Note that the second mixed derivative of the log-likelihood function is

$$\frac{\partial^2 l}{\partial \mu \partial \sigma} = \frac{\partial}{\partial \sigma}\left(\frac{\partial l}{\partial \mu}\right) = \frac{\partial}{\partial \sigma}\left(\frac{1}{\sigma^2}\cdot \sum_{j=1}^n (\ln X_j - \mu)\right) = -\frac{2n}{\sigma^3}\cdot\sum_{j=1}^n(\ln X_j - \mu).$$

The corresponding entry in the information matrix is

$$\mathbf{I}(\mu,\sigma)_{12} = \mathbf{I}(\theta)_{21} = -\mathbf{E}_X\left[\frac{\partial^2 l}{\partial \mu \partial \tau}\right] = \frac{2n}{\sigma^3}\sum_{j=1}^n \mathbf{E}_X\left[\ln X_j - \mu\right] = 0.$$

Therefore, the information matrix is

$$\mathbf{I}(\mu,\sigma) = \begin{pmatrix} n/\sigma^2 & 0 \\ 0 & 2n/\sigma^2 \end{pmatrix}.$$

Thus, the covariance matrix is

$$\mathbf{Cov}(\mu,\sigma) = \mathbf{I}^{-1}(\mu,\sigma) = \begin{pmatrix} \sigma^2/n & 0 \\ 0 & \sigma^2/2n \end{pmatrix}. \tag{6.39}$$

6.4.4 MLE for Poisson Distribution

When a sample $\mathbf{X} = \{X_j : 1 \leq j \leq n\}$ of size n is drawn from **Poisson** $[\lambda]$, the likelihood associated with one observation, $X = x$, is by (1.17):

$$f(x;\lambda) = \frac{\lambda^x}{x!}\cdot e^{-\lambda}.$$

The likelihood function based on $\mathbf{X}$ is

$$L(\lambda) = \frac{\lambda^w}{\prod_{i=1}^n (x_i)!}\cdot e^{-n\lambda},$$

where $w = \sum_j x_j$ is the value of a sufficient statistic, $W = \sum_{j=1}^n X_j$.

The log-likelihood function based on $\mathbf{X}$ is

$$l(\lambda) = \ln L(\lambda) = w \ln \lambda - n\lambda - C, \quad C = \sum_{i=1}^n \ln\left((x_i)!\right)$$

Differentiating the log-likelihood, we have

$$l'(\lambda) = \frac{w}{\lambda} - n.$$

Equating the derivative to zero and solving for λ, we obtain the MLE for Poisson distribution

$$l'(\lambda) = \frac{w}{\lambda} - n = 0 \iff \hat{\lambda} = \frac{w}{n}. \tag{6.40}$$

6.4.4.1 Information for Poisson Distribution

Since $W \sim \mathbf{Poisson}\,[n\lambda]$, its moments are

$$\mathbf{E}[W] = n\lambda \quad \text{and} \quad \mathbf{Var}(W) = n\lambda.$$

Thus, the estimate $\hat{\lambda}$ is unbiased and has variance

$$\mathbf{Var}\left(\hat{\lambda}\right) = \mathbf{Var}\left(\frac{W}{n}\right) = \frac{\lambda}{n}.$$

To calculate the information bound, we differentiate the log-likelihood function $l(\lambda)$ again to obtain

$$l''(\lambda) = -\frac{w}{\lambda^2}.$$

Then the information is

$$I(\lambda) = -\mathbf{E}\left[l''(\lambda)\right] = \frac{1}{\lambda^2}\mathbf{E}\left[w\right] = \frac{n\lambda}{\lambda^2} = \frac{n}{\lambda}.$$

Note that

$$I(\lambda) = \frac{1}{\mathbf{Var}[\hat{\lambda}]}.$$

Therefore, the MLE is efficient in the Cramér–Rao sense.

6.4.5 MLE for Exponential Distribution

Suppose that observations $\mathbf{X} = \{X_j : 1 \le j \le n\}$ are independently drawn from an exponential distribution with parameter θ.

For an observation, $X = x$, using (1.33), the exponential distribution has its probability density function given by

$$f(x) = \frac{1}{\theta}\,e^{-x/\theta}.$$

The likelihood function based on $\mathbf{X}$ is

$$L(\theta) = \frac{1}{\theta^n}e^{-\frac{w}{\theta}},$$

where $w = \sum_j x_j$ is the value of a sufficient statistic, $W = \sum_{j=1}^n X_j$.

The log-likelihood function based on $\mathbf{X}$ is

$$l(\theta) = \ln L(\theta) = -n\ln\theta - \frac{w}{\theta}.$$

Differentiating the log-likelihood, we have

$$l'(\theta) = -\frac{n}{\theta} + \frac{w}{\theta^2}.$$

Equating the derivative to zero and solving for θ, we obtain the MLE for an exponential distribution

$$l'(\lambda) = -\frac{n}{\theta} + \frac{w}{\theta^2} = 0 \Leftrightarrow -n + \frac{w}{\theta} = 0 \Leftrightarrow \hat{\theta} = \frac{w}{n} = \bar{X}. \tag{6.41}$$

Recall that for data censored from above at u, by (6.23) the likelihood function is of the form

$$L(\theta) = \left[\prod_{i=1}^{n} f(x_i, \theta) \right] (S(u))^m,$$

where n is the number of uncensored observations and m is the number of censored observations.

For the exponential distribution,

$$L(\theta) = \frac{1}{\theta^n} \exp\left\{ -\frac{1}{\theta} \sum_{i=1}^{n} x_i - \frac{m \cdot u}{\theta} \right\}.$$

The log-likelihood function is

$$l(\theta) = -n \ln \theta - \frac{1}{\theta} \left[\sum_{i=1}^{n} x_i + m \cdot u \right].$$

Differentiating the log-likelihood function with respect to x and equating it to zero, we obtain

$$l'(\theta) = -\frac{n}{\theta} + \frac{1}{\theta^2} \left[\sum_{i=1}^{n} x_i + m \cdot u \right] = 0 \Leftrightarrow -n + \frac{1}{\theta} \left[\sum_{i=1}^{n} x_i + m \cdot u \right] = 0.$$

Thus, the MLE for an exponential distribution with data censored from above at u is

$$\hat{\theta} = \frac{\sum_{i=1}^{n} x_i + m \cdot u}{n}. \tag{6.42}$$

For a left-truncated data at d, using (6.24), the likelihood function is of the form

$$L(\theta) = \frac{\prod_{i=1}^{n} f(\theta, x_i) \cdot (S(\theta, u))^m}{(1 - F(\theta, d))^{n+m}},$$

where u is the censoring point (e.g., a policy limit), d is the truncation point (e.g., a deductible), n is the number of uncensored observations, and m is the number of censored observations.

For an exponential distribution the likelihood function is:

$$L(\theta) = \frac{1}{\theta^n} \exp\left\{ -\frac{1}{\theta} \sum_{i=1}^{n} x_i - \frac{mu}{\theta} \right\} \cdot \frac{1}{\exp\left\{ -\frac{1}{\theta} \cdot d(n+m) \right\}} =$$

$$= \frac{1}{\theta^n} \exp\left\{ -\frac{1}{\theta} \left(\sum_{i=1}^{n} x_i + mu - d(n+m) \right) \right\}.$$

The log-likelihood function is

$$l(\theta) = -n \ln \theta - \frac{1}{\theta} \left[\sum_{i=1}^{n} x_i + mu - d(n+m) \right].$$

Differentiating the log-likelihood function with respect to θ and equating it to zero, we obtain

$$l'(\theta) = -\frac{n}{\theta} + \frac{1}{\theta^2}\left[\sum_{i=1}^{n} x_i + mu - d(n+m)\right] = 0 \Leftrightarrow$$

$$-n + \frac{1}{\theta}\left[\sum_{i=1}^{n} x_i + mu - d(n+m)\right] = 0.$$

Thus, the MLE for an exponential distribution with data that is left-truncated at d and censored from above at u is

$$\hat{\theta} = \frac{\sum_{i=1}^{n} x_i + mu - d(n+m)}{n}. \tag{6.43}$$

6.4.5.1 Information for Exponential Distribution

Going back to unrestricted data and calculating the second derivative of the log-likelihood function, we have

$$l''(\theta) = \frac{n}{\theta^2} - \frac{2}{\theta^3}\sum_{i=1}^{n} x_i.$$

Calculating the information, we obtain

$$\mathbf{I}(\theta) = -\mathbf{E}\left[\frac{d^2 l}{d\theta^2}\right] = -\frac{n}{\theta^2} + \frac{2}{\theta^3}\sum_{i=1}^{n}\mathbf{E}[x_i] =$$

$$= -\frac{n}{\theta^2} + \frac{2n\theta}{\theta^3} = -\frac{n}{\theta^2} + \frac{2n}{\theta^2} = \frac{n}{\theta^2}.$$

Taking the inverse of this expression, we obtain the asymptotic lower bound for the variance of $\hat{\theta}$:

$$\mathbf{I}^{-1}(\theta) = \frac{\theta^2}{n}$$

Note that

$$\mathbf{Var}(\hat{\theta}) = \mathbf{Var}\left(\frac{\sum_{i=1}^{n} x_i}{n}\right) = \frac{1}{n^2}\mathbf{Var}\left(\sum_{i=1}^{n} x_i\right) =$$

$$= \frac{1}{n^2}\sum_{i=1}^{n}\mathbf{Var}(x_i) = \frac{1}{n^2} \cdot n\theta^2 = \frac{\theta^2}{n}.$$

Therefore, the MLE is efficient in the Cramér–Rao sense.

6.4.6 MLE for Inverse Exponential Distribution

Suppose that observations $\mathbf{X} = \{X_i : 1 \le i \le n\}$ are independently drawn from an inverse exponential distribution with parameter θ. Then the vector of observations

$\mathbf{Y} = \{Y_i = 1/X_i : 1 \leq i \leq n\}$ is exponential with parameter $\alpha = 1/\theta$. By (6.41), the MLE for an exponential distribution is

$$\hat{\alpha} = \frac{1}{n} \sum_{i=1}^{n} Y_i.$$

Therefore, the MLE for an inverse exponential distribution is

$$\hat{\theta} = \frac{1}{\hat{\alpha}} = \frac{n}{\sum_{i=1}^{n} y_i} = \frac{n}{\sum_{i=1}^{n} 1/x_i}. \tag{6.44}$$

The same result can be obtained directly from the definition of the **pdf** of the inverse exponential distribution.

For an observation, $X = x$, the inverse exponential distribution has its probability density function given by

$$f(x) = \frac{\theta}{x^2} e^{-\theta/x}.$$

The likelihood function based on $\mathbf{X}$ is

$$L(\theta) = \frac{1}{\prod_{i=1}^{n} x_i^2} \theta^n \exp\left\{-\theta \sum_{i=1}^{n} \frac{1}{x_i}\right\}.$$

The log-likelihood function based on $\mathbf{X}$ is

$$l(\theta) = \ln L(\theta) = -2 \sum_{i=1}^{n} \ln x_i + n \ln \theta - \theta \sum_{i=1}^{n} \frac{1}{x_i}.$$

Differentiating the log-likelihood, we have

$$l'(\theta) = \frac{n}{\theta} - \sum_{i=1}^{n} \frac{1}{x_i}.$$

Equating the derivative to zero and solving for θ, we obtain the MLE for an inverse exponential distribution:

$$l'(\lambda) = \frac{n}{\theta} - \sum_{i=1}^{n} \frac{1}{x_i} = 0 \Leftrightarrow \hat{\theta} = \frac{n}{\sum_{i=1}^{n} 1/x_i}$$

6.4.6.1 Information for Inverse Exponential Distribution

Going back to unrestricted data and calculating the second derivative of the log-likelihood function, we have

$$l''(\theta) = -\frac{n}{\theta^2}.$$

Calculating the information, we obtain

$$\mathbf{I}(\theta) = -\mathbf{E}\left[\frac{d^2l}{d\theta^2}\right] = \mathbf{E}\left[\frac{n}{\theta^2}\right] = \frac{n}{\theta^2}.$$

Taking the inverse of this expression, we obtain the asymptotic lower bound for the variance of $\hat{\theta}$:

$$\mathbf{I}^{-1}(\theta) = \frac{\theta^2}{n}$$

6.4.7   MLE for Gamma Distribution

Suppose that observations $\mathbf{X} = \{X_j : 1 \le j \le n\}$ are independently drawn from a gamma-distributed population with the shape parameter α, the scale parameter θ, and the common density function, given by (1.38),

$$f(x, \alpha, \theta) = \frac{1}{\theta^\alpha \, \Gamma(\alpha)} \, x^{\alpha - 1} \, e^{-x/\theta} \quad \text{for} \ \ 0 < x < \infty.$$

The likelihood function based on $\mathbf{X}$ is

$$L(\alpha, \theta) = \frac{1}{\theta^{n\alpha} \, \Gamma(\alpha)^n} \, \prod_{i=1}^{n} x_i^{\alpha - 1} \, \exp\left(-\frac{w}{\theta}\right),$$

where $w = \sum_{i=1}^{n} x_i$ is the sum of observed X-values that is the observation of $W = \sum_{j=1}^{n} X_j$.

The log-likelihood function based on $\mathbf{X}$ is

$$l(\alpha, \theta) = \ln L(\alpha, \theta) = n\alpha \ln \theta - \frac{w}{\theta} - n \ln \Gamma(\alpha) + (\alpha - 1) \sum_{i=1}^{n} \ln x_i.$$

Suppose α is known. Let us evaluate the MLE of θ. Note that $l(\alpha, \theta)$ can be rewritten as

$$l(\theta) = n\alpha \ln \theta - \frac{w}{\theta} + C, \ \ C = -n \ln \Gamma(\alpha) + (\alpha - 1) \sum_{i=1}^{n} \ln x_i.$$

The expression for C does not contain θ.

Differentiating $l(\alpha, \theta)$ with respect to θ, we have

$$\frac{\partial l}{\partial \theta} = -\frac{n\alpha}{\theta} + \frac{w}{\theta^2}.$$

Equating the derivative to zero and solving for θ, we obtain the MLE of θ for gamma distribution:

$$-\frac{n\alpha}{\theta} + \frac{w}{\theta^2} = 0 \Leftrightarrow -n\alpha + \frac{w}{\theta} = 0 \Leftrightarrow \hat{\theta} = \frac{w}{n\alpha} \tag{6.45}$$

If the shape parameter is $\alpha = 1$, the maximum of $\ln L(\theta)$ may occur at $\theta = 0$, which is usually excluded from consideration, since it does not depend on the data.

Suppose θ is known. Let us evaluate the MLE of α. Note that $l(\alpha, \theta)$ can be rewritten as

$$l(\alpha) = n\alpha \ln \theta - n \ln \Gamma(\alpha) + (\alpha - 1) \sum_{i=1}^{n} \ln x_i + C.$$

The expression for C does not contain α.

Differentiating $l(\alpha, \theta)$ with respect to α, we have

$$\frac{\partial l}{\partial \alpha} = n \ln \theta + \sum_{i=1}^{n} \ln x_i - n\psi(\alpha),$$

where

$$\psi(\alpha) = \frac{d}{d\alpha} \ln \Gamma(\alpha) = \frac{\Gamma'(\alpha)}{\Gamma(\alpha)}$$

is the logarithmic derivative of the gamma function or **digamma function**[6].

This function has a series representation of

$$\psi(\alpha) = -\gamma - \sum_{k=0}^{\infty} \left(\frac{1}{\alpha + k} - \frac{1}{k+1} \right),$$

which in the case of α being a positive integer is reduced to $\psi(1) = -\gamma$:

$$\psi(n) = -\gamma + \sum_{k=1}^{n-1} \frac{1}{k}, \quad n = 2, 3, \dots$$

Here, $\gamma \approx 0.5772156649\dots$ is known as **Euler's constant**.

Equating the derivative to zero, we have

$$n \ln \theta + \sum_{i=1}^{n} \ln x_i + n \left(\gamma + \sum_{k=0}^{\infty} \left(\frac{1}{\alpha+k} - \frac{1}{k+1} \right) \right) = 0 \Leftrightarrow$$

$$\sum_{k=0}^{\infty} \left(\frac{1}{\alpha+k} - \frac{1}{k+1} \right) = -\frac{1}{n} \left(n \ln \theta + \sum_{i=1}^{n} \ln x_i \right) - \gamma \Leftrightarrow$$

$$\sum_{k=0}^{\infty} \frac{\alpha - 1}{(\alpha+k)(k+1)} = \frac{1}{n} \left(n \ln \theta + \sum_{i=1}^{n} \ln x_i \right) + \gamma.$$

Solving for α to obtain the MLE of α for gamma distribution will require numerical methods.

6.4.7.1 Information for Gamma Distribution

Since $W \sim$ **Gamma** $[n\alpha, \theta]$, its moments are

$$\mathbf{E}[W] = n\alpha\theta \quad \text{and} \quad \mathbf{Var}(W) = n\alpha \cdot \theta^2.$$

Thus, the MLE has mean and variance as follows:

$$\mathbf{E}\left[\hat{\theta}\right] = \mathbf{E}\left[\frac{W}{n\alpha}\right] = \theta \quad \text{and} \quad \mathbf{Var}\left(\hat{\theta}\right) = \mathbf{Var}\left(\frac{W}{n\alpha}\right) = \frac{\theta^2}{n\alpha}$$

It follows that MLE is unbiased and its mean square error coincides with the variance.

To calculate the information bound, we differentiate $l'(\theta)$ again to obtain

$$\frac{\partial^2 l}{\partial \theta^2} = \frac{n\alpha}{\theta^2} - \frac{2w}{\theta^3}.$$

Then the information is

$$I(\theta) = -\mathbf{E}\left[l''(\theta)\right] = -\frac{n\alpha}{\theta^2} + \frac{2}{\theta^3} \mathbf{E}[W] = -\frac{n\alpha}{\theta^2} + \frac{2}{\theta^3} n\alpha\theta = -\frac{n\alpha}{\theta^2} + \frac{2n\alpha}{\theta^2} = \frac{n\alpha}{\theta^2}.$$

Note that

$$I(\theta) = \frac{1}{\mathbf{Var}[\hat{\theta}]}.$$

Therefore, the MLE is efficient in the Cramér–Rao sense.

6.4.8   MLE for Pareto Distribution

Suppose that observations $\mathbf{X} = \{X_i\}$ are independently drawn from a Pareto-distributed population with parameters α and θ, and with the common density and cumulative distribution functions, given by (1.53), as

$$f(x, \alpha, \theta) = \frac{\alpha \cdot \theta^\alpha}{(\theta + x)^{\alpha+1}} \quad \text{and} \quad F(x, \alpha, \theta) = 1 - \left(\frac{\theta}{x + \theta}\right)^\alpha.$$

Suppose there are n uncensored observations, $x_1, x_2, \ldots, x_n$, plus c observations censored from above at u and all observations truncated from below at d.

The likelihood function based on $\mathbf{X}$ is

$$L(\alpha, \theta) = \frac{\prod_{i=1}^{n} f(x_i, \alpha, \theta) \cdot S(u, \alpha, \theta)^c}{S(d, \alpha, \theta)^{n+c}} =$$

$$= \frac{\alpha^n \cdot \theta^{n\alpha}}{\prod_{i=1}^{n}(\theta + x_i)^{(\alpha+1)}} \cdot \frac{\theta^{c\alpha}}{(u + \theta)^{c\alpha}} \cdot \frac{(d + \theta)^{\alpha(n+c)}}{\theta^{\alpha(n+c)}} =$$

$$= \frac{\alpha^n}{\prod_{i=1}^{n}(\theta + x_i)^{(\alpha+1)}} \cdot \frac{(d + \theta)^{\alpha(n+c)}}{(u + \theta)^{c\alpha}}.$$

The log-likelihood function based on $\mathbf{X}$ is

$$l(\alpha, \theta) = n \ln \alpha + \alpha(n + c) \ln(d + \theta) - c\alpha \ln(u + \theta) -$$
$$- (\alpha + 1) \sum_{i=1}^{n} \ln(\theta + x_i).$$

For a fixed θ, differentiating $l(\alpha, \theta)$ with respect to α, we obtain

$$\frac{\partial l}{\partial \alpha} = \frac{n}{\alpha} + \left[(n + c)\ln(d + \theta) - c\ln(u + \theta) - \sum_{i=1}^{n} \ln(\theta + x_i)\right] =$$

$$= \frac{n}{\alpha} + \left[\sum_{i=1}^{n+c} \ln(d_i + \theta) - \sum_{i=1}^{n+c} \ln(\theta + x_i)\right],$$

where $x_i = u$ for all $i > n$ and d_i are varying deductibles. Thus,

$$\hat{\alpha} = -\frac{n}{K}, \quad K = \sum_{i=1}^{n+c} \ln(d_i + \theta) - \sum_{i=1}^{n+c} \ln(\theta + x_i). \tag{6.46}$$

If we fix α instead and differentiate $l(\alpha, \theta)$ with respect to θ, we obtain:

$$\frac{\partial l}{\partial \alpha} = \frac{\alpha(n + c)}{d + \theta} - \frac{c\alpha}{u + \theta} - \sum_{i=1}^{n} \frac{\alpha + 1}{\theta + x_i}.$$

Note that to find the critical points of l (the roots of the equation $\partial l / \partial \theta = 0$) is equivalent to finding the roots of a polynomial of degree $n + 1$, which is not always possible analytically. However, it is possible in some limited situations such as two data points and certain restrictions on u and d.

6.4.8.1   Information for Pareto Distribution

Considering unrestricted data, the likelihood function is

$$L(x, \alpha, \theta) = \frac{\alpha^n \cdot \theta^{n\alpha}}{\prod_{i=1}^{n} (x_i + \theta)^{\alpha+1}}.$$

The log-likelihood function is

$$l(x, \alpha, \theta) = n \ln \alpha + n\alpha \ln \theta - (\alpha + 1) \sum_{i=1}^{n} \ln (x_i + \theta).$$

For a fixed θ, taking the derivative with respect to α, we obtain

$$\frac{\partial l}{\partial \alpha} = \frac{n}{\alpha} + n \ln \theta - \sum_{i=1}^{n} \ln (x_i + \theta).$$

Equating to zero and solving for α, we have

$$\hat{\alpha} = \frac{n}{\sum_{i=1}^{n} \ln (x_i + \theta) - n \ln \theta}.$$

Differentiating again,

$$\frac{\partial l^2}{\partial \alpha^2} = -\frac{n}{\alpha^2}.$$

Taking the expected value, we have

$$\mathbf{I}(\alpha) = -\mathbf{E}\left[\frac{\partial l^2}{\partial \alpha^2}\right] = \frac{n}{\alpha^2}.$$

Taking the inverse of this expression, we have

$$\mathbf{I}^{-1}(\theta) = \frac{\alpha^2}{n}.$$

This is the Cramér–Rao lower bound for the asymptotic variance of $\hat{\alpha}$.

For a fixed α, taking the derivative of l with respect to θ, we obtain

$$\frac{\partial l}{\partial \theta} = \frac{n\alpha}{\theta} - (\alpha + 1) \sum_{i=1}^{n} \frac{1}{x_i + \theta}.$$

Finding critical points of the function l will lead to dealing with a polynomial of the $(n+1)^{th}$ degree. Unless $n = 2$, which will already require solving a cubic equation, we may need numerical techniques to find its roots.

Differentiating with respect to θ again, we obtain

$$\frac{\partial^2 l}{\partial \theta^2} = -\frac{n\alpha}{\theta^2} + (\alpha + 1) \sum_{i=1}^{n} \frac{1}{(x_i + \theta)^2}.$$

The information matrix is

$$\mathbf{I}(\theta) = -\mathbf{E}_X\left[\frac{d^2 l}{d\theta^2}\right] = \frac{n\alpha}{\theta^2} - (\alpha + 1) \sum_{i=1}^{n} \mathbf{E}_X\left[\frac{1}{(x_i + \theta)^2}\right].$$

Calculating the expectation of $1/(X + \theta)^2$, we have

$$
\begin{aligned}
\mathbf{E}_X \left[\frac{1}{(X + \theta)^2} \right] &= \int_0^\infty \frac{1}{(x + \theta)^2} \cdot \frac{\alpha \cdot \theta^\alpha}{(x + \theta)^{\alpha+1}} \, dx = \\
&= \alpha \cdot \theta^\alpha \int_0^\infty \frac{1}{(x + \theta)^{\alpha+3}} \, dx = -\frac{\alpha \cdot \theta^\alpha}{(\alpha + 2)} \cdot \frac{1}{(x + \theta)^{\alpha+2}} \Big|_0^\infty = \\
&= \frac{\alpha}{(\alpha + 2)\theta^2}.
\end{aligned}
$$

Thus, the information is

$$
\mathbf{I}(\theta) = \frac{n\alpha}{\theta^2} - \frac{n\alpha(\alpha + 1)}{(\alpha + 2)\theta^2} = \frac{n\alpha}{\theta^2} \left(1 - \frac{\alpha + 1}{\alpha + 2} \right) = \frac{n\alpha}{(\alpha + 2)\theta^2}. \tag{6.47}
$$

Taking the inverse of the information, we obtain

$$
\mathbf{I}^{-1}(\theta) = \frac{(\alpha + 2)\theta^2}{n\alpha}.
$$

This is the Cramér–Rao lower bound for variance of the estimator $\hat{\theta}$.

6.4.9 MLE for Weibull Distribution

Suppose that observations $\mathbf{X} = \{X_j : 1 \leq j \leq n\}$ are independently drawn from a Weibull-distributed population with a parameter τ, which is fixed, and θ. Then the vector of observations, $\mathbf{Y} = \{Y_i = X_i^\tau : 1 \leq i \leq n\}$, is exponential with parameter $\alpha = \theta^\tau$. By (6.41), the MLE for an exponential distribution is

$$
\hat{\alpha} = \frac{1}{n} \sum_{i=1}^n Y_i \Leftrightarrow \hat{\theta}^\tau = \frac{1}{n} \sum_{i=1}^n X_i^\tau.
$$

Therefore, the MLE of θ for a Weibull distribution is

$$
\hat{\theta} = \sqrt[\tau]{\frac{\sum_{i=1}^n x_i^\tau}{n}}. \tag{6.48}
$$

The same result can be obtained directly from the definition of the **pdf** of the inverse exponential distribution.

For an observation, $X = x$, the inverse exponential distribution has its probability density function given by

$$
f(x, \tau, \theta) = \frac{\tau x^{\tau-1}}{\theta^\tau} e^{-(x/\theta)^\tau}.
$$

The likelihood function of θ is

$$
L(\theta) = \prod_{i=1}^n f(x_i, \theta) = \frac{\tau^n}{\theta^{n\tau}} \left(\prod_{i=1}^n x_i^{\tau-1} \right) e^{-\sum_{i=1}^n x_i^\tau / \theta^\tau}.
$$

The log-likelihood function is

$$
l(\theta) = n \ln \tau - n\tau \ln \theta + (\tau - 1) \sum_{i=1}^n \ln x_i - \frac{1}{\theta^\tau} \sum_{i=1}^n x_i^\tau.
$$

Differentiating $l(\theta)$, we obtain

$$l'(\theta) = -\frac{n\tau}{\theta} + \frac{\tau}{\theta^{\tau+1}} \sum_{i=1}^{n} x_i^\tau.$$

Equating to zero and solving for θ, we obtain the MLE of θ

$$-n + \frac{1}{\theta^\tau} \sum_{i=1}^{n} x_i^\tau = 0 \Leftrightarrow \hat{\theta} = \sqrt[\tau]{\frac{\sum_{i=1}^{n} x_i^\tau}{n}},$$

which coincides with formula (6.48).

Note that if n is the number of uncensored observations, c is the number of censored observations, d_i is the truncation point for each observation (0 if untruncated), x_i is the observation if uncensored or the censoring point if censored, then the parameter θ is estimated as

$$\hat{\theta} = \sqrt[\tau]{\frac{1}{n} \sum_{i=1}^{n+c} (x_i^\tau - d_i^\tau)}. \tag{6.49}$$

6.4.9.1 Information for Weibull Distribution

Going back to an unrestricted data and differentiating $l'(\theta)$, we obtain

$$l''(\theta) = \frac{n\tau}{\theta^2} - \frac{\tau(\tau+1)}{\theta^{\tau+2}} \sum_{i=1}^{n} x_i^\tau.$$

Taking the expected value, we have

$$\mathbf{I}(\theta) = -\mathbf{E}\left[\frac{d^2 l}{d\theta^2}\right] = \frac{\tau(\tau+1)}{\theta^{\tau+2}} \cdot n\mathbf{E}[X^\tau] - \frac{n\tau}{\theta^2}.$$

For a Weibull distribution the kth raw moment is

$$\mathbf{E}\left[X^k\right] = \theta^k \Gamma\left(1 + \frac{k}{\tau}\right).$$

Therefore,

$$\mathbf{E}\left[X^\tau\right] = \theta^\tau \Gamma\left(1 + \frac{\tau}{\tau}\right) = \theta^\tau \Gamma\left(2\right) = \theta^\tau.$$

Hence,

$$\mathbf{I}(\theta) = \frac{\tau(\tau+1)}{\theta^{\tau+2}} \cdot n\theta^\tau - \frac{n\tau}{\theta^2} = \frac{\tau(\tau+1)n}{\theta^2} - \frac{n\tau}{\theta^2} = \frac{n\tau^2}{\theta^2}.$$

Taking the inverse of this expression, we have

$$\mathbf{I}^{-1}(\theta) = \frac{\theta^2}{n\tau^2}.$$

This is the Cramér–Rao lower bound for variance of the estimator $\hat{\theta}$.

6.4.10 MLE for Beta Distribution

Suppose that observations $\mathbf{X} = \{X_i : 1 \leq i \leq n\}$ are independently drawn from a Beta-distributed population with parameters a, b, and θ. For a beta distribution, the probability density function is of the form

$$f(x, a, b, \theta) = \frac{\Gamma(a+b)}{\Gamma(a)\Gamma(b)} \left(\frac{x}{\theta}\right)^a \left(1 - \frac{x}{\theta}\right)^{b-1} \frac{1}{x}, \ 0 < x < \theta.$$

Suppose $b = 1$. Then, since $\Gamma(1) = 1$ and $\Gamma(n) = (n-1)!$, the **pdf** becomes

$$f(x, a, \theta) = \frac{a x^{a-1}}{\theta^a}, \ 0 < x < \theta.$$

For n uncensored observations $x_1, x_2, \ldots, x_n$, the likelihood function is

$$L(a, \theta) = \frac{a^n \prod_{i=1}^{n} x_i^{a-1}}{\theta^{na}}.$$

The log-likelihood function is

$$l(a, \theta) = n \ln a - na \ln \theta + (a-1) \sum_{i=1}^{n} \ln x_i.$$

Differentiating $l(a, \theta)$ with respect to a, we obtain

$$\frac{\partial l}{\partial a} = \frac{n}{a} - n \ln \theta + \sum_{i=1}^{n} \ln x_i.$$

Equating the derivative to zero and solving for a, we obtain the MLE of a:

$$\hat{a} = \frac{n}{n \ln \theta - \sum_{i=1}^{n} \ln x_i} = \frac{n}{\sum_{i=1}^{n} \ln \theta - \ln x_i} =$$
$$= -\frac{n}{\sum_{i=1}^{n} \ln(x_i/\theta)} = -\frac{n}{\ln \prod_{i=1}^{n}(x_i/\theta)} \tag{6.50}$$

Suppose $a = 1$. Then, since $\Gamma(1) = 1$ and $\Gamma(n) = (n-1)!$, the **pdf** becomes

$$f(x, b, \theta) = \frac{b}{\theta}\left(1 - \frac{x}{\theta}\right)^{b-1}, \ 0 < x < \theta.$$

For n uncensored observations $x_1, x_2, \ldots, x_n$, the likelihood function is

$$L(b, \theta) = \frac{b^n \prod_{i=1}^{n}(1 - x_i/\theta)^{b-1}}{\theta^n}.$$

The log-likelihood function is

$$l(b, \theta) = n \ln b - n \ln \theta + (b-1) \sum_{i=1}^{n} \ln\left(1 - \frac{x_i}{\theta}\right).$$

Differentiating $l(b, \theta)$ with respect to b, we obtain

$$\frac{\partial l}{\partial b} = \frac{n}{b} + \sum_{i=1}^{n} \ln\left(1 - \frac{x_i}{\theta}\right).$$

Equating the derivative to zero and solving for b we obtain the MLE of b:

$$\hat{b} = -\frac{n}{\sum_{i=1}^{n} \ln(1 - x_i/\theta)} \tag{6.51}$$

6.4.10.1 Information for Beta Distribution

If $b - 1$, differentiating $\partial l / \partial a$ with respect to a again, we have

$$\frac{\partial^2 l}{\partial a^2} = -\frac{n}{a^2}.$$

Then the information is

$$I(a) = -\mathbf{E}\left[l''(a)\right] = \frac{n}{a^2}.$$

Taking the inverse of this expression, we have

$$\mathbf{I}^{-1}(a) = \frac{a^2}{n}.$$

This is the Cramér–Rao lower bound for variance of the estimator $\hat{a}$.

If $a = 1$, differentiating $\partial l / \partial b$ with respect to b again, we have

$$\frac{\partial^2 l}{\partial b^2} = -\frac{n}{b^2}.$$

Then the information is

$$I(b) = -\mathbf{E}\left[l''(b)\right] = \frac{n}{b^2}.$$

Taking the inverse of this expression, we have

$$\mathbf{I}^{-1}(b) = \frac{b^2}{n}.$$

This is the Cramér–Rao lower bound for variance of the estimator $\hat{b}$.

6.4.11 MLE for Uniform Distribution

The Cramér–Rao conditions assume that the underlying density function, $f(x, \theta)$, is continuous and differentiable in θ, having continuous first two moments of its logarithmic derivative.

The **super-efficiency phenomenon** is a situation when the Cramér–Rao regularity conditions fail. An example of such phenomenon is a family of uniform distributions, where the density is defined as

$$f(x, \theta) = \frac{1}{\theta} \quad \text{for} \quad (0 < x < \theta) \quad \text{and} \quad f(x, \theta) = 0 \quad \text{elsewhere.}$$

For this function regularity conditions break at the endpoint, θ.

Having observed a sample $\mathbf{X} = \{X_i : 1 \le i \le n\}$ of size n drawn from $\mathbf{Unif}(0, \theta)$, one may attempt to derive MLE for θ. In this case, $W = \max_{1 \le i \le n} X_i$ is a sufficient statistic. The likelihood function based on the sample is

$$L(\theta) = \frac{1}{\theta^n} \quad \text{for} \quad [(x_1 < \theta) \bigcap (x_2 < \theta) \ldots (x_n < \theta)] \Leftrightarrow w < \theta.$$

The maximum value (taken over $\theta > w$) is attained at $\hat{\theta} = w$. Thus, the MLE of θ is

$$\hat{\theta} = W = \max_{1 \le j \le n} X_i.$$

For a uniform distribution $U[0, \theta]$ with grouped data, the MLE of θ is

$$\hat{\theta} = c_j \left(n/n_j \right), \tag{6.52}$$

where c_j is the upper bound of highest finite interval and n_j is the number of observations below c_j.

6.4.11.1 Variance and Bias for Uniform Distribution

To calculate its variance of $\hat{\theta}$, let us first understand its distribution. The **CDF** of $\hat{\theta}$ is

$$F_{\hat{\theta}}(x) = \mathbf{P}\left(\max\{x_1, x_2, \ldots, x_n\} \leq x\right) = \prod_{i=1}^{n} \mathbf{P}\left(x_i \leq x\right) = \prod_{i=1}^{n} \frac{x}{\theta} = \frac{x^n}{\theta^n}.$$

Therefore, the **pdf** of $\hat{\theta}$ is

$$f_{\hat{\theta}}(x) = \frac{n}{\theta^n} x^{n-1}.$$

Calculating the expected value of $\hat{\theta}$, we obtain

$$\mathbf{E}[\hat{\theta}] = \int_0^\theta \frac{n}{\theta^n} x^{n-1} \cdot x \, dx = \frac{n}{\theta^n} \int_0^\theta x^n \, dx = \frac{n}{\theta^n} \cdot \frac{\theta^{n+1}}{n+1} = \frac{n}{n+1} \theta.$$

Calculating the second raw moment of $\hat{\theta}$, we have

$$\mathbf{E}[\hat{\theta}^2] = \int_0^\theta \frac{n}{\theta^n} x^{n-1} \cdot x^2 \, dx = \frac{n}{\theta^n} \int_0^\theta x^{n+1} \, dx = \frac{n}{\theta^n} \cdot \frac{\theta^{n+2}}{n+2} = \frac{n}{n+2} \theta^2.$$

Thus, the variance is

$$\mathbf{Var}\left(\hat{\theta}\right) = \mathbf{E}[\hat{\theta}^2] - \mathbf{E}[\hat{\theta}]^2 = \frac{n}{n+2} \theta^2 - \left(\frac{n}{n+1}\right)^2 \theta^2 = n\theta^2 \left(\frac{1}{n+2} - \frac{n}{(n+1)^2}\right) =$$

$$= \frac{n\theta^2}{(n+2)(n+1)^2} \left(n^2 - 2n + 1 - n^2 - 2n\right) = \frac{n\theta^2}{(n+2)(n+1)^2}.$$

Alternatively, the ratio, W/θ has beta distribution, **Beta** $[n, 1]$. By (1.30) and (1.32), for a beta-distributed random variable with parameters a and b,

$$\mathbf{E}[X] = \frac{a}{a+b} \quad \text{and} \quad \mathbf{Var}(X) = \frac{ab}{(a+b)^2 \cdot (a+b+1)}.$$

Therefore,

$$\mathbf{E}[W] = \mathbf{E}[\hat{\theta}] = \frac{n}{n+1} \cdot \theta \quad \text{and} \quad \mathbf{Var}(W) = \mathbf{Var}(\hat{\theta}) = \frac{n}{(n+1)^2(n+2)} \theta^2.$$

Since $\mathbf{E}[\hat{\theta}] \neq \theta$, the MLE of θ is biased and its bias is

$$\mathbf{Bias}(\theta) = \mathbf{E}[\hat{\theta}] - \theta = \theta \left(\frac{n}{n+1} - 1\right) = -\frac{\theta}{n+1}.$$

Calculating the mean square error of $\hat{\theta}$, we have

$$\mathbf{MSE}(\theta) = \mathbf{E}\left[(\hat{\theta} - \theta)^2)\right] = \mathbf{Var}\left(\hat{\theta}\right) + \left(\mathbf{Bias}(\theta)\right)^2 =$$

$$= \theta^2 \left[\frac{n}{(n+1)^2(n+2)} + \left(\frac{1}{n+1}\right)^2\right] = \frac{2\theta^2}{(n+1)(n+2)}.$$

Unlike many other maximum likelihood estimates, this example shows that as the sample size increases, the variance that typically has the magnitude of n^{-1} tends to zero **faster** with the order of $O(n^{-2})$, and the same applies to the mean square error.

6.4.11.2 Uniform Distribution on $(\theta, 2\theta)$

Suppose that a sample is drawn from a uniform population on $(\theta, 2\theta)$, $X \sim \mathbf{Unif}(\theta, 2\theta)$. Although this situation looks similar to the previously considered one, there are several deviations. Despite the unique unknown parameter, θ, the sufficient statistic has two components:

$$V = \min_{1 \le i \le n} X_i \quad \text{and} \quad W = \max_{1 \le i \le n} X_i$$

The joint probability density function for $\mathbf{X}$ has the value determined by $V = v$ and $W = w$, as follows:

$$f(\mathbf{x}, \theta) = \theta^{-n} \cdot n(n-1)(w-v)^{n-2}$$

when $\theta < v < w < 2\theta$ and it vanishes outside of the region $\bigcap_{j=1}^{n} (\theta < x_j < 2\theta)$.

Note that as follows from definitions of V and W, the inequality $0 < W - V < \theta$ holds, and this implies that the maximum value of the likelihood function in θ is achieved when $\theta = w - v$.

Direct calculations involving double integration over the region $(\theta < v < w < 2\theta)$ lead to conclusion for the mean square error:

$$\mathbf{MSE}(\theta) = \mathbf{E}\left[(W - V) - \theta\right]^2 = \frac{6\theta^2}{(n+1)(n+2)}$$

Again, irregularity leads to super-efficiency. In regular cases, the mean square error would be of magnitude $O(n^{-1})$, rather than $O(n^{-2})$.

6.5 The Delta Method

The **delta method** is a method of estimating the variance of a function of a random variable $g(X)$ from the variance of the random variable X. This technique is based on **linearization** of $g(X)$ in a **small vicinity** of the expectation, $\mu = E[X]$.

Note that it is often difficult to estimate the variance of nonlinear functions of the random variables. However, the variance of a linear function is known:

$$\mathbf{Var}(aX + b) = a^2 \mathbf{Var}(X)$$

The delta method proposes to linearize a function by using its Taylor series and omitting all terms past the linear term. The Taylor series is usually constructed around the *mean* of the random variable.

Recall that for any n differentiable function g, the Taylor series around x_0 is:

$$g(x) = g(x_0) + g'(x_0)(x - x_0) + \frac{g''(x_0)}{2!}(x - x_0)^2 + \ldots$$

$$\ldots + \frac{g^{(n)}(x_0)}{n!}(x - x_0)^n + o\left((x - x_0)^n\right),$$

where $o\left((x - x_0)^n\right)$ is a function such that

$$\lim_{x \to x_0} \frac{o(x - x_0)^n}{(x - x_0)^n} = 0.$$

Considering only a linear term,

$$g(x) \approx g(x_0) + g'(x_0)(x - x_0).$$

Then for a random variable X,

$$\mathbf{Var}\left(g(X)\right) \approx \mathbf{Var}\left(g(X_0) + g'(X_0)(X - X_0)\right) = \left(g'(X_0)\right)^2 \mathbf{Var}\left(X\right), \; X_0 = \mathbf{E}[X].$$

If $\mathbf{X} = (X_1, X_2, \ldots, X_n)$ is the vector of the random variables, constructing the Taylor series around a point $\mathbf{X}_0$, we obtain the following expressions for the variance of the function $g(\mathbf{X})$:

1. One variable:

$$\mathbf{Var}\left(g(X)\right) \approx \mathbf{Var}(X) \left.\left(\frac{dg}{dX}\right)^2\right|_{X=X_0}$$

2. Two variables:

$$\mathbf{Var}\left(g(X)\right) \approx \mathbf{Var}(X) \left.\left(\frac{\partial g}{\partial X}\right)^2\right|_{X=X_0} + 2\mathbf{Cov}(X, Y) \left.\frac{\partial g}{\partial X}\frac{\partial g}{\partial Y}\right|_{X=X_0, Y=Y_0} +$$

$$+ \mathbf{Var}(Y) \left.\left(\frac{\partial g}{\partial Y}\right)^2\right|_{Y=Y_0}$$

3. General:

$$\mathbf{Var}\left(g(\mathbf{X})\right) \approx \left.(\partial \mathbf{g})'\right|_{\mathbf{X}=\mathbf{X}_0} \Sigma \left.(\partial \mathbf{g})\right|_{\mathbf{X}=\mathbf{X}_0},$$

$$\partial \mathbf{g} = \left(\frac{\partial g}{\partial X_1}, \frac{\partial g}{\partial X_2}, \cdots, \frac{\partial g}{\partial X_n}\right)',$$

where Σ is the *covariance matrix*, defined by

$$\Sigma = \begin{bmatrix} \sigma_1^2 & \sigma_{12} & \cdots & \sigma_{1n} \\ \sigma_{21} & \sigma_2^2 & \cdots & \sigma_{2n} \\ \vdots & \vdots & \ddots & \vdots \end{bmatrix}$$

6.6 Confidence Intervals Based on MLE

In this section we focus on constructing confidence intervals for an unknown parameter α based on its MLE estimate $\hat{\alpha}$. There are various ways of doing this, including exact and approximate methods as well as a **boostraping** technique. We focus on the first two methods. Note that being able to construct exact confidence intervals for a parameter is actually an exception and is generally not possible.

6.6.1 Normal Confidence Intervals for an MLE

A **normal confidence interval** for a quantity estimated by maximum likelihood is constructed by adding and subtracting $z_p \cdot \sigma$, where z_p is an appropriate standard normal percentile and σ is the estimated standard deviation.

As an illustration to determining a normal confidence interval for an MLE estimate, suppose we are given that a random variable has probability density function $f(x, \alpha)$, where the parameter α is estimated using maximum likelihood. Given a random sample $X_1, X_2, \ldots, X_n$ of observations of X, we would like to construct a $p\%$ normal confidence interval for $\mathbf{P}(X < x^*)$.

Applying a standard MLE method, we construct the likelihood and log-likelihood functions as

$$L(\alpha) = \prod_{i=1}^{n} f(X_i, \alpha), \; l(\alpha) = \ln L(\alpha) = \sum_{i=1}^{n} \ln f(X_i, \alpha).$$

Differentiating $l(\alpha)$, equating the derivative to zero, and solving for α, we obtain $\hat{\alpha}$, the MLE estimate of α.

To calculate asymptotic variance of $\hat{\alpha}$, we differentiate $l'(\alpha)$ again and then apply the definition of the information, obtaining

$$I(\alpha) = -\mathbf{E}\left[l''(\mathbf{X}, \alpha)\right].$$

Thus, the lower bound for the asymptotic variance of $\hat{\alpha}$ is

$$\widehat{\mathbf{Var}}(\hat{\alpha}) = \frac{1}{I(\alpha)}.$$

Let $g(\alpha) = \widehat{\mathbf{P}}(X < x^*)$. Given the **pdf** $f(x, \alpha)$, we can evaluate the the cumulative distribution function as

$$F_X(x, \alpha) = \int_0^x f(t, \alpha)\, dt.$$

Therefore,

$$g(\alpha) = \widehat{\mathbf{P}}(X < x^*) = F_X(x^*, \hat{\alpha}).$$

Evaluating $g(\alpha)$ at $\alpha = \hat{\alpha}$ and applying the delta method, we have

$$\mathbf{Var}\left(g(\alpha)\right) = \widehat{\mathbf{Var}}\left(\widehat{\mathbf{P}}(X < x^*)\right) \approx \mathbf{Var}(\alpha) \left(\frac{dg}{d\alpha}\right)^2 \bigg|_{\alpha = \hat{\alpha}}.$$

The pth percentile confidence interval for $g(\alpha) = \widehat{\mathbf{P}}(X < x^*)$ is then

$$\left(g(\hat{\alpha}) - z_{(1+p)/2}\sqrt{\widehat{\mathbf{Var}}\left(g(\hat{\alpha})\right)}, g(\hat{\alpha}) + z_{(1+p)/2}\sqrt{\widehat{\mathbf{Var}}\left(g(\hat{\alpha})\right)}\right).$$

If the quantity for the left-hand side of the confidence interval is *negative*, it should be replaced by zero, since the function being estimated (the probability) is always non-negative. Similarly, if the quantity for the right-hand side of the confidence interval is *greater than one*, it should be replaced by one, since the function being estimated (the probability) is always less or equal to one.

6.6.2 Non-Normal Confidence Intervals for an MLE

The use of normal confidence intervals assumes the maximum likelihood estimator is normally distributed, which is true asymptotically but is not true for small samples, and building separate confidence intervals for each parameter separately is optimal.

An alternative method for building confidence intervals is to solve an inequality for the log-likelihood equation. The confidence interval consists of the k-dimensional region in which the log-likelihood function is greater than c for some constant c, where k is the number of parameters. Based on the theory of likelihood ratio tests, to obtain the confidence of p, a quantity c is selected to be the maximum log-likelihood minus $0.5w$, where w is the $100p^{th}$ percentile of the chi-square distribution with k degrees of freedom, where k is the number of parameters being estimated.

As an illustration to determining a non-normal confidence interval for an MLE estimate, suppose we are given that a random variable has probability density function $f(x, \alpha)$, where the parameter α is estimated using maximum likelihood. Given a random sample $X_1, X_2, \ldots, X_n$ of observations of X, we would like to construct a $p\%$ non-normal confidence interval for $\mathbf{P}(X < x^*)$.

Applying a standard MLE method, we construct the likelihood and log-likelihood functions as

$$L(\alpha) = \prod_{i=1}^{n} f(X_i, \alpha), \ l(\alpha) = \ln L(\alpha) = \sum_{i=1}^{n} \ln f(X_i, \alpha).$$

Differentiating $l(\alpha)$, equating the derivative to zero, and solving for α, we obtain $\hat{\alpha}$, the MLE estimate of α, and then we can calculate $l_{max} = l(\hat{\alpha})$. Our goal is to select a region,

$$\{\alpha | l(\alpha) > c\}, \ \text{for a constant } c > 0.$$

Calculating c as the difference of the maximum value of the log-likelihood function and $0.5w$, where w is the $100p^{th}$ percentile of the chi-square distribution with 1 degree of freedom (since there is only one parameter), we have

$$c = l_{max} - 0.5 \cdot \chi_p.$$

Thus, the region becomes

$$\{\alpha | l(\alpha) > l_{max} - 0.5 \cdot \chi_p\}.$$

Depending on the structure of the function $l(\alpha)$, the inequality might be either solved analytically or using numerical methods. A popular approach involves a Solver functionality in Excel.

6.7 Advantages and Disadvantages of the MLE Method

Maximum likelihood estimators have higher probability of being close to the estimated quantities and are more often unbiased. In addition, the method can be applied in a large variety of estimation problems, including censored and truncated data. As a result, it often supersedes both the method of moments and the method of percentile matching.

Maximum likelihood estimators have certain properties that are considered to be desirable when it comes to estimation techniques. For example, they are asymptotically unbiased, with a minimum variance, and are asymptotically normal. This property can be used in building confidence intervals, as well as hypothesis testing.

The disadvantages of the MLE method include computational difficulty in many cases, as well as being biased for samples of a small size. The technical difficulties can be overcome by using an appropriate package available in most statistical software.

Conclusion

In this chapter we presented the three most popular methods of point estimation. They were accompanied by relatively simple notions of what can be viewed as optimal estimators.

The method of maximum likelihood estimation (MLE) received the most detailed consideration due to its special place among other statistical methods of estimating the parameters of a probability distribution. In addition to its definition, application, and main technique, its asymptotic efficiency was also explained. The technique known as the delta-method highlighted asymptotic normality of various estimates applicable in estimation practice.

Comparison of methods provided throughout the chapter brought out their relative strengths and illustrated advantages of maximum likelihood method in situations when regularity conditions were satisfied.

In the following exercises readers will strengthen their understanding of the ideas developed in this chapter.

Exercises

6.1. You have the following sample of loss sizes:

$$4 \quad 6 \quad 9 \quad 12 \quad 23 \quad 57 \quad 112 \quad 150$$
$$\sum x_i = 373, \quad \sum x_i^2 = 39{,}099$$

You are to fit the losses to a Pareto distribution using the method of moments, matching the first two moments.

Using the fitted distribution, estimate the probability that a claim is greater than 100.

6.2. Claim sizes are as follows:

$$2000 \quad 2500 \quad 3000 \quad 4500 \quad 6500$$

A lognormal distribution is fitted to the claim sizes using the method of moments, matching the first two moments.

Determine the estimate of σ^2.

6.3. You are given the following losses:

$$110 \quad 160 \quad 160 \quad 185 \quad 210 \quad 260 \quad 310 \quad 410 \quad 510 \quad 810$$

Calculate the smoothed empirical estimate of the 70th percentile.

6.4. You observe a sample of four losses:

$$25 \quad 40 \quad 70 \quad 120$$

You fit these losses to a Weibull distribution, matching the 20th and the 60th smoothed empirical percentiles.

Calculate the estimated mode of the distribution.

6.5. You are given the following losses:

$$1500 \quad 1700 \quad 2100 \quad 2600 \quad 2700 \quad 2900$$

You fit an inverse exponential to the loss distribution using maximum likelihood.

Determine the resulting estimate of the probability of a loss below 2000.

6.6. The following claim experience is observed:

Claim Size X	Number of Claims
0 – 2000	25
2000 – 4000	15
4000 – ∞	10

You fit an exponential to the claim size distribution using maximum likelihood.
Determine the estimate of the mean claim size.

6.7. Data are being fit to a distribution with the following probability function:

n	Probability of n
0	0.2
1	$0.8 - \theta$
2	θ

The only possible values for the distribution are 0, 1, and 2, and $0 \leq \theta \leq 0.8$.
You have the following data:

Value	Number of Observations
0	10
1	25
2	5

Calculate the value of θ of the fitted distribution using maximum likelihood.

6.8. Claim counts follow a geometric distribution with parameter β. You are given the
following data for 261 policyholders:

Number of Claims	Number of Policyholders
0	214
1	76
2	41
3	29
≥ 4	5

Calculate the maximum likelihood estimate of β.

6.9. An insurance coverage has an ordinary deductible of 600 and a maximum covered loss of 10,200. Reported losses, including the deductible, are

$$1100 \quad 2200 \quad 4300 \quad 8400$$

There are three additional losses above 10,200.

The data is fitted to an exponential distribution using maximum likelihood.

Determine the mean of the fitted distribution.

6.10. In a mortality study, you have the following data for five individuals:

i	d_i	u_i	x_i
1	4	25	0
2	0	0	45
3	0	35	0
4	15	0	50
5	34	0	60

where d_i is the entry time, u_i is the withdrawal time, x_i is the death time.

The data are fitted to a Weibull distribution with $\tau = 4$. You are given that $\Gamma(5/4) = 0.9064$.

Determine the maximum likelihood estimate of mean survival time.

6.11. You have the following data for losses from an insurance coverage:

Range	Number of Observations
$(0, 2000)$	20
$[2000, 6000)$	30
$[6000, 11{,}000]$	41
$(11{,}000, \infty)$	0

The underlying distribution is assumed to be uniform on $[0, \theta]$. The parameter θ is estimated using maximum likelihood.

Determine θ.

6.12. There are three classes of policyholders.

(i) In class X, losses follow a gamma distribution with parameters $\alpha = 3$ and θ.

(ii) In class Y, losses follow an exponential distribution with mean 2θ.

(iii) In class Z, losses follow an exponential distribution with mean 3θ.

The following losses are observed:

Class	Observations
X	300, 400, 800
Y	200, 900
Z	500, 1100, 1300

Estimate θ using maximum likelihood.

6.13. You are given the following observations of X:

$$5.0 \quad 2.9 \quad 4.5 \quad 7.0 \quad 5.1$$

A lognormal distribution with parameters μ and σ is fit to these observations using the maximum likelihood method.

Estimate the μ and σ.

6.14. An insurance coverage has an ordinary deductible of 750 and a maximum covered loss of 15,000. Reported losses, including the deductible, are

$$2000 \quad 3000 \quad 5000 \quad 9000$$

There are two losses above the maximum covered loss. The loss distribution is fitted to Pareto with $\theta = 6000$.

Determine the maximum likelihood estimator of α.

6.15. Losses follow a distribution with probability density function

$$f(x, a) = \frac{ax^{a-1}}{100^a}, \quad 0 < x < 100.$$

You are given the following sample of losses:

$$10 \quad 15 \quad 35 \quad 45 \quad 45$$

Determine the maximum likelihood estimate of a.

6.16. Claim counts follow a Poisson distribution. You have the following information about a book of business:

Number of Claims	Number of Policyholders
0	75
≥ 1	25

The distribution is fitted using maximum likelihood.

Calculate the fitted probability of three claims.

6.17. For an inverse Pareto distribution with fixed θ, calculate the maximum likelihood estimate of τ and the lower bound of the asymptotic variance of $\hat{\tau}$.

6.18. You are given the following two observations:

$$6 \qquad 8$$

The observations are fitted to a Pareto distribution with $\alpha = 2$. The parameter θ is estimated using maximum likelihood.

Determine the absolute difference between the true information and the observed information if the parameter estimate $\hat{\theta}$ is used to approximate θ in the information expressions.

6.19. A random variable X has mean 4 and variance 5.

Using the delta method, approximate the variance of X^3.

6.20. Claim size X follows a single-parameter Pareto distribution with known parameter $\theta = 50$. The parameter α is estimated as 2, with variance 1.

Determine the variance of the estimate for $\mathbf{P}(X > 100)$.

6.21. Claim size X follows a two-parameter Pareto distribution with estimated parameters $(\alpha, \theta) = (2, 50)$. The covariance matrix is

$$\begin{pmatrix} 0.7 & 0.3 \\ 0.3 & 0.5 \end{pmatrix}.$$

Determine the variance of the estimate for $\mathbf{P}(X > 100)$.

6.22. The parameter θ of a uniform distribution on $[0, \theta]$ is estimated using maximum likelihood methods to be $\hat{\theta} = 30$. The variance of $\hat{\theta}$ is 0.0054.

Let $\hat{\nu}$ be the estimated variance of the uniform distribution.

Using the delta method, estimate the variance of $\hat{\nu}$.

6.23. You are given the following:

i) A random variable has probability density function

$$f(x) = ax^{a-1}, \ 0 \le x \le 1, \ a > 0.$$

ii) The parameter a is estimated using maximum likelihood.

iii) A random sample of observations of X is

$$0.2 \qquad 0.5 \qquad 0.7 \qquad 0.7 \qquad 0.8.$$

Construct a 95% *normal* confidence interval for $\mathbf{P}(X < 0.6)$.

6.24. You are given the following:

i) A random variable has probability density function

$$f(x) = ax^{a-1}, \ 0 \le x \le 1, \ a > 0.$$

ii) The parameter a is estimated using maximum likelihood.

iii) A random sample of observations of X is

$$0.2 \qquad 0.5 \qquad 0.7 \qquad 0.7 \qquad 0.8.$$

Construct a 95% *non-normal* confidence interval for a.

6.25. A population follows a normal distribution with mean 20 and unknown variance σ^2. A sample of 30 observations is used to estimate σ, the square root of the population's variance.

Calculate the Cramér–Rao lower bound for the variance of an unbiased estimator of σ if the true value of σ is 15.

6.26. Observations $\{X_k : \ 1 \le k \le n\}$ share a common density:

$$f(x|\mu) = \frac{\mu^4}{3!} x^3 \cdot e^{-\mu \cdot x} \ \text{ for } \ x > 0,$$

where $\mu > 0$ is a targeted parameter.

Determine the maximum likelihood estimator for μ.

6.27. Claim size X follows a single-parameter Pareto distribution with known parameter $\theta = 150$. The parameter α is estimated using maximum likelihood.

A random sample of observations of X is

$$162 \qquad 170 \qquad 176 \qquad 220 \qquad 237.$$

Construct a 95% normal confidence interval for $\mathbf{P}(X < 300)$.

6.28. A random variable follows a uniform distribution on $[0, \theta]$. A sample of 150 observations of the random variable has maximum 60. The parameter θ is estimated using maximum likelihood.

Construct a 90% non-normal confidence interval for θ.

Solutions

6.1. For Pareto distribution with parameters θ and α, the survival function is of the form

$$S_X(x) = \left(\frac{\theta}{\theta + x}\right)^\alpha.$$

By (6.4), using the method of moments, the parameters of the Pareto distribution are estimated as

$$\hat{\alpha} = \frac{2(\hat{\mu}_2' - \hat{\mu}_1^2)}{\hat{\mu}_2' - 2\hat{\mu}_1^2}, \ \hat{\theta} = \frac{\hat{\mu}_1 \cdot \hat{\mu}_2'}{\hat{\mu}_2' - 2\hat{\mu}_1^2},$$

$$\text{where} \ \hat{\mu}_1 = \frac{1}{n}\sum_{i=1}^{n}X_i, \ \hat{\mu}_2' = \frac{1}{n}\sum_{i=1}^{n}X_i^2$$

We are given

$$\sum x_i = 373, \quad \sum x_i^2 = 39{,}099.$$

Therefore,

$$\hat{\mu}_1 = \frac{1}{8}\cdot 373 = 46.625, \ \hat{\mu}_2' = \frac{1}{8}\cdot 39{,}099 = 4887.375.$$

Calculating $\hat{\alpha}$ and $\hat{\theta}$, we obtain

$$\hat{\alpha} = \frac{2(4887.375 - 46.625^2)}{4887.375 - 2\cdot 46.625^2} = \frac{5426.96875}{539.59375} = 10.0575$$

$$\hat{\theta} = \frac{46.625\cdot 4887.375}{4887.375 - 2\cdot 46.625^2} = \frac{227{,}873.86}{539.59375} = 422.3063.$$

Estimating the probability that a claim is greater than 100, we obtain

$$\hat{\mathbf{P}}\left(X > 100\right) = \hat{S}_X(100) = \left(\frac{\hat{\theta}}{\hat{\theta} + 100}\right)^{\hat{\alpha}} = \left(\frac{422.3063}{422.3063 + 100}\right)^{10.0575} =$$

$$= 0.8085^{10.0575} = \mathbf{0.118}.$$

6.2. By (6.6), using the method of moments, the parameters of the lognormal distribution are estimated as

$$\hat{\mu} = 2\ln\hat{\mu}_1 - \frac{1}{2}\ln\hat{\mu}_2', \ \hat{\sigma}^2 = \ln\hat{\mu}_2' - 2\ln\hat{\mu}_1,$$

$$\text{where} \ \hat{\mu}_1 = \frac{1}{n}\sum_{i=1}^{n}X_i, \ \hat{\mu}_2' = \frac{1}{n}\sum_{i=1}^{n}X_i^2.$$

Calculating $\hat{\mu}_1$ and $\hat{\mu}_2'$, we have

$$\hat{\mu}_1 = \frac{1}{n}\sum x_i = \frac{1}{5}\left(2000 + 2500 + 3000 + 4500 + 6500\right) = \frac{1}{5}\cdot 18{,}500 = 3700$$

$$\hat{\mu}_2' = \frac{1}{n}\sum x_i^2 = \frac{1}{5}\cdot 10^6\left(4 + 2.5^2 + 9 + 4.5^2 + 6.5^2\right) = \frac{1}{5}\cdot 10^6 \cdot 81.75 = 16.35\cdot 10^6.$$

Hence,

$$\hat{\sigma}^2 = \ln\left(16.35 \cdot 10^6\right) - 2\ln 3700 = 16.6097 - 16.4322 = \mathbf{0.1777}.$$

6.3. Note that $n = 10$, $p = 0.7$. Calculating $(n+1)p$, we have $(n+1)p = 11 \cdot 0.7 = 7.7$. Since $(n+1)p$ is not an integer, using formula (6.11) for the smoothed empirical estimate of the $100p^{th}$ percentile, we obtain

$$\hat{\pi}_{0.7} = (7.7 - 7) \cdot 410 + (8 - 7.7) \cdot 310 = \mathbf{380}.$$

6.4. Calculating the 20th and the 60th smoothed empirical percentiles, we have

$$n = 4, \; p = 0.2, \; q = 0.6, \; (n+1)p = 5 \cdot 0.2 = 1, \; (n+1)q = 5 \cdot 0.6 = 3.$$

Since both $(n+1)p$ and $(n+1)q$ are integers, the 20th and the 60th smoothed empirical percentiles are

$$\hat{\pi}_p = 25, \; \hat{\pi}_q = 70.$$

Using the method of percentile matching, the parameters of the Weibull distribution are estimated, as in (6.15):

$$\hat{\tau} = \frac{\ln\left(\frac{\ln(1-p)}{\ln(1-q)}\right)}{\ln\left(\frac{\hat{\pi}_p}{\hat{\pi}_q}\right)}, \; \hat{\theta} = \frac{\hat{\pi}_p}{(-\ln(1-p))^{\ln\left(\frac{\hat{\pi}_p}{\hat{\pi}_q}\right)/\ln\left(\frac{\ln(1-p)}{\ln(1-q)}\right)}}$$

Hence,

$$\hat{\tau} = \frac{\ln\left(\frac{\ln(0.8)}{\ln(0.4)}\right)}{\ln\left(\frac{25}{70}\right)} = 1.3719$$

$$\hat{\theta} = \frac{25}{(-\ln(0.8))^{1/1.3719}} = 74.6059.$$

The mode of a Weibull distribution with parameters θ and τ is given by

$$m = \theta \left(\frac{\tau - 1}{\tau}\right)^{1/\tau}.$$

Hence, the estimated mode of the distribution is

$$\hat{m} = \theta \left(\frac{0.3719}{1.3719}\right)^{1/1.3719} = 28.8097 \approx \mathbf{28.81}.$$

6.5. The probability density and the cumulative distribution functions for the inverse exponential distribution with parameter θ are

$$f(x, \theta) = \frac{\theta e^{-\theta/x}}{x^2}, \quad F(x) = e^{-\theta/x}.$$

Using (6.44), the MLE for an inverse exponential distribution is

$$\hat{\theta} = \frac{n}{\sum_{i=1}^{n} 1/x_i}.$$

Therefore, using our data, we have

$$\hat{\theta} = \frac{6}{\frac{1}{1500} + \frac{1}{1700} + \frac{1}{2100} + \frac{1}{2600} + \frac{1}{2700} + \frac{1}{2900}} = \frac{600}{\frac{1}{15} + \frac{1}{17} + \frac{1}{21} + \frac{1}{26} + \frac{1}{27} + \frac{1}{29}} =$$

$$= \frac{600}{0.2831} = \mathbf{2119.46}.$$

Thus,

$$\widehat{\mathbf{P}}\left(X < 2000\right) = e^{-2119.463/2000} = \mathbf{0.3465}.$$

6.6. The mean of the exponential distribution is parameter θ. Thus, we need to estimate θ.

For grouped data,

$$\mathbf{P}\left(X \in I_j = [c_{j-1}, c_j]\right) = F(c_j) - F(c_{j-1}) = S(c_{j-1}) - S(c_j).$$

The cumulative distribution and the survival functions for the exponential distribution with parameter θ are

$$F(x) = 1 - e^{-x/\theta}, \quad S(x) = e^{-x/\theta}.$$

Hence, the probabilities for each interval are

$$\mathbf{P}\left(X \in I_1\right) = \mathbf{P}\left(X \in [0, 2000)\right) = F(2000) = 1 - e^{-2000/\theta}$$
$$\mathbf{P}\left(X \in I_2\right) = \mathbf{P}\left(X \in [2000, 4000)\right) = S(2000) - S(4000) = e^{-2000/\theta} - e^{-4000/\theta}$$
$$\mathbf{P}\left(X \in I_3\right) = \mathbf{P}\left(X \in [4000, \infty)\right) = S(4000) = e^{-4000/\theta}.$$

Therefore, the likelihood function is

$$L(\theta) = \left(1 - e^{-2000/\theta}\right)^{25} \left(e^{-2000/\theta} - e^{-4000/\theta}\right)^{15} e^{-4000 \cdot 10/\theta} = \left(1 - e^{-2000/\theta}\right)^{40} e^{-2000 \cdot 35/\theta}.$$

Let $x = e^{-2000/\theta}$. Then,

$$L(x) = (1 - x)^{40} x^{35}.$$

The log-likelihood function is

$$l(x) = 40 \ln(1 - x) + 35 \ln x.$$

Differentiating the log-likelihood function with respect to x and equating it to zero, we obtain

$$l'(x) = -\frac{40}{1 - x} + \frac{35}{x} = \frac{35(1 - x) - 40x}{x(1 - x)} = \frac{35 - 75x}{x(1 - x)} = 0 \Rightarrow$$

$$x = \frac{35}{75} = \frac{7}{15} = 0.4667.$$

Solving for θ, we obtain

$$e^{-2000/\theta} = 0.4667 \Leftrightarrow -\frac{2000}{\theta} = \ln 0.4667 = -0.7621 \Leftrightarrow \hat{\theta} = \frac{2000}{0.7621} = \mathbf{2624.19}.$$

6.7. In this problem n has trinomial distribution. The probability of ten 0's is 0.2^{10}, so 0.2^{10} is the likelihood of ten 0's. Similarly, $(0.8 - \theta)^{25}$ is the likelihood of twenty five 1's, and θ^5 is the likelihood of five 2's. Multiplying them together, as well as by a trinomial coefficient for all possible orders, since the order of the observations is not specified, we obtain

$$L(\theta) = \frac{40!}{10!25!5!} 0.2^{10}(0.8 - \theta)^{25}\theta^5.$$

Taking logarithms on both sides, we have

$$l(\theta) = \ln L(\theta) = \ln \frac{40!}{10!25!5!} + 10\ln 0.2 + 25\ln(0.8 - \theta) + 5\ln\theta.$$

Differentiating,

$$\frac{dl}{d\theta} = -\frac{25}{0.8 - \theta} + \frac{5}{\theta} = \frac{4 - 30\theta}{\theta(0.8 - \theta)} = \frac{2(2 - 15\theta)}{\theta(0.8 - \theta)}.$$

Finding the critical points, we get

$$\theta = \frac{2}{15} = 0.1\overline{333}, 0, \text{ or } 0.8.$$

$\theta = 0.1\overline{333}$ is the local maximum. The other two roots are the foreign ones.

Thus, the answer is $\hat{\theta} = \mathbf{0.13}$.

6.8. Let $p = \beta/(1 + \beta)$. Then, $1 - p = 1/(1 + \beta)$ and

$$p_0 = \frac{1}{1 + \beta} = 1 - p, \quad p_n = \left(\frac{\beta}{1 + \beta}\right)^n \cdot \frac{1}{1 + \beta} = p^n(1 - p).$$

Thus, the likelihood function is

$$L(p) = p_0^{214} \cdot p_1^{76} \cdot p_2^{41} \cdot p_3^{29} \cdot \left(1 - \sum_{k=0}^{3} p_k\right)^5 =$$

$$= (1 - p)^{214} \cdot (p(1 - p))^{76} \cdot \left(p^2(1 - p)\right)^{41} \cdot \left(p^3(1 - p)\right)^{29} \cdot \left(p^4\right)^5.$$

Note that the last term in the expression for $L(p)$ is p^4. Indeed,

$$1 - \sum_{k=0}^{3} p_k = 1 - (1 - p)\sum_{k=0}^{3} p^k = 1 - (1 - p) \cdot \frac{1 - p^4}{1 - p} = p^4.$$

Therefore,

$$L(p) = (1 - p)^{360} p^{265}.$$

Taking a logarithm of this function, we obtain

$$l(p) = 360\ln(1 - p) + 265\ln p.$$

Differentiating l,

$$l'(p) = -\frac{360}{1-p} + \frac{265}{p} = \frac{265 - 625p}{p(1-p)}.$$

Equating this derivative to zero and solving for p, we have

$$\hat{p} = \frac{265}{625} \approx 0.4240 \Leftrightarrow 1 - \hat{p} = 0.5760 = \frac{1}{1 + \hat{\beta}} \Rightarrow \hat{\beta} = \mathbf{0.7361}.$$

6.9. Modeling ground-up losses, we have

$$L(\theta) = \frac{\prod_{i=1}^{n} f(\theta, x_i) \cdot (S(\theta, u))^m}{(1 - F(\theta, d))^{n+m}},$$

where u is the policy limit, d is the deductible, n is the number of uncensored observations, and m is the number of censored observations.

Using (6.43), the MLE for an exponential distribution with data that is left-truncated at d and censored from above at u is

$$\hat{\theta} = \frac{\sum_{i=1}^{n} x_i + mu - d(n+m)}{n}.$$

Using our data

$$\theta = \frac{1100 + 2200 + 4300 + 8400 + 3 \cdot 10{,}200 - 600 \cdot 7}{4} =$$

$$= \frac{42{,}400}{4} = 10{,}600.$$

6.10. For Weibull distribution

$$\mathbf{E}[X] = \theta \cdot \Gamma\left(1 + \frac{1}{\tau}\right).$$

For $\tau = 4$,

$$\mathbf{E}[X] = \theta \cdot \Gamma\left(1 + \frac{1}{4}\right) = \theta \cdot \Gamma\left(\frac{5}{4}\right) = 0.9064 \cdot \theta.$$

Our uncensored data consists of death points $x_2 = 45$, $x_4 = 50$, and $x_5 = 60$. There are two censored observations: $u_1 = 25$ and $u_3 = 35$. Finally, the truncation points are d_i.

Using (6.49), if n is the number of uncensored observations, c is the number of censored observations, d_i is the truncation point for each observation (0 if untruncated), x_i is the observation if uncensored or the censoring point if censored, and the parameter θ is estimated as

$$\hat{\theta} = \sqrt[\tau]{\frac{1}{n} \sum_{i=1}^{n+c} (x_i^\tau - d_i^\tau)}.$$

Thus,

$$\hat{\theta} = \sqrt[4]{\frac{1}{3}\left(45^4 + 50^4 + 60^4 + 25^4 + 35^4 - 4^4 - 15^4 - 34^4\right)} = 53.0800.$$

Therefore, the estimated of mean survival time is

$$\mathbf{E}[X] = 0.9064 \cdot \theta = 0.9064 \cdot 53.0800 = 48.1117 \approx \mathbf{48.11}.$$

6.11. If the data are grouped, but all groups are bounded (there is no group with an upper bound of infinity), then the MLE is the lower of the following two items:

1. The upper bound of the highest interval with data

2. The lower bound of the highest interval with data times the total number of observations divided by the number of observations below that number, according to (6.52)

The upper bound of the highest interval with data is 11,000. This is the first comparison point.

The lower bound of the highest interval with data is 6000. The total number of observations is $n = 20 + 30 + 41 = 91$. The number of observations below 6000 is $m = 20 + 30 = 50$. Thus, the second comparison point is

$$6000 \cdot \frac{91}{50} = 10{,}920.$$

Finding the minimum, we obtain the MLE of θ:

$$\hat{\theta} = \min\{11{,}000, 10{,}920\} = 10{,}920.$$

6.12. The probability density function for the exponential distribution with parameter θ is

$$f(x, \theta) = \frac{1}{\theta} e^{-x/\theta}.$$

The probability density function for the gamma distribution with parameters θ and α is

$$f(x, \theta, \alpha) = \left(\frac{x}{\theta}\right)^{\alpha} e^{-x/\theta} \cdot \frac{1}{x} \cdot \frac{1}{\Gamma(\alpha)}.$$

For $\alpha = 3$,

$$f(x, \theta) = \left(\frac{x}{\theta}\right)^3 e^{-x/\theta} \cdot \frac{1}{x} \cdot \frac{1}{\Gamma(3)} = \frac{x^2}{2} \cdot \frac{1}{\theta^3} e^{-x/\theta}.$$

Thus, the likelihood function is

$$L(\theta) = \frac{1}{2^3} (300 \cdot 400 \cdot 800)^2 \cdot \frac{1}{\theta^9} \cdot \exp\left\{ -\frac{1}{\theta} (300 + 400 + 800) \right\} \cdot$$

$$\cdot \frac{1}{4\theta^2} \cdot \exp\left\{ -\frac{1}{2\theta} (200 + 900) \right\} \cdot \frac{1}{27\theta^3} \cdot \exp\left\{ -\frac{1}{3\theta} (500 + 1100 + 1300) \right\} =$$

$$= A \cdot \frac{1}{\theta^{14}} \cdot e^{-3016.67/\theta}, \quad \text{where } A \text{ is a constant.}$$

The log-likelihood function is

$$l(\theta) = -14 \ln \theta - \frac{3016.67}{\theta} + \ln A.$$

Differentiating the log-likelihood function with respect to x and equating it to zero, we obtain

$$l'(\theta) = -\frac{14}{\theta} + \frac{3016.67}{\theta^2} = 0 \Leftrightarrow -14 + \frac{3016.67}{\theta} = 0 \Leftrightarrow \theta = \frac{3016.67}{14} = \mathbf{215.48}.$$

6.13. Using (6.38), the MLE for μ and σ for lognormal distribution is

$$\hat{\mu} = \bar{Y} = \frac{1}{n} \cdot \sum_{j=1}^{n} \ln X_j, \quad \hat{\sigma} = \sqrt{\frac{1}{n} \sum_{i=1}^{n} (\ln X_i)^2 - \hat{\mu}^2}.$$

Hence,

$$\hat{\mu} = \frac{1}{5} (\ln 5 + \ln 2.9 + \ln 4.5 + \ln 7 + \ln 5.1) = \frac{7.7534}{5} = 1.5507 \approx \mathbf{1.55}$$

$$\hat{\sigma}^2 = \frac{1}{5} \left((\ln 5)^2 + (\ln 2.9)^2 + (\ln 4.5)^2 + (\ln 7)^2 + (\ln 5.1)^2 \right) - 1.5507^2 =$$

$$= 2.4854 - 2.4047 = 0.0808 \Rightarrow \hat{\sigma} = \mathbf{0.2842}.$$

6.14. For a Pareto distribution, using (6.46),

$$\hat{\alpha} = -\frac{n}{K}, \quad K = \sum_{i=1}^{n+c} \ln(d_i + \theta) - \sum_{i=1}^{n+c} \ln(\theta + x_i),$$

where n is the number of uncensored observations and c is the number of censored observations.

For the same deductible d,

$$K = (n + c) \ln(\theta + d) - \sum_{i=1}^{n+c} \ln(\theta + x_i) = \ln(\theta + d)^{n+c} - \ln \prod_{i=1}^{n+c} (\theta + x_i).$$

For our data,

$$K = \ln \frac{6750^6}{8000 \cdot 9000 \cdot 11{,}000 \cdot 15{,}000 \cdot 21{,}000^2} = \ln \frac{6.75^6}{8 \cdot 9 \cdot 11 \cdot 15 \cdot 21^2} =$$

$$= \ln 0.0181 = -4.0144.$$

Therefore,

$$\hat{\alpha} = \frac{4}{4.0144} = \textbf{0.9964}.$$

6.15. This is beta distribution with parameters $\theta = 100$, a and $b = 1$. Using (6.50), for a beta distribution with $b = 1$, the MLE estimate of the parameter a is

$$\hat{a} = -\frac{n}{\ln\left(\prod_{i=1}^{n} x_i/\theta\right)}.$$

For our data,

$$\hat{a} = -\frac{5}{\ln\left(0.1 \cdot 0.15 \cdot 0.35 \cdot 0.45^2\right)} = \frac{5}{6.8465} = 0.7303 \approx \textbf{0.73}.$$

6.16. For a Poisson distribution, we have

$$p_0 = e^{-\lambda} = \frac{75}{100} = 0.75$$
$$Pr\left(N \geq 1\right) = 1 - p_0 = 0.25.$$

Calculating λ, we obtain

$$\lambda = -\ln 0.75 = 0.2877.$$

Hence, the fitted probability of three claims is

$$p_3 = \frac{\lambda^3}{3!} \cdot e^{-\lambda} = \frac{0.2877^3}{6} \cdot 0.75 = 0.002976 \approx \textbf{0.003}.$$

6.17. For the inverse Pareto distribution with parameters θ and τ, the probability density function is

$$f(x, \theta, \tau) = \frac{\tau \cdot \theta \cdot x^{\tau-1}}{(x + \theta)^{\tau+1}}.$$

For a fixed θ, given n data points, $x_1, x_2, \ldots, x_n$, the likelihood function is

$$L(\tau) = \frac{\tau^n \cdot \theta^n \cdot \prod_{i=1}^{n} x_i^{\tau-1}}{\prod_{i=1}^{n}(x_i + \theta)^{\tau+1}}.$$

Then the log-likelihood function is

$$l(\tau) = \ln L(\tau) = n \ln \tau + n \ln \theta + (\tau - 1) \sum_{i=1}^{n} \ln x_i - (\tau + 1) \sum_{i=1}^{n} \ln(x_i + \theta).$$

Differentiating the log-likelihood function with respect to τ, we obtain

$$l'(\tau) = \frac{n}{\tau} + \sum_{i=1}^{n} \ln x_i - \sum_{i=1}^{n} \ln(x_i + \theta).$$

Equating this expression to zero and solving for τ, we obtain the the MLE of τ for an inverse Pareto distribution with a fixed parameter θ:

$$\hat{\tau} = \frac{n}{\sum_{i=1}^{n} \ln(x_i + \theta) - \sum_{i=1}^{n} \ln x_i} = \frac{n}{\sum_{i=1}^{n} \ln\left((x_i + \theta)/x_i\right)}$$

Differentiating again, we have

$$l''(\tau) = -\frac{n}{\tau^2}.$$

The information matrix has a single entry whose value is

$$I(\tau) = -\mathbf{E}\left[l''(\tau)\right] = \frac{n}{\tau^2}.$$

Therefore, the lower bound of the asymptotic variance $Var(\hat{\tau})$ of $\hat{\tau}$ is

$$(I(\tau))^{-1} = \frac{\tau^2}{n}.$$

6.18. For a Pareto distribution with parameters θ and $\alpha = 2$ the probability density function is

$$f(x, \theta) = \frac{2\theta^2}{(x + \theta)^3}.$$

Given n data points, $x_1, x_2, \ldots, x_n$, the likelihood function is

$$L(\theta) = \frac{2^n \cdot \theta^{2n}}{\prod_{i=1}^{n}(x_i + \theta)^3}.$$

Then the log-likelihood function is

$$l(\theta) = \ln L(\theta) = n \ln 2 + 2n \ln \theta - 3 \sum_{i=1}^{n} \ln(x_i + \theta).$$

Differentiating the log-likelihood function with respect to θ, we obtain

$$l'(\theta) = \frac{2n}{\theta} - \sum_{i=1}^{n} \frac{3}{x_i + \theta}.$$

Let us calculate the MLE of θ for two observations, $x_1 = 6$ and $x_2 = 8$. We have

$$\frac{4}{\theta} - \frac{3}{\theta + 6} - \frac{3}{\theta + 8} = 0 \Leftrightarrow 4(\theta + 6)(\theta + 8) - 3\theta(\theta + 8) - 3\theta(\theta + 6) = 0 \Leftrightarrow$$

$$4(\theta^2 + 14\theta + 48) - 3\theta^2 - 24\theta - 3\theta^2 - 18\theta = 0 \Leftrightarrow$$

$$4\theta^2 + 56\theta + 192 - 6\theta^2 - 42\theta = 0 \Leftrightarrow -2\theta^2 + 14\theta + 192 = 0 \Leftrightarrow \theta^2 - 7\theta - 96 = 0 \Leftrightarrow$$

$$D = 49 + 4 \cdot 96 = 433, \quad \theta_{1,2} = \frac{-7 \pm \sqrt{433}}{2} = \begin{bmatrix} 13.9043 \\ -6.9043 \end{bmatrix}.$$

Assuming θ is positive, the MLE of θ is $\hat{\theta} = 13.9043$.

The *observed* information is $-l''(\theta = \hat\theta)$. Differentiating $l'(\theta)$, we have

$$l''(\theta) = -\frac{2n}{\theta^2} + \sum_{i=1}^{n} \frac{3}{(x_i + \theta)^2}.$$

For $n = 2$ and two observations $x_1 = 6$ and $x_2 = 8$, we have

$$-l''(\theta = 13.9043) = \frac{4}{13.9043^2} - \frac{3}{19.9043^2} - \frac{3}{21.9043^2} = 0.006865.$$

This is the observed information.

Calculating the information using the *true* formula, recall that by (6.47), for Pareto distribution with fixed α, the information is

$$\mathbf{I}(\theta) = \frac{n\alpha}{(\alpha + 2)\theta^2}.$$

For $n = 2$, $\theta = \hat\theta$, and $\alpha = 2$, we have

$$I(\theta) = \frac{2 \cdot 2}{4 \cdot 13.9043^2} = \frac{1}{13.9043^2} = 0.00517.$$

This is the true information.

Thus, absolute difference between the true information and the observed information is then

$$0.006865 - 0.00517 = \mathbf{0.001695}.$$

6.19. The delta method is a method of estimating the variance of a transformed random variable from the variance of the initial random variable.

By the delta method formula for one variable,

$$\mathbf{Var}\,(g(X)) \approx \mathbf{Var}(X) \left(\frac{dg}{dx}\right)^2.$$

In our case,

$$g(x) = x^3, \quad g'(x) = 3x^2.$$

Evaluating $g'(x)$ at $x_0 = \mathbf{E}[X] = 4$, we obtain

$$\mathbf{Var}\left(X^3\right) = \mathbf{Var}\,(g(X)) \approx 5 \cdot (3 \cdot 16)^2 = 5 \cdot 48^2 = 5 \cdot 2304 = 11{,}520.$$

Alternatively,

$$g(x) = x^3, \quad g'(x) = 3x^2, \quad g''(x) = 6x.$$

Writing the Taylor series around the mean $x_0 = 4$, we have

$$g(x) \approx g(4) + g'(4)(x - 4) + \frac{g''(4)}{2}(x - 4)^2 = 64 + 48(x - 4) + 12(x - 4)^2.$$

Hence,

$$\mathbf{Var}\left(X^3\right) = \mathbf{Var}\,(64 + 48(x - 4)) = 48^2 \mathbf{Var}\,(X) = 2304 \cdot 5 = 11{,}520.$$

6.20. Let $g(\alpha) = \widehat{\mathbf{P}}(X > 100)$. For a single-parameter Pareto distribution the survival function is
$$S_X(x) = \left(\frac{\theta}{x}\right)^\alpha.$$

Therefore,
$$g(\alpha) = \left(\frac{50}{100}\right)^\alpha = \left(\frac{1}{2}\right)^\alpha.$$

By the delta method formula for one variable,
$$\mathbf{Var}\left(g(\alpha)\right) \approx \mathbf{Var}(\alpha)\left(\frac{dg}{d\alpha}\right)^2.$$

Differentiating g with respect to α, we have
$$\frac{dg}{d\alpha} = \left(\frac{1}{2}\right)^\alpha \ln\frac{1}{2} = -\left(\frac{1}{2}\right)^\alpha \ln 2.$$

Hence,
$$\mathbf{Var}\left(\widehat{\mathbf{P}}(X > 100)\right) \approx \mathbf{Var}(\alpha)\left(\frac{dg}{d\alpha}\right)^2 =$$
$$= 1 \cdot \left(\frac{1}{2}\right)^{2\alpha}(\ln 2)^2 = 1 \cdot \left(\frac{1}{2}\right)^4 (\ln 2)^2 = \mathbf{0.03003}.$$

6.21. Let
$$g(\alpha, \theta) = \widehat{\mathbf{P}}(X > 100) = \left(\frac{\theta}{100 + \theta}\right)^\alpha.$$

By the delta method formula for two variables,
$$\mathbf{Var}\left(g(X)\right) \approx (\partial\mathbf{g})'\Sigma(\partial\mathbf{g}) = \mathbf{Var}(X)\left(\frac{\partial g}{\partial x}\right)^2 + 2\mathbf{Cov}(X,Y)\frac{\partial g}{\partial x}\frac{\partial g}{\partial y} +$$
$$+ \mathbf{Var}(Y)\left(\frac{\partial g}{\partial y}\right)^2, \text{ where } \partial\mathbf{g} = \left(\frac{\partial g}{\partial x}, \frac{\partial g}{\partial y}\right).$$

Calculating partial derivatives with respect to each variable, we obtain
$$\frac{\partial g}{\partial \alpha} = \left(\frac{\theta}{100 + \theta}\right)^\alpha \ln\left(\frac{\theta}{100 + \theta}\right) = \left(\frac{50}{150}\right)^2 \ln\left(\frac{50}{150}\right) = \left(\frac{1}{3}\right)^2 \ln\left(\frac{1}{3}\right) = -0.1221$$
$$\frac{\partial g}{\partial \theta} = \alpha\left(\frac{\theta}{100 + \theta}\right)^{\alpha-1}\frac{100 + \theta - \theta}{(100 + \theta)^2} = \alpha\left(\frac{\theta}{100 + \theta}\right)^{\alpha-1}\frac{100}{(100 + \theta)^2} = 2 \cdot \frac{50}{150} \cdot \frac{100}{150^2} =$$
$$= 2 \cdot \frac{1}{3} \cdot \frac{2}{3} \cdot \frac{1}{150} = 0.00296.$$

Therefore,
$$\mathbf{Var}\left(\widehat{\mathbf{P}}(X > 100)\right) \approx (-0.1221 \ \ 0.00296)\begin{pmatrix} 0.7 & 0.3 \\ 0.3 & 0.5 \end{pmatrix}\begin{pmatrix} -0.1221 \\ 0.00296 \end{pmatrix} =$$
$$= (-0.0846 \ \ -0.03514)\begin{pmatrix} -0.1221 \\ 0.00296 \end{pmatrix} = \mathbf{0.0102},$$

where values in the last two equalities are calculated as follows:

$$-0.0846 = -0.1221 \cdot 0.7 + 0.00296 \cdot 0.3$$
$$-0.03514 = -0.1221 \cdot 0.3 + 0.00296 \cdot 0.5$$
$$0.0102 = -0.0846(-0.1221) - 0.03514(0.00296)$$

6.22. For $X \in U[0, \theta]$, $\mathbf{Var}(X) = \theta^2/12$. Let $g(\theta) = \hat{v} = \theta^2/12$. By the delta method formula for one variable,

$$\mathbf{Var}\left(g(\theta)\right) \approx \mathbf{Var}(\theta) \left(\frac{dg}{d\theta}\right)^2.$$

Differentiating g with respect to θ, we have $dg/d\theta = \theta/6$. Hence,

$$\mathbf{Var}\left(g(\theta)\right) \approx 0.0054 \cdot \left(\frac{30}{6}\right)^2 = 0.0054 \cdot 25 = \mathbf{0.135}.$$

6.23. Given n data points, $x_1, x_2, \ldots, x_n$, the likelihood function is

$$L(a) = a^n \prod_{i=1}^{n} x_i^{a-1}.$$

Then the log-likelihood function is

$$l(a) = n \ln a + (a - 1) \sum_{i=1}^{n} \ln x_i.$$

Differentiating the log-likelihood function with respect to θ and equating it to zero, we obtain,

$$l'(a) = \frac{n}{a} + \sum_{i=1}^{n} \ln x_i = 0 \Rightarrow \hat{a} = -\frac{n}{\sum_{i=1}^{n} \ln x_i}.$$

Using our data, the MLE estimate of the parameter a is

$$\hat{a} = -\frac{5}{\ln 0.2 + \ln 0.5 + 2 \ln 0.7 + \ln 0.8} = \frac{5}{3.2391} = 1.5436.$$

To calculate asymptotic variance,

$$l''(a) = -\frac{n}{a^2} \Rightarrow -\mathbf{E}\left[l''(a)\right] = \frac{n}{a^2} \Rightarrow \hat{Var}(\hat{a}) = \frac{a^2}{n}.$$

Using $n = 5$ and $a = \hat{a} = 1.5436$, we have

$$\widehat{\mathbf{Var}}(\hat{a}) = \frac{1.5436^2}{5} = 0.4766.$$

Let $g(a) = \hat{\mathbf{P}}\left(X < 0.6\right)$. Since $f(x) = ax^{a-1}$, the cumulative distribution function is

$$F_X(x) = \int_0^x at^{a-1} \, dt = t^a \big|_0^x = x^a.$$

Therefore,

$$g(a) = \widehat{\mathbf{P}}\,(X < 0.6) = F_X(0.6) = 0.6^a.$$

Evaluating $g(a)$ at $a = \hat{a} = 1.5436$, we have

$$g(1.5436) = 0.6^{1.5436} = 0.4545.$$

By the delta method formula for one variable,

$$\mathbf{Var}\,(g(a)) \approx \mathbf{Var}(a)\left(\frac{dg}{da}\right)^2.$$

Differentiating g with respect to a, we have

$$\frac{dg}{da} = 0.6^a \ln 0.6 = 0.6^{1.5436} \cdot \ln 0.6 = -0.2322.$$

Hence,

$$\widehat{\mathbf{Var}}\left(\widehat{\mathbf{P}}\,(X < 0.6)\right) \approx \mathbf{Var}(a)\left(\frac{dg}{da}\right)^2 = 0.4766 \cdot (0.2322)^2 = 0.02569.$$

The 95th percentile confidence interval for $g(a) = \widehat{\mathbf{P}}\,(X < 0.6)$ is

$$g(a) \pm 1.96\sqrt{\widehat{\mathbf{Var}}\,(g(a))} = 0.4545 \pm 1.96\sqrt{0.02569} =$$
$$= 0.4545 \pm 0.3141 = \mathbf{(0.1404,\ 0.7687)}.$$

This is a wide confidence interval, but there were only five observations in the sample.

6.24. There is only one parameter. We select a region in which

$$l(a) = n \ln a + (a - 1)\sum_{i=1}^{n} \ln x_i > c \quad \text{for some } c.$$

Using $n = 5$ and our data,

$$\sum_{i=1}^{5} \ln x_i = \ln 0.2 + \ln 0.5 + 2\ln 0.7 + \ln 0.8 = -3.2391.$$

Thus, the region becomes:

$$\{a | l(a) = 5\ln a - 3.2391(a - 1) > c\}.$$

We have calculated in the exercise the MLE estimate of the parameter a to be $\hat{a} = 1.5436$.

Thus, the maximum value of the log-likelihood function is

$$l_{max} = 5\ln(1.5436) - 3.2391(0.5436) = 0.4098.$$

The 95th percentile of chi-square with one degree of freedom is $\chi_{0.95} = 3.841$. Thus,

$$c = l_{max} - 0.5 \cdot \chi_{0.95} = 0.4098 - 0.5 \cdot 3.841 = -1.5107.$$

Hence, the region becomes

$$\{a | 5\ln a - 3.2391(a-1) > -1.5107\}.$$

This is a nonlinear equation,

$$5\ln x - 3.2391(x-1) = -1.5107,$$

requires a numerical technique to solve. Plotting this equation[1], we have the following:

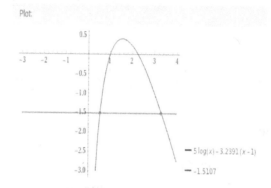

Using the Excel Solver functionality, we obtain the following interval for a:

$$I = (0.5536, 3.3176)$$

6.25. We have shown in section 6.4.3.1, formula (6.39), that the variance of the parameter estimate $\widehat{\sigma}$ is

$$\mathbf{Var}(\widehat{\sigma}) = \frac{\sigma^2}{2n}.$$

Therefore, using the given information,

$$\mathbf{Var}(\widehat{\sigma}) = \frac{\sigma^2}{60} = \frac{15^2}{60} = \frac{225}{60} = \mathbf{3.75}.$$

6.26. The likelihood function is

$$L(\mu) = \prod_{k=1}^{n} f(x|\mu) = \left(\frac{1}{6}\right)^n \cdot \mu^{4n} \cdot \prod_{k=1}^{n} x_k^3 \cdot e^{-\mu \cdot (\sum_{k=1}^{n} X_k)}.$$

The log-likelihood is

$$l(\mu) = L(\mu) = C + 4n\ln\mu - \mu \cdot \sum_{k=1}^{n} X_k, \quad C = 3\sum_{k=1}^{n}\ln X_k - n\ln 6.$$

---

[1]https://www.wolframalpha.com

Constant C does not contain parameter μ.

Differentiating $l(\mu)$ with respect to μ, we have

$$\frac{dl}{d\mu} = \frac{4n}{\hat{\mu}} - \sum_{k=1}^{n} X_k.$$

Soving for μ, we obtain the MLE:

$$\frac{4n}{\hat{\mu}} - \sum_{k=1}^{n} X_k = 0 \Leftrightarrow \hat{\mu} = \frac{4n}{\sum_{k=1}^{n} X_k} = \frac{4}{\bar{X}},$$

with $\bar{X}$ being defined as the sample mean.

Alternatively, we recognize that the given density function,

$$f(x|\mu) = \frac{\mu^4}{3!} x^3 \cdot e^{-\mu \cdot x} \quad \text{for} \quad x > 0,$$

is the **pdf** for the gamma distribution with parameters $\alpha = 4$ and $\theta = 1/\mu$. Using (6.45), the MLE for θ is

$$\hat{\theta} = \frac{\bar{X}}{\alpha}.$$

Therefore, the MLE for μ is

$$\hat{\mu} = \frac{1}{\hat{\theta}} = \frac{\alpha}{\bar{X}} = \frac{4}{\bar{X}}.$$

6.27. For a single-parameter Pareto distribution, the **pdf** is

$$f(x, \alpha) = \frac{\alpha \theta^\alpha}{x^{\alpha+1}}.$$

Given n data points, $X_1, X_2, \ldots, X_n$, the likelihood function is

$$L(\alpha) = \alpha^n \theta^{n\alpha} \frac{1}{\prod_{i=1}^{n} X_i^{\alpha+1}}.$$

Then the log-likelihood function is

$$l(\alpha) = n \ln \alpha + n\alpha \ln(\theta) - (\alpha + 1) \sum_{i=1}^{n} \ln X_i.$$

Differentiating the log-likelihood function with respect to α and equating it to zero, we obtain

$$l'(\alpha) = \frac{n}{\alpha} + n \ln(\theta) - \sum_{i=1}^{n} \ln X_i = 0 \Rightarrow \hat{\alpha} = \frac{n}{\sum_{i=1}^{n} \ln X_i - n \ln(\theta)}.$$

Using our data, the MLE estimate of the parameter α is

$$\hat{a} = \frac{5}{\ln 162 + \ln 170 + \ln 176 + \ln 220 + \ln 237 - 5 \cdot \ln 150} = 4.1584.$$

To calculate asymptotic variance,

$$l''(a) = -\frac{n}{\alpha^2} \Rightarrow -\mathbf{E}\left[l''(a)\right] = \frac{n}{\alpha^2} \Rightarrow \hat{\mathbf{V}}\mathrm{ar}(\hat{\alpha}) = \frac{\alpha^2}{n}.$$

Using $n = 5$ and $\alpha = \hat{\alpha} = 4.1584$, we have

$$\widehat{\mathbf{V}\mathrm{ar}}(\hat{\alpha}) = \frac{\alpha^2}{5} = 3.4584.$$

Let $g(\alpha) = \widehat{\mathbf{P}}\left(X < 300\right)$. For a single-parameter Pareto distribution, the cumulative distribution function is

$$F_X(x) = 1 - \left(\frac{\theta}{x}\right)^\alpha.$$

Therefore,

$$g(\alpha) = \widehat{\mathbf{P}}\left(X < 300\right) = F_X(300) = 1 - 0.5^\alpha.$$

Evaluating $g(\alpha)$ at $\alpha = \hat{\alpha} = 4.1584$, we have

$$g(\hat{\alpha}) = g(4.1584) = 1 - 0.5^{4.1584} = 0.9440.$$

By the delta method formula for one variable,

$$\mathbf{Var}\left(g(\alpha)\right) \approx \mathbf{Var}(\alpha) \left.\left(\frac{dg}{d\alpha}\right)^2\right|_{\alpha=\hat{\alpha}}.$$

Differentiating g with respect to α, we have

$$\frac{dg}{d\alpha} = 0.5^\alpha \ln 2.$$

Evaluating the derivative at $\hat{\alpha}$,

$$\left.\frac{dg}{d\alpha}\right|_{\alpha=\hat{\alpha}} = 0.5^{4.1584} \ln 2 = 0.0388.$$

Hence,

$$\widehat{\mathbf{Var}}\left(\widehat{\mathbf{P}}\left(X < 300\right)\right) \approx 3.4584 \cdot (0.0388)^2 = 0.0052.$$

The 95th percentile confidence interval for $g(\alpha) = \widehat{\mathbf{P}}\left(X < 300\right)$ is

$$g(\hat{\alpha}) \pm z_{1+p/2} \sqrt{\widehat{\mathbf{Var}}\left(g(\hat{\alpha})\right)} = 0.9440 \pm 1.96\sqrt{0.0052} = (0.8025, 1.0855).$$

Since the probability is always less than or equal to one, the confidence interval is $(0.8025, 1)$.

6.28. The likelihood function for a uniform distribution with n individual data points is

$$L(\theta) = \frac{1}{\theta^n}.$$

The log-likelihood function is

$$l(\theta) = -n \ln(\theta) \quad \text{for} \quad \theta > 60.$$

This function is maximized at $\hat{\theta} = 60$ as

$$l_{max} = l(60) = -150 \ln(60) = -614.1517.$$

We are looking for a region of θ such that

$$\{\theta | l(\theta) = -n \ln(\theta) > c\}.$$

The 90th percentile of chi-square with one degree of freedom is $\chi_{0.90} = 2.7055$. Thus,

$$c = l_{max} - 0.5 \cdot \chi_{0.90} = -614.1517 - 0.5 \cdot 2.7055 = -615.5045.$$

Hence, the region becomes

$$\{\theta | -150 \ln(\theta) > -615.5045\}.$$

Solving for θ, we have

$$\ln(\theta) < 4.1034 \Leftrightarrow \theta < e^{4.1034} = 60.5436.$$

Hence, the confidence interval is

$$I = (60, 60.5436).$$

Appendix A

One-Sample K–S Table

The table gives the critical values $D_{n,\alpha}$ as described in Kolmogrov–Smirnov test.

n \ α	0.001	0.010	0.020	0.050	0.100	0.150	0.200
1		0.99500	0.99000	0.97500	0.95000	0.92500	0.90000
2	0.97764	0.92930	0.90000	0.84189	0.77639	0.72614	0.68377
3	0.92063	0.82900	0.78456	0.70760	0.63604	0.59582	0.56481
4	0.85046	0.73421	0.68887	0.62394	0.56522	0.52476	0.49265
5	0.78137	0.66855	0.62718	0.56327	0.50945	0.47439	0.44697
6	0.72479	0.61660	0.57741	0.51926	0.46799	0.43526	0.41035
7	0.67930	0.57580	0.53844	0.48343	0.43607	0.40497	0.38145
8	0.64098	0.54180	0.50654	0.45427	0.40962	0.38062	0.35828
9	0.60846	0.51330	0.47960	0.43001	0.38746	0.36006	0.33907
10	0.58042	0.48895	0.45662	0.40925	0.36866	0.34250	0.32257
11	0.55588	0.46770	0.43670	0.39122	0.35242	0.32734	0.30826
12	0.53422	0.44905	0.41918	0.37543	0.33815	0.31408	0.29573
13	0.51490	0.43246	0.40362	0.36143	0.32548	0.30233	0.28466
14	0.49753	0.41760	0.38970	0.34890	0.31417	0.29181	0.27477
15	0.48182	0.40420	0.37713	0.33760	0.30397	0.28233	0.26585
16	0.46750	0.39200	0.36571	0.32733	0.29471	0.27372	0.25774
17	0.45440	0.38085	0.35528	0.31796	0.28627	0.26587	0.25035
18	0.44234	0.37063	0.34569	0.30936	0.27851	0.25867	0.24356
19	0.43119	0.36116	0.33685	0.30142	0.27135	0.25202	0.23731
20	0.42085	0.35240	0.32866	0.29407	0.26473	0.24587	0.23152
25	0.37843	0.31656	0.30349	0.26404	0.23767	0.22074	0.20786
30	0.34672	0.28988	0.27704	0.24170	0.21756	0.20207	0.19029
35	0.32187	0.26898	0.25649	0.22424	0.20184	0.18748	0.17655
40	0.30169	0.25188	0.23993	0.21017	0.18939	0.17610	0.16601
45	0.28482	0.23780	0.22621	0.19842	0.17881	0.16626	0.15673
50	0.27051	0.22585	0.21460	0.18845	0.16982	0.15790	0.14886
Over 50	$\dfrac{1.94947}{\sqrt{n}}$	$\dfrac{1.62762}{\sqrt{n}}$	$\dfrac{1.51743}{\sqrt{n}}$	$\dfrac{1.35810}{\sqrt{n}}$	$\dfrac{1.22385}{\sqrt{n}}$	$\dfrac{1.13795}{\sqrt{n}}$	$\dfrac{1.07275}{\sqrt{n}}$

Appendix B

One-Sample A–D Table

The following are tables of critical values the one-sample Anderson–Darling test.

Dist \ α	0.001	0.0025	0.005	0.010	0.025	0.050	0.100	0.150	0.200	0.250
Specified	5.9671		4.4971	3.8784	3.0775	2.4922	1.9330	1.6212		1.2479
Exponential		2.534	2.244	1.959	1.591	1.321	1.062	0.916	0.816	0.736
Gumbel/Weibull				1.038	0.877	0.757	0.637			0.474
Logistic			1.001	0.906	0.769	0.660	0.523			0.426
Normal			1.1578	1.0348	0.8728	0.7514	0.6305		0.5091	
Lognormal			1.063	1.013	0.861	0.795	0.750		0.756	
			1.34	0.93	0.94	0.89	0.80		0.39	

Gamma

k \ α	0.005	0.01	0.025	0.05	0.1	0.25
1	1.227	1.092	0.917	0.786	0.657	0.486
2	1.190	1.062	0.894	0.768	0.604	0.477
3	1.178	1.052	0.886	0.762	0.639	0.475
4	1.173	0.048	0.883	0.759	0.637	0.473
5	1.170	1.045	0.881	0.758	0.635	0.472
6	1.168	1.043	0.880	0.757	0.635	0.472
8	1.165	1.041	0.878	0.755	0.634	0.471
10	1.164	1.040	0.877	0.754	0.633	0.471
12	1.162	1.038	0.876	0.754	0.633	0.471
15	1.162	1.038	0.876	0.754	0.632	0.470
20	1.161	1.037	0.875	0.753	0.632	0.470
>	1.159	1.035	0.873	0.752	0.631	0.470

Bibliography

[1] Weishaus, Abraham. *Study Manual for Exam C/Exam 4*. ASM, 2011.

[2] Klugman, Stuart et al. *Loss Models: From Data to Decisions*. Wiley, SOA, 2019.

[3] Casella, George and Berger, Roger. *Statistical Inferences*. Duxbury Advanced Series, 2nd edition, 2002.

[4] Bühlmann, Hans. "Experience Rating and Credibility". *ASTIN Bulletin*, no. 1 (1967): 99–207.

[5] Robbins, Herbert. "An Empirical Bayes Approach to Statistics". *Proc. Third Berkeley Symposium on Mathematical Statistatistics and Probability, University of California Press*, no. 1 (1956): 157–163.

[6] Abramowitz, Milton and Stegun, Irene. *Handbook of Mathematical Functions with Formulas, Graphs, and Mathematical Tables*. New York: Dover, 1972.

[7] Fisher, Ronald. "On the Mathematical Foundations of Theoretical Statistics". *Philosophical Transactions of the Royal Society A.*, no. 222 (1922): 309–368.

[8] Ross, Sheldon. *First Course in Probability*. Prentice Hall, 5th edition, 1997.

Index

CPSIA information can be obtained
at www.ICGtesting.com
Printed in the USA
LVHW061754051021
699606LV00003B/17